W9-AZB-398

BOOKS BY LESLIE FORD

THE GIRL FROM
THE MIMOSA CLUB

LESLIE FORD

The Girl from the Mimosa Club

CHARLES SCRIBNER'S SONS

NEW YORK

TO

THE BALTIMORE POLICE

WITH RESPECT AND WITH MANY THANKS

FOR THEIR GREAT HELP AND

CONSTANT HUMOR

—*Leslie Ford*

THE GIRL FROM
THE MIMOSA CLUB

Johnny Brayton squeezed his car in to the curb between a snow-ball stand and a beat-up cart of canteloupes, sweet corn and lima beans, turned off his engine and put the keys in his pocket. He buttoned the second button of his fresh seersucker coat, picked up his coco straw hat, put it on with unusual care, picked up his shiny new briefcase, opened the street-door and eased his decently black-shod feet to the blistering pavement. He grinned suddenly. When he got around to writing his future memoirs, this was where he would start. He could see the first page of the deluxe edition.

"The eminent career of the Honorable John Summerfield Brayton, 17th (or whichever) Chief Justice of the Supreme Court of the United States, began on Sunday morning, the 25th of July, in the lousy purlieus of the Pine Street Police Station for Women in the City of Baltimore.

"A graduate of Gilman Country School, Princeton University and the University of Virginia Law School, and having served his country the required two years, dodging onerous duties with distinction, the future Chief Justice passed the Maryland Bar Examination with no distinction, and at the age of twenty-six entered the practice of the law as yard bird in the presumably respectable firm of Cadbury, Dewar and Grimes.

"His first distinguished appearance in his chosen profession was on that Sunday morning, temperature 96 degrees, relative humidity 100 per cent, when he was summoned to represent a police haul of night-spot sitters and strippers, on behalf of his firm's lucrative client, Baltimore's brilliant impresario Solly Herman, lowdown proprietor of a lowdown joint trading as the Mimosa Club, raided the night before, while the Honorable John S. Brayton was sweating it out at a Little Season dance in honor of one of Baltimore's richer but less promising debutantes at the Elkridge Kennels."

He got the rest of the way out of his car, shut the door and backed against it to avoid too intimate contact with a horse, bells a-jingle, hitched to a cart full of watermelons. Perched on the emerald mound was a little colored kid holding a half-cut melon. "Hi, mister!"

"Hi there." Johnny Brayton grinned back at him, feeling suddenly at home, and amended his memoirs from "lousy purlieus" to "colorful precincts." Then he grinned again, unbuttoned his seersucker coat and tossed his coco straw hat back through the window onto the car floor. If he couldn't impress a six-year old colored kid on a cart load of watermelons, he wasn't likely to impress either his present clients or the court. That was further apparent the minute he entered the station house doors.

"—You the kid Grimes sent to spring the Mimosa gang?"

The nervous character in a green, short-sleeved, open-neck nylon shirt, green slacks, pointed black-and-white perforated shoes, chewing a sodden cigar, who'd eyed him with a sinking heart as he came through the doors, caught up with him before he reached the police desk.

"Mr. Grimes sent me to represent them," Johnny said with dignity.

"Okay, chum. I'm Joe Anselo. You don't have to worry. Just take it easy." Joe Anselo was clearly trying to reassure himself, not John Brayton. "—Solly said I was to tell you, don't make a production, just get 'em the hell out of here. Quick an' easy, see? I got the dough." He shoved a wad of bills into Johnny's hand. "You don't do nothin' but plead 'em guilty, pay the fines an' get 'em out, see? This here's a lady judge. They ain't pullin' nothin' on her like they would on a man, see? Cripes, it's hot."

Anselo wiped his fish-belly brow with a hairy arm. The sweat looked cold to Brayton.

"You got it, Mac, ain't you? The big deal's on at Central, which the dicks got Solly on a numbers charge. So as he don't want any stink over here. Just get 'em out and stick around till I shove 'em in taxis, see? And there's one we got to go easy on. Miss Reeves.— Miss we got to call her, account of Solly got this torch. H-bomb. It's her first time in. You got it, ain't you?"

"I've got it, Mac," Johnny said amiably. He heard a commotion and looked at the far end of the room along a passage beside the wide oak staircase. A female turnkey was unlocking the silver-barred gate. He saw his first clients. The golden girls of the rose-colored spots. It took him a full moment to readjust.

He turned back to Anselo. "They . . . look different in daylight, don't they."

Anselo shot him a suspicious glance. "You a comedian, Mac?"

"No." Johnny stuffed the wad of bills into his briefcase. "Just understating what I assumed must be a fact. If the Mimosa Club's still in business."

"Okay, I get it. That's the courtroom. No crackin' wise in there, see?" He was sweating again. "You sure you—"

"Leave it to me, chum."

Johnny Brayton moved toward the courtroom door with an ease that he hoped Joe Anselo mistook for confidence, and in another moment had made a further revision of his future biography. For "first distinguished appearance in his chosen profession" read "his first job was purely routine." Quick, and easy. The woman judge wore her judicial black robes, the officers of the Racket Squad (Morals Division) gave their testimony, the four strippers and five sitters pleaded guilty and were fined and dismissed. The girl Miss Reeves was a blonde in a red dress, ten dollars for disorderly conduct. In fifteen minutes it was over and nothing left for the legal representative of Solly Herman, trading as the Mimosa Club, but to pay up and go on home and have his breakfast. Or so he thought until he went out into the station house lobby and saw Anselo and Miss Reeves.

Anselo spread his hands helplessly. "Look, I'm tryin' to get her to come on. I got the taxi. Come on, Miss Reeves."

"I won't," Miss Reeves said flatly. She had on the red off-the-shoulder evening dress she'd slept in and red shoes. She was standing there, her hands on her hips washerwoman-fashion, her long bobbed blonde hair tossed back, chin up, her blue eyes flashing under lashes an inch thick with mascara. "You tell Solly Herman I'm through. He told me the one thing you didn't worry about in Baltimore was cops. They're fixed. Nobody ever goes to jail. So I've just spent a whole night in one and I'm through. Anyway I've got a friend coming."

"Not Solly, Miss Reeves. He's—"

"Not Solly. My maiden aunt. We always pick each other up after Saturday night jail. It's an old family custom."

Counsellor Brayton moved peaceably in. "You go on, Joe. I'll stick around with Miss Reeves till her aunt comes."

"Don't bother," Miss Reeves said. "I'm quite at home here by now, thank you."

"Okay, okay." Anselo retired down the steps to his other charges.

Johnny turned back to the girl in the red dress. "It's possible your maiden aunt hasn't got the word yet, Miss Reeves," he said gravely.

"She will have. As soon as I can borrow a dime to call a cab. I left my bag at the Mimosa Club."

"Why bother the poor old lady?" The counsellor's tone was eminently reasonable. "My car's across the street. I'll be happy to drop you anywhere you'd like to go. In the public interest, if you'll allow me to say so. It's Sunday morning. That rig you've got on . . ."

Up to that point neither gravity nor reason had impressed her. He saw her hesitate now, looking down at her bare shoulders and slinky red skirt.

"Well . . . all right," she said reluctantly. "If it isn't too much trouble."

"None at all." He smiled at her. "Unless you live to hell and gone out in the country. But you look like an urban type, to me."

She laughed suddenly. "It's just a few blocks."

"Let's go then."

Her laughter, light and crystal-clear, surprised him. Then in the door, looking down into the street with the children around the watermelon carts and a dignified group of colored people obviously on their way to worship, she hesitated again, drawing back.

"Now what's the trouble?"

"—Nothing. I . . . I just feel so naked. Like I had a bikini on in church."

"Allow me." John Brayton took off his seersucker jacket. "Your cloak, your Majesty. I'd rather you didn't walk through a puddle on it." He laid it round her bare shoulders.

"Oh, thanks! It's silly . . . but I just didn't think about how I'd look. Let's hurry, shall we?"

"It's that dark green one-tone job across the street."

He hadn't meant that he didn't want to be seen crossing the street with her, but that must have been the way she took it, because she flashed down the littered concrete steps and was across the street and in the car before he was half-way there.

"Park Avenue," she said. "Just above Monument, on the right hand side. I'll show you."

He'd expected a downtown fleabag of some kind, but Park Avenue didn't surprise him. A lot of the fine old houses, built wall to wall solidly lining both sides of the once elegant street, had been turned into rooming houses. He started the car and swung east on Mulberry, waiting for her to say something. But she didn't. She sat huddled down, her eyes straight ahead. Her silence made him uncomfortably aware of himself, sitting expectantly behind the wheel, ready with his superior wisdom to advise and counsel the repentant Magdalene, assuaging her remorse. Aware also that he was beginning to feel a little silly.

He glanced at her and was surprised, even startled, at the delicate sensitive lines of her face, lost in a concentrated reverie that was entirely unselfconscious and had nothing to do with repentance or remorse. And certainly nothing whatsoever to do with Johnny Brayton of the Baltimore Braytons.

The damned girl's just thinking.

It struck him as so funny that he laughed aloud.

She looked up at him then. "What's the matter?"

"Nothing. Just that you're a funny girl. That's all."

"I don't feel very funny.—It's straight ahead, in the middle of this block. The red brick house with the new white trim."

He was surprised again as he saw the house, with its white marble steps and polished brass rail, in one of the blocks that had escaped the blight or been recovered from it. The fashionable dentist all the Braytons went to had his offices in the brownstone mansion a few doors along. He drew up to the curb. Miss Reeves put her hand out to open the car door.

"If you wouldn't mind waiting, I'll dash in and put something on and bring you your coat. I don't want to shock my landlady. I won't be but a second. And . . . thanks a lot! I'm very grateful. Really."

"Now wait a minute, Miss Reeves," Johnny Brayton heard himself saying. He took her hand and laid it calmly back on her lap. "Today's the first time I've been in court—"

"I thought so." Her blue eyes lighted suddenly. "You were so solemn . . . so according to the book."

"That's plenty from you, young woman.—And how did you know? I thought this was your first time too."

She was still amused. "Well, it was. But my . . . I mean, I've seen a lot of movies and trials on television. I don't mean you weren't wonderful. You were."

"That's better. But it's not what we're talking about. I don't think my first client just says 'Thanks' and walks off. I think she at least buys me a cup of coffee."

"Then you'd better see Solly. He's your client, not me. But I doubt if he's free, unless he got an awful lot of bail awful quick."

"Objection sustained. But it wasn't Solly I loaned my coat to and furnished transportation home for.—Just how long would it take you to get some of that gunk scraped off, Miss Reeves, get a shower and get sufficiently dressed to go somewhere and eat?"

She shook her head. "You take your duties too seriously. It's a bad precedent to establish—feeding your clients' hired help."

"It's myself I want to feed. There's no cook at the Braytons' till nine on Sundays. For getting rid of Anselo for you, you owe me something. I'm offering to settle for one cup of coffee. I'll even buy it."

"No. If I owe it to you, I'll make it for you." She pressed down the door handle. "But I need more than a shower. Give me half an hour. And maybe you can find some cream, if you want it. And a paper. Then come straight through to 1-B."

"We could go to the Belvedere or the Stafford. I don't want to shock your landlady either."

"It's all right. And don't get out, will you? I'll just dash while the street's clear."

She got out quickly. She'd managed to loop her long skirt up under her belt so that at any distance she merely looked like a girl in a red dress and red shoes with a light jacket round her shoulders. And she had nice long legs, in fact, very nice, Johnny Brayton observed as she went gracefully up the steps and through the white-louvered summer doors.

2

As Johnny Brayton looked at the clock on the dash a disquieting realization of what he'd done came sharply into his mind. It was twenty minutes past ten. Half an hour—just when the streets would be full of people on their way to church. Including members of his own family from his home in Mt. Vernon Place, just a couple of blocks away. It occurred to him that hunting a bottle of cream through the Sunday streets in shirtsleeves and a bow tie was in itself unfitting. Not to mention that waiting half an hour to see a girl he'd just got out of jail didn't add much to his prestige and dignity as a fledgling member of the bar. Furthermore somebody was sure to see him.

He could hear his mother's voice suddenly from one of the most vivid of disciplinary moments, when, aged thirteen, he was caught at a movie for adults only, as baffling as it had been dull. *You're always seen, love. It's an immutable truth. Usually by the least likely, most righteous and most poisonous person you know. You can be perfectly innocent but they'll never think so. The skating rink and a knock-kneed cousin were my downfall. I had to write "You're always seen" a hundred times. You write it once, in your little head, Johnny. It'll save you endless trouble, love.*

Of course, it wasn't that he was ashamed to be seen with the girl, exactly, but at the same time there was no doubt it would be a little difficult to explain, to family or friends. *After all, let's face it. She's nothing but a tramp. A female sitter. You better get your coat and beat it home, Johnny, my friend. Better still, go home and send Horace around for it.*

His mother was having a lot of people in to lunch, anyway. But when he turned left to get to Howard Street, to avoid the church people on Cathedral, and saw a dingy shop with a pile of Sunday papers on a box in front, he pulled over to the curb. After all, it had been his idea, not hers. No point in being rude just because the girl had been in jail. He'd hand her the paper, collect his coat and that would be that. Simple, no complications. Quick and easy.

Then when he was paying for the paper he heard himself saying, "You don't happen to have any cream, do you?"

The man went to the Coke machine and took out a bottle. "Watch it," he said. "The cap's loose."

"Stick it in a bag, will you?"

Johnny Brayton got back in his car. The side view of her face there beside him had slipped back, blotting out the image of her as one of the Mimosa gang—the wide-open thoughtful blue eyes, the complete lack of embarrassment, or of consciousness of him as anything but a person offering her a lift. The more he tried to shake it out of his mind the tighter it stuck. It was like the memory of a time in Quebec once when he'd heard a brief snatch of an unknown melody through an open window that someone had closed abruptly. He'd never heard the rest, and it haunted him for months.

If she'd just said something, he thought. It struck him then that what she'd said had been very clear. She'd agreed to the coffee, there in front of the house, just as the easiest way to get rid of him. Remembering her entire lack of enthusiasm, he grinned, a little lop-sidedly, and wiped his forehead with a sticky shirt sleeve. A girl like that, used to heels . . . . The skin on the back of his neck crawled, cold in spite of the heat. Now he'd thought of it, his I-brought-you-home, you-owe-me-something routine didn't seem quite so debonair or amusing. In fact it was now obvious the thing to do was go in and have coffee, with dignity and decorum—let her see he wasn't a heel, just a casual decent guy with nothing in mind, nothing at all—and be on his way.

He parked across from the white marble steps, put the paper under his arm, picked up the bag with the bottle of cream in it, got out, holding the cream carefully, backed against the door to close it, and heard the sudden screech of scorching rubber as a car braked to a surprised stop, virtually against his chest.

"Johnny! Why for heaven sakes! Of all people! What on earth are you . . . where's your coat? I thought you were in court this morning!"

Oh, no. It couldn't be. *But, oh yes.* It was. The immutable truth right there in front of his face. If Camilla Anne, his sister-in-law, wife of his elder brother Pug, was not the most righteous person he knew, she was certainly the most poisonous, and the least likely member of the family or their exclusive circle to be seen on Park Avenue on Sunday morning at a quarter to eleven. She didn't even live downtown. She lived out in Homeland where there were front gardens for the children. But with people for lunch, Camilla Anne was a sure bet to be right in there, rearranging the seating and the flowers, a general pain in the broader portion of the human anatomy. Just a nice ordinary girl, marriage had turned her into one of the most managing, most ambitious little snobs in Baltimore. Perpetually bright, perpetually gay, she was childishly eager to please everybody, in her own enchanted circle. To people who weren't it it, she was kind, as became the lady of the manor, unless it looked as if they were trying to get in it. Then she became a cruel little snot who made Johnny's blood freeze with rage one minute, curdling with mortification the next. And there she was, her eagerly smiling face leaning brightly across the front seat, John Brayton backed against the furnace heat of his car and with an almost overpowering desire to use the cream bottle as a blunt instrument.

"We were so glad for you, dear! Weren't you lucky all the important people were out of town? You must have been terribly excited!"

"It was purely routine," Johnny said stiffly. "And you'd better move on, Camilla Anne. You're blocking things."

Cars were edging around her, too polite to sound their horns.

"Oh, I can get in here a second. I want to hear all about it."

She swerved her car in to the curb in front of him, got out and swooped back. "We nearly died laughing when we heard it. Imagine you with all those dreadful women! I bet it was awful, wasn't it?"

"No, it wasn't. They were—"

"Why, *Johnny!* Don't *tell* me! You haven't fallen for one of those. . . . Oh, Johnny, wouldn't that be a scream! I'm going to tell Daddy Brayton! He'll . . . oh, look! What's that!"

She stuck a rose-tipped forefinger out, her happy face screwed up with alarm. "Johnny! You're dripping! All over your shoes . . . what is it? It looks like cream, or something!"

It did, and it was. The blasted bottle would have to tip and spring a leak, the way his hands were throttling it instead of Camilla Anne.

"It is cream," he said calmly. He dropped the sodden bag and wrapped his handkerchief around the bottle. "Cream for coffee."

"Why, Johnny!" Her face lighted teasingly. "Why John Brayton! It *is* one of those girls! That's where your coat is! Why . . . you wolf in lawyer's clothing! I'm gonna tell! I'm gonna tell on you!"

"Look, Camilla Anne. Some day, somebody's going to put a bullet hole right through your offensive little skull. Now shut up, will you? What I do is my business, not yours."

"Well, it *is* my business," Camilla Anne said hotly. "Look at you! Sunday morning! Disgracing yourself and disgracing the Family! And you needn't think I won't tell! I'm plenty broad-minded, but I'm not going to let you walk out of the arms of a woman like that and sit down at Mother's luncheon table with all her guests—"

"That's enough, Cam." His voice was dangerously quiet. "You've got a filthy mind and a foul mouth. Go scrub both of 'em. And tell my mother to count me out for lunch. Any reason you care to give is fine with me."

He walked abruptly away, across the street and up the steps into the vestibule, leaving her there staring avid-eyed. Let her stand. Let her stare. Let her take down the street number and hot-foot it to his father and the Family. The Family was always capitalized, the way Camilla Anne said it. He heard her then, door slam, engine roar, gears grate. *The hell with you, Camilla Anne.*

How in God's name Ma puts up with her I'll never know. That was the automatic reaction to every encounter with Camilla Anne. A few times she'd been such strong poison that even his mother had gagged. Then all she did was close her eyes a moment, to open them, tranquilly clear again, with never a word spoken. With the thought of his mother—"To our serene and lovely Ma," was the way the four of them always addressed their joint presents to her— he was conscious for an instant of the vague anxiety, formless, a sort of hollow sensation in the pit of his stomach, that he'd been aware of lately whenever he thought of her. It disappeared as he looked down at the bank of brass mail boxes on the wall, hunting for Miss Reeves of 1-B. But there was no Miss Reeves. In the slot for 1-B the card said "Miss Kerry O'Keefe." She probably shared an apartment. He pressed the bell and waited, and heard a door click open at the back end of the hall.

The house was a typical three-story Baltimore row house with a hallway running back to a garden area on a walled alley. The floors and stairs were waxed and polished, a bowl of pink zinnias sat under a gilt mirror on a mahogany table against the wall. In back, the door to 1-B was standing a few inches ajar. At least she hadn't felt she needed to use the one-way seeing eye contraption set in it so she could see callers without being seen by them—a wise precaution in a business like hers, no doubt. He knocked and waited.

"Come in!"

He stepped into a tiny foyer. The wall was pale peach, hanging on it a mellowed panel of a deeper peach Chinese Brocade. Luxury he hadn't expected. He revised that idea when he stopped in an archway looking into what had been a glassed-in verandah and was now a living room. It was almost Spartan, the only furniture a sofa, a dropleaf table, some chairs and an old cherrywood chest of drawers. But in the lined drapes and the slip covers on the sofa and the one arm chair there was a spring riot of color, in the chintz with great yellow and pink hyacinths and jade green leaves on a dusty blue background the color of the walls. Through the tilted slats of the blue venetian blinds, at the end of the room he could see into a small city garden, a feathery tree in the center, with a pair of yellow canvas deck chairs and a white iron table under it in the shade.

"Sorry, just a minute." Her voice came from across the room where a section of the former porch had been partitioned off. "I'm scrambling eggs. You know these servantless houses."

It was so blithe a mimicry of so many of John Brayton's aunts, cousins and friends that he grinned as he put the paper on the sofa. There was no sign of a second person present. "I've got the cream, slightly spilled," he said, and then she was there in the kitchen door.

There was a long moment when his heart was still, listening to the haunting melody complete at last. He stood looking at her, not actually surprised, as if some way he'd known he would see her fresh, clean and clear as sunlight. And she was no longer the calmly unselfconscious young lady in the car. The sensitive face was faintly flushed, the long black lashes, shiny as silk, drooped under his gaze, shading the defensive blue of her wide-set eyes. He wouldn't have thought she'd be shy, or that she was nearly as young. Her hair, darker because it was still damp from washing, was sleeked rippling back into a pony tail, showing the fine lines of her heart-shaped face

19

and delicate head above her slender body in a simple white cotton dress, as soft and cool as snow.

"It isn't Miss Reeves. It's Kerry . . . Kerry O'Keefe." Johnny Brayton spoke her name gently.

She nodded, her lashes drooping again. "I should have told you."

"Kerry. You're so lovely, Kerry. Why . . . do you do it?"

In an instant her eyes darkened. "Do what? But let me guess. Work for Solly. Well, perhaps it's for the same reason you do. Or don't you call it working for him representing him in court? He wouldn't be in business five minutes if he didn't have a smart lawyer on his payroll."

"Sorry," Johnny said. "The mistake's mine."

She laughed and took the cream bottle. "Just so we get things straight is all. No big pots calling little kettles black. And anyway, I've quit—you haven't. So let's skip it, shall we? I've put the coffee outside. You go on, I'll bring the eggs and stuff."

He stood a moment looking around him. "Who's the decorator?" he asked, as she came back with a tray with bacon and scrambled eggs on it.

"O'Keefe." Her eyes lighted with amusement. "Nothing a girl can't do when she gets two rooms, bath, kitchen and a garden cheap if she'll take it from scratch because the landlady's run out of money remodelling the rest of an old house. And I'm proud of my garden. I never expected to have a tree all of my own."

"So you're not urban. You're really a country girl at heart." He smiled gravely at her.

"Small town, anyway.—Except that my tree's a mimosa. Maybe you'll feel defiled sitting under it."

"I said it was a mistake. You said let's skip it."

"Sorry. The mistake's mine." Her laughter made him think of the sunlight glancing through the feathery foliage of the tree.

"It's self-service, al fresco." She'd plugged the coffee pot and toaster in from a kitchen outlet down to the table under the window. And afterwards, when they'd pushed the dishes back through the screen into the sink, they sat in the yellow deck chairs under the tree, the golden hours weaving a gossamer web. Johnny Brayton watched her gravely, aware that something profoundly important in his life was happening to him there in the summer stillness. At what point he knew he had fallen in love with a girl he knew nothing about he couldn't have told, but he did know it, and know the same magic was moving in her heart as deeply as his own. Only once he touched her, just the snowy fold of her skirt, awkwardly, as he'd never touched a girl before. And only once he asked her a question, where she was born.

"That's odd, you know," she said lightly. "It was twenty-two years ago. I've told so many people so many places, from Nome to Puerto Cabello, I've even got myself mixed up. But I know where you were born. Right here in North Baltimore. Nobody could miss that."

"Stuffy, you mean?"

"No, I don't. Just nice and casual. Sort of civilized, I guess."

"I was afraid you'd think I was a heel, pushing my way in. You didn't want me to come, did you?"

"Not very much. For lots of reasons."

"But you're not sorry, are you?"

She shook her head. "Glad, really."

"Look, Kerry. You've got to quit—"

"We said we'd skip that, didn't we?" she said evenly. "Let's talk about you, not me."

"There's not much. I passed the bar and got a job three weeks ago. Apprentice lawyer. I'd starve if I didn't live at home . . . just around in Mt. Vernon Place. There are four of us—a brother and sister married, and my favorite kid sister, nineteen, about to be. When the lad gets out of the Army. He's okay, very old Baltimore, or his family is. Stuffy, I guess."

He grinned at her, but she shook her head, laughing. "It wasn't me that said it."

"I guess family ties are stronger here than most places," Johnny Brayton said. "And I don't mean Old Family stuff. Maybe it's because kids are a part of things. As soon as you can climb on a pony you're taken in hand and older people start showing you the way to go. Handing on their traditions to the new people coming along. So your parents' and grandparents' friends are yours too. Maybe it's a mold you get set in. Some people call it a code. It's hard to explain."

And why am I trying? What is it I'm doing? Whistling in the dark? The picture of his regal and uncompromising grandmother Mrs. John Summerfield came into his mind—with a companion piece entitled "Camilla Anne Informs The Family."

"Isn't your father a doctor? A very well-known one?"

"Not to his children. The family stuff means Ma, in ours. She's the old Baltimorean, the one that stuck us on a horse and taught us to shoot and hunt and not tell lies and make excuses for ourselves. Father we see at dinner, if he happens to be at home." He gave her a wry smile. "You can see this isn't an area of deep devotion."

"You don't like him much, do you."

"We've never had the chance. I don't mean he isn't a very charming, sophisticated, distinguished guy. He is. But his children amuse him. We're experimental mammals. Higher than laboratory rats but not much. Why he married and had a family we've never figured out. Except that Ma's father was a great internist and his chief, so it didn't hurt his career.—As for Ma, she's a dreamy gal. For her you could tear any one of us in a thousand pieces."

Kerry saw his smile fade. "You're worried about her," she said gently. "She isn't . . . ill, is she?"

"She'd never let us know it if she was." He shook his head. "I don't know what it is. She's one of those very serene, casual people. Lots of fun—sails, shoots, rides, that sort of thing. This is the first summer we haven't gone to Gibson Island. Father always stayed in town but we didn't. But it's okay, because he spends most of his time with a patient of his. A Mrs. Ristwich . . . Mrs. Richwitch, we call her. She's an oil widow from Texas, very loaded. She came to him to get diagnosed last Spring and she's been under foot ever since."

"Does your mother mind—"

"I can't imagine it. There's always been some dame on his trail. This one's just richer and more persistent. Anyway, the ordinary passions don't move him. His interest in dames is prying them loose from a couple of million bucks for medical education. And he's too cagey to—"

The phone had rung half a dozen times when they were having coffee, but she'd shaken her head when he stopped talking, waiting for her to go to answer it, and it had rung only one ring. It rang twice now, and a third time as she got to her feet.

He stood watching her run up the steps and through the dutch door out of sight, and in a moment saw her come back, watched her in the golden glow of a new passion, strangely unreal, strangely tender. He watched her gravely, knowing it wasn't going to be an easy thing and that all the ties he'd been telling her about weren't simple strands to be brushed aside at his convenience. But not

22

knowing, mercifully not, that there'd be a time when he would stand in that same door torn with agony, saying "I wish I'd rotted in hell before the day I ever met you" ... a time deep behind the sable wings of the rain-cold night when he would have to choose between this girl and his mother, and the words he'd so lightly spoken—"For her you could tear any one of us in a thousand pieces" —were the bitterest of gall and burning pain.

She came part way toward him, her face a little pale.

"Johnny—you've got to go now," she said quickly. "I'm sorry, but I've ... got to get downtown. About a ... a job."

The golden glow shattering, the tenderness freezing in a sudden sick despair, made Johnny Brayton's voice harsher than he meant it, his words more brutal.

"You mean, the female sitter goes back for—"

"That's right!" Her eyes flashed cobalt fire and her chin went up. "And I'd like you to leave and leave at once."

She ran back up the steps into the house.

"Oh Kerry." He followed her, sicker with himself than he was with her. "I'm sorry. I didn't mean it. It's just that something's happened to me today I didn't know could happen ... not like this."

"I ... didn't either. And I ... I'm sorry."

"Not sorry, Kerry—"

"I didn't mean that. I mean, about this morning ... and about now. I know it must seem so ... so horrible to you. But I can't help it." She clenched her fists tightly. "I have to have a job. I have to work—"

"But not this kind of work, Kerry. My God, you don't understand—"

"I understand all right. I know what your family would think— how dreadful it would be for them. In a place like Baltimore—as you've told me. But it can't be helped, Johnny. So just go away. You've had your coffee, and here's your coat. The rest was just ... just midsummer madness."

He shook his head. "This is for keeps, Kerry. My family'll—"

"Your family'll think you're stark raving mad. So please go." She thrust his coat into his hands. "And thanks, so much! I don't know what I'd have done."

She went quickly through the arch to the door and opened it. "Listen to me, Kerry."

"I can't, Johnny. I've got to hurry. Really."

"When'll you be back?"

"I don't know."

"Then what's your phone number?"

She hesitated. "I'm not always here. But you . . . you could leave a message." She gave him the number. "Goodbye, Johnny."

As he turned back she closed the door quickly. There was nothing he could do but stand there looking helplessly at it, the mirrored disk a sightless eye as cold as it was blind.

He was moving blindly himself as he went down the steps, almost colliding with the man in tan slacks and brown linen coat there who half grunted an apology and moved off down the street. It wasn't until Johnny was waiting for the traffic light at the corner that a sudden memory flashed into his mind and Kerry's pallor and frantic hurry, her taut voice and clenched fists, focussed suddenly, their meaning plain. The sweat broke out, clammy cold, on the palms of his hands as he swung around to look back.

Sergeant Trumper of the Rackets Division had turned and was walking slowly up toward her house.

"—This fellow Trumper . . ." Johnny could hear Mr. Grimes, his first week at the office. ". . . Coming in here at three o'clock. Rackets Division. I want you all to take a good look at him. He's a cool cookie. Don't let him get you in any casual conversation at a bar."

Watching him now in the side view mirror, Johnny saw him reach the house, slowing down as he passed it. The light changed to orange. Johnny shot through it and turned left, cursing himself for a fool as he remembered that Cathedral was a one-way street and he had two extra blocks to go before he could get back to her. In his own sweaty anxiety he remembered Joe Anselo's as he'd tried to hurry the girls out of Pine Street, and the all-too-smooth coopera-tion of the police. He was sick with apprehension, and sicker when he got around in Park again. The detective was gone. Kerry O'Keefe was gone too.

If he's taken her back to Pine Street . . . But he hadn't. Barging over there, he found that out, his relief turning clammy cold again as the desk sergeant said "By the way, mister, aren't you the lawyer Solly Herman had over here this morning?"

His voice had taken on a different tone. "Why don't you go down to Central Headquarters? That's where she'd be if they've taken her in for questioning.—If you all are so worried about her."

I'm just tying her tighter to Solly Herman. He was surer about that as he glanced back, going out, and saw the desk sergeant quietly picking up the telephone. *I'd better call Mr. Grimes. No. I hadn't. I'd better leave it lay. I'd better go on home and sit tight.*

He put his car in the old carriage house in Peabody Alley behind the house in Mt. Vernon Place and sat, his elbows on the wheel, his head in his hands. When he closed his eyes, her face was there. It was her face as it had been, fresh and clear, the silken lashes drooped, her cheeks warm, when he first saw her coming out of the kitchen, and changing then as it had changed, lighted with laughter or grave as it had been as she listened to him under the tree, the ache that was pain but not pain growing inside him, profoundly new and incredibly lovely.

I guess I never knew what love was all about before.

He got out of the car, started across the garden to the back door, remembered Camilla Anne and turned back, through the carriage house into the alley and along it to Cathedral Street and up toward Mt. Vernon Place. Then as he was about to cross it he stopped, his jaw hardening. *The hell with Camilla Anne.* He turned right toward his home, halfway along the block.

The Braytons' was the second of the pair of brownstone houses there, built with a common cornice and common interior wall but separate entrances. In other places they might be called a double house. In Baltimore they were two units in the row-house tradition that holds, grim or handsome, for mansion and tenement. Without space between for even a wayward ailanthus seedling, their only rear access through the alley in back, the pair were set between the Barton Jacobs and Walters houses, in the solid unbroken façade of brick, brownstone and granite forming the once sacrosanct, still distinguished block, on the south side of the plaza that sets off at the Charles Street intersection the magnificent column that was the nation's first monument to its first president.

Half-way along, Johnny saw the familiar figure that brought the familiar clutch that always stopped him. He braced himself, resisting the instant impulse to turn back. It was instinctive, common to all four of the Brayton children, what the sight of their father always did to them, a mechanism to protect them from the uncanny perception, the amused, faintly mocking smile that seemed to comment on nothing but their baser traits, reducing to absurdity all their pathetic attempts at self-respect. *As if we were a lot of comic frogs up for dissection.* It was his younger sister's passionate outburst for some reason Johnny had forgot, remembering only the frustration and the violence. *I hate him! He's just a sadist, that's what he is!*

Just clinical, Johnny thought as he saw him now, a tall slender man, immaculately elegant in a gray raw silk suit, a panama hat in his hand, coming down the brownstone steps toward a shining limousine standing at the curb, a uniformed chauffeur holding the door open.

Johnny felt the flush at the back of his neck. He knew he'd been seen. When his father got over to the car he'd stop and wait for him. And the reason Dr. Brayton had not already stopped was apparent. It was what Johnny's grandmother Mrs. Summerfield called That Woman Next Door. His father was pretending not to see their neighbor Mrs. Inga Remstad coming down the steps of the other of the two houses, the one nearer Johnny. And Mrs. Remstad was not an easy woman not to see.

It wouldn't hurt him to speak to her. You can't be that choosy about your neighbors. Not any more you can't. But Johnny felt better. It was an effect Mrs. Remstad always had on him. There was a kind of warm earthiness about her that was partly flesh and partly spirit. She was a handsome woman, voluptuous even, but there was something else, a responsive gaiety that twinkled in her eyes, as Scandinavian blue as her hair was yellow. If she didn't move in the Braytons' rarefied circles at least she and Johnny were friends, and had been since he was ten and his baseball went through her conservatory window, second floor back. And if she rented the first and third floors of her house, she wasn't the only householder on Mt. Vernon Place who did so.

"Hi, Mrs. Remstad." He stopped, waiting for her to reach the sidewalk.

"Hi, Johnny." She smiled at him. But instead of going on she stopped.

"That's a very fancy new car you've got, Doctor." Her voice was low and throaty, husky in a spine-warming way. But what astonished Johnny was the impish malice in her smile as she stood there, forcing his father to look around. "The sick business must be looking up, these days."

"Oh, how do you do, Mrs. Remsen. It's not my car—"

"'Course not. I see it's got a Texas license. And the name's Remstad, Doctor." She winked at Johnny and went along.

He's angry. It was only a spark, instantly vanished, but for Johnny Brayton a revelation. His father wasn't wholly exempt from human passions. That such a trivial assault on his dignity should bring that out was an added shock, and an instant release. For the first time in his life Johnny faced his father without fear and without awe.

"Well, Johnny." The ironically dissecting eyes were on him once more. "I'm told you had your . . . baptism of fire today." Dr. Brayton paused, faintly amused. "—In court, I mean."

Johnny raised his own brows slightly. "Hearsay evidence is never trustworthy, sir," he said easily. "As for court, it was routine."

He saw the flicker of surprise, even interest, in his father's eyes—another spark instantly vanished, because Mrs. Remstad was returning. She was there as the Texas car left the curb and Johnny reached the bottom step.

"It's just too hot," she said. "We're in for a storm, I guess."

She glanced up at the sulphur murkiness of the sky and along the street at the car. "—That was real mean of me." She was apparently upset about it. "I just don't know what got into me."

"I wouldn't worry." Johnny grinned at her.

"I'm not worrying." Her pink and white face, usually smiling, was set, stubbornly resentful. "But I just get tired of being treated like I wasn't here. Like I was dirt. I've lived next door to you people twenty-six going on twenty-seven years—before you were born—and you're the only one speaks to me on the street."

"Oh, Mrs. Remstad. My mother—"

"Your mother's a perfect lady. I have to give her that. It's your father that's got so high and mighty. Specially now he's got this fancy car and shoffer."

"Well, he doesn't—"

But Mrs. Remstad was really wound up. "I'm not in his class. I don't pretend to be. But I got feelings, like anybody else. You people don't know I'm on earth. But you'd be surprised what I know about you. Watching you go out and come in all these years. Like you kids out skating . . . I'd see you duck behind the bushes

28

when he came home. And that Texas car here all the time. I'd get pretty sick of it if I was you. But here comes your grandmother's car."

She recognized it before Johnny did. There was something disturbing about such watchful interest. *She must be horribly lonely in there,* he thought uncomfortably. That the day would come when the watch Mrs. Inga Remstad kept would have a shattering significance in their lives was an idea as fantastic as it was remote to him then.

"Johnny . . . ask Madam if she's ready, will you?" Occam, his grandmother's driver and general custodian for forty-odd withered years, was leaning over the front seat. "Tell her we have two more parties and a storm's coming up."

"Well, so long, Johnny." Mrs. Remstad moved on.

Johnny went up the Brayton steps and opened the front door. "Hi, Gran," he said. He remembered Camilla Anne again and stiffened for the attack direct.

"Hello, dear." His grandmother Mrs. Summerfield was sailing through the double doors of the gold-and-white front parlor, a handsome old Turk with a glint in her eye and a handsome smell of fine old bourbon on her breath. "That woman, Johnny . . . what did she say to your father?"

He looked at her blankly, not having expected that. "Why, nothing, actually. Just that—"

"He looked as if he smelled a polecat." Mrs. Summerfield was highly amused. "His own fault. He should have bought that house when he bought this. In '29 they were giving them away. If he doesn't like a trollop—"

"You don't know she's a trollop, Gran."

"I know your grandfather's eyes used to light up when he saw her. A showgirl of some kind. You'd know more about that than I would, I expect."

Johnny's jaw hardened. He'd expected a frontal assault, not a surreptitious smash with a blunt instrument from ambush behind Mrs. Remstad. Then he saw the reason. His mother was in the parlor door. His heart plummeted. Her face was white, her dark eyes as drained as the flesh around her lips.

"Mother . . . Occam's waiting. Help Gran down the steps, Johnny, please."

"I don't need any help, but I'd enjoy an escort."

29

She took his arm and marched through the door and down to the sidewalk. The attack direct came then.

"Disgracing the Family, eh?" Mrs. Summerfield was still amused. "Occam, Johnny's disgracing us. With a stripper. Or a sitter. Which is it, Johnny?" She patted the old man's arm. "But don't you worry. I'll give him the money to buy her off.—A rake in the Family."

"Not a rake, Gran." He managed to speak quietly. "And it isn't funny."

Her eyes bored into his, an angry flush darkening her cheeks.

"And not a damned fool either—or are you?" She got in the car. "Shut the door. If you have to fall in love, do it with somebody of your own kind. Your sister's engaged to be married. Do you want an open scandal to ruin that? Her brother running with jailbirds? And your mother looks like death on a pale horse as it is, with this Richwitch woman always here. If you have to be a fool don't you dare to let her know it. I'm ashamed of you Johnny. Go on, Occam."

As Johnny went back up the steps, aware of Mrs. Remstad looking down at him as she closed her upstairs windows, his anger drained out of him. *What did you expect, you knew it was coming.* The hall was empty, suddenly darkening, still with the ominous stillness that comes before the storm breaks and the lightning leaps. He stood an instant outside the mahogany panelled room across from the parlor that the young Braytons called the Common Room. "Ma?"

"She's gone upstairs, Johnny." Old Horace was coming out to turn on the lights and close the windows. "She isn't feeling so well, I expect. She doesn't want to be disturbed."

He went up the marble staircase curving handsomely to the second floor, and past his father's study door, on the side of the house next to Mrs. Remstad's. His mother's sitting room was across the hall on the other side. He put his hand on the doorknob, hesitating, as if in some way he'd forfeited his right to walk in through the door that was so warmly, with so much love and affection, always open to him and his brother and sisters. It was her face, down there in the hall, the drained eyes and white flesh around her lips. He raised his hand and knocked on the ivory panel. *The first time I've ever knocked. It's Father. He's the only one who always knocks.* That came up out of his mind without his ever having been consciously aware of it before.

As he knocked again, a curious incident slipped into his mind. It had happened in the Spring when a well-known painter was visiting them. "Your mother is an extraordinarily beautiful woman," he'd said to Johnny, and his father, standing near them, had glanced over at her with a flicker of surprise and sudden interest in his eyes, as he'd looked at Johnny a few minutes ago.

She's probably in her bedroom. He turned the doorknob, opened the door quietly in case she was resting, and saw her then at her desk, the pen in her hand racing across the blue note paper in front of her. He opened the door wider and stepped onto the pale eggshell cotton carpet. Before he could speak she was up like an arrow, as swift and as straight, whirling around at him, the fires of all hell blazing in her dark eyes.

In the stunned instant that Johnny Brayton stood there, unbelievably staring, he saw her hand relax on the back of the chair, her eyes close. She let herself down into the chair again, her pallor softening as she moved her hand across her forehead.

"Oh, I'm so sorry, Johnny," she whispered.

She opened her eyes. "You startled me, love," she said lightly. "And I certainly must have startled you. But please, darling." She smiled and got up. "Forgive me . . . it's been a difficult day. Would you mind if we don't—"

"Look, Ma." He was still too dazed to sound as he'd planned, casual and adult in explaining what had happened, explaining Kerry, matter-of-fact in reassuring her that there'd be no open scandal to ruin anybody's life and plans. "I want to tell you why—"

"Oh, don't, love. It was quite all right. Camilla Anne told me you'd met an old school friend." There wasn't a shadow in her eyes, dark with a translucent depth like the brown-black water of a cypress garden, as she looked at him with a tranquil smile. "There was nothing world-shaking about the luncheon, sweet. A few visiting doctors and an assortment of your sister's future in-laws, charming people if somewhat unbending for my taste. But she adores them. I don't think they approve of her trekking off for weekends at Army camps. Nor do I. But Camilla Anne assured us it's entirely correct these days."

She smiled at him. "But I wish it was over. The child's so happy. It's the first time in her life she's really been confident of herself. It would break my heart if anything happened to hurt her."

She came across the room to him. "Johnny dear. I'm tired, love.

I don't feel like talking. So do you mind? Tomorrow. But not now."

"Okay."

She took his face between her hands, cool on his burning cheeks, bending it down to kiss his forehead. "I love you, Johnny." She smiled at him, her eyes swimming with sudden tears but her voice serenely steady. "There's chicken in the ice box and I told Bessie to save you at least half a pecan pie. And I sequestered the bottle of old Scotch a future in-law brought. It's in your room. Good night, my lamb."

"Good night, Ma."

He stopped in the doorway. "I just don't want you to think I'm a complete bastard, Ma," he said quietly.

"I should think I have more valid information about that than you, love." She smiled again. "And I assure you it's never occurred to me that you were, or are, or could be. There must be some mistake. It's probably the heat." She looked out of the window. "The storm's passing us. Too bad. We really need the break. Good night, dear."

She closed the door. He heard the latch click and then the bolt as she locked it quietly.

Johnny Brayton went slowly up to the third floor. If his mother's locking her door behind him wasn't meant directly for him, the effect was the same—as what she'd said to him was in effect what his grandmother had said.—His sister's happiness, her new confidence. *It'll break my heart if anything happens.*

At the top of the stairs he paused a moment, listening to the faint incessant murmur of his aunt Miss Elizabeth Brayton's television in the room in front of his. The 1840 house had been solidly built or they'd all have been as somewhat more than fey as she was, sitting there glued to the TV panel, seldom coming out except to wander vaguely around the house at night, careful to tiptoe as she passed her brother's door. He went on into his own room. The air conditioner was on. It was cool and quiet, the storm passing over, the summer twilight touching the framed picture of his younger sister Lolly, the changeling child. It had been taken when she was first engaged and the heart-glow was in her eyes, dark like their mother's, the new confidence shining in her small pointed face, very moving to Johnny as he looked at it.

"They don't have to worry. I wouldn't ever hurt you, baby."

He said it aloud to her, remembering the terror-ridden nights she'd heard the ghosts tapping, until their mother had the fireplace chimney in her room above her father's study closed up so the swallows couldn't nest in it.

Tap, tap, tap . . .

He looked around, startled, and saw his door opening. If it had been a ghost he'd hardly have been more surprised than he was to see the wraith-like figure of Miss Elizabeth Brayton peering in at him.

"Nothing happened, did it?"

He looked blankly at her.

"At lunch. Your mother asked me to come down so there wouldn't be thirteen. I said subtract Camilla Anne. But some poisons take hours to have effect."

"Not Camilla Anne," Johnny said.

"It was the crab cocktail I had in mind. But my brother says my brains are addled from too much crime on television. The woman with the oil seems to be what's addled his. Nobody can go on playing God forever. But it was the thirteen that worried me. I shouldn't wish to be responsible for a disaster. Your mother already has too much to try her. Excuse me now, dear, I'm sure the commercial's over."

She faded out as wraith-like as she'd appeared, leaving Johnny alone. Finally alone. Until the sunlit face of the girl in the yellow deck chair under the tree slipped back, the warmth and the loveliness returning.

Maybe she's home now. He picked up the phone and dialled the number she'd given him, holding his breath a little, waiting.

"—This is Miss Reeves' apartment."

Before he could swallow his dismay at hearing the name Reeves again, Kerry O'Keefe's voice was going on.

"Miss Reeves is not at home. This is a tape recording. You will have twelve seconds to give your name and telephone number. She will call you when she comes in."

He was still holding the receiver when the twelve seconds were gone and her voice was gone, the dial tone zinging in his ear, the iridescent image shattered into the tawdry dust of the Pine Street Police Station . . . dream stuff reduced to brutal reality, to Joe Anselo and the sullen crew being herded out of the cell block, into court, into taxis.

As she thrust her door shut behind Johnny Brayton, Kerry O'Keefe could see him through the disk of the one-way glass. He was still standing there, his heart with its tenderness and deep distress speaking to her more clearly than any of his words had done.

"Oh, Johnny . . . I'm sorry! I'm so sorry!"

She listened to him going along the hall to the front door. *If only I could have told him. He must think I'm horrible.* She pressed her head against the painted wood, swallowing back the ache in her throat, her mouth flooding with salt unshed tears. *I never knew you could just fall in love, all of a sudden. I've got to see him. Maybe I can tell him.*

She heard the other tread then, coming swiftly along the hall. Through the one-way glass she could see the man in the brown linen coat, and opened the door before he knocked.

"Well, he caught me flat-footed." Sergeant Dave Trumper, assigned to the Rackets Division at Central Headquarters, Baltimore City Police, stepped in and pushed the door shut. "I didn't expect you'd get rid of him that quick."

He went across the living room, shut the dutch door into the garden and tilted up the blue venetian blinds. The deck chairs were still by the iron table under the tree, still with the warmly intimate air he'd noticed over the cedar fence the half-dozen times he'd come and found the two of them still out there, unconscious of him or of time.

"If I'd thought he'd recognize me I'd have stayed in the car. What'd you want to drag one of Solly Herman's law boys back home with you for?"

"I didn't drag him home," Kerry said warmly. "I had to get out of Pine Street without Joe Anselo—"

"I know. I was in the captain's office. But I didn't expect him to spend the day."

"Neither did I. I didn't even expect him to come in. But I didn't want him to get curious and ask about me.—Coffee?"

He nodded, watching her go out to the kitchen, his bleak sea-grey eyes expressionless. He took off his coat, hung it on the back of a chair and stood there, waiting. When the sharp jab at the doorbell came he moved silently across the room to the door, looking through the glass. Kerry O'Keefe standing breathless in the kitchen heard the urgent knocking, then the feet bolting out along the hall. Trumper came back.

"Your friend Brayton. Come to tell you to cheese it, the cops." He took a cigarette out of his coat pocket and lighted it. "You've sure fouled the deal up, Officer O'Keefe. Unless you've resigned."

She came in and put the coffee on the table. "Resigned, or been fired?"

"You? Fired?" He filled his cup and reached for the sugar bowl. "You're the Rackets Division's fair-haired girl today, lady. I'd 'a told you before if I'd thought you were interested. I thought you'd decided to wait and read about it in the Sunpaper tomorrow morning."

She flushed at the sardonic twitch at one corner of his thin lips.

"It was a three million dollar take-in station you uncovered for us in the room behind the ladies' john. We're proud of you. Especially when it wasn't what we sent you down there for. It was a fine job, Officer O'Keefe. A very fine job."

Kerry bent her head quickly to keep him from seeing a different kind of flush on her cheeks. In the six months she'd worked with Sergeant Trumper this was the first word of praise she'd heard. There'd been a solid wall of antagonism that she'd thought at first was personal and learned slowly was a basic antagonism to women in police work. It was no place for women . . . *and especially you, O'Keefe, you're just not the type.* His flat face, expressionless as old leather, had never relaxed to make a tough job easier for her. It wasn't until last night, in the instant of panic when the cell block gate clanged shut behind her, that she'd ever imagined she could feel a wild rush of gratitude, much less affection, for him. So praise from him had real meaning.

He was stirring his coffee intently when she came back with a cup for herself and sat down on the sofa.

"Look, Kerry." It was the first time he'd ever called her anything but O'Keefe or Officer O'Keefe. "For God's sake—what do you think you're trying to prove?"

His face hadn't changed but his voice was curiously gentle.

"Why, nothing. Not a thing, Sergeant Trumper."

"Sure you are. I'm not the greatest detective in the world but I can see through a rookie cop like you. What do you think I've been doing the last three hours?—Cooling my heels, stalling 'em off at Headquarters, because every time I came here I looked through the fence at you and this guy out there under the apple-blossom tree. And you didn't even know when I knocked the top off the garbage can. I saw the guy. What are you going to do, Kerry? Let him break his heart and break your own? You want to let him go on thinking you're a lousy tramp?"

"—Could I . . . tell him?"

"Not and stay with Rackets you can't. His firm represents other outfits we've got an eye on. That's why I'm asking you."

"Asking me what?"

"If you're going to keep your job or get your guy."

She looked at him, her eyes widening.

"Because that's the story, kid. I saw you two out there. That was the big deal, Kerry. It don't come along more'n once, maybe twice in anybody's life. You going to kick it in the teeth? Look. I got a wife and three kids. You tell me I can have J. Edgar's job tomorrow if I dump 'em and I'll laugh in your face. They're what I live for. And look at you last night. When that gate shut, I was sick at my stomach."

She felt the rush of gratitude and the real affection again. "I . . . I heard you say you were going to stay around all night. And thanks, Dave. I . . . I thought I couldn't take it, till then."

"I was scared you'd fold and give the show away."

"I know. You're just so damned tough, aren't you?" She laughed, blinking to keep the sudden moisture out of her eyes.

"Sure I'm tough. I got to be. But you don't. Why don't you quit—"

"I'm not quitting." Her chin went up. "When the Inspector picked me out for special training I promised I'd stay a year—"

"Oh, for Chrissake, Kerry. Nobody expects a woman to keep a promise."

"Maybe that's one of the things I'm trying to prove. You don't expect a woman—"

"I expect a woman to act like a woman, and—"

He saw her eyes light then as the phone rang, until she heard the second ring. "So you gave the guy your number. Or Reeves' number." He got to his feet. "Okay if I get this? I told 'em I'd be here."

She heard him answer and listen. Then he said, "—Okay, took it like a soldier." And a pause before he said, "That's what I'm finding out. I'll call you."

He came back. "Your boy friend's combing the jails."

"Oh, no!"

"The desk sergeant at Pine Street just phoned in. Says he told Brayton to try Headquarters. We get any more people interested, you're going to be under cover like the Washington Monument."

He looked at her silently for a moment. "That was the Chief," he said evenly. "He wants to know if you can take it or if you can't."

"I can take it. I promised a year. I'm not quitting."

"Okay, Officer."

He reached in the pocket of his coat on the chair and took out a packet of papers. "Here you are." He tossed them over to her. "Your new credentials. You're a gal called Kitty Kelly, an out-of-work hostess from a Miami joint. Description on the back page."

He got up. "How long's it going to take you to pack?"

Her face was pale as she looked at him silently.

"—You're going away, Kerry. Till the heat's off. You're a fool not to quit. But it's up to you, and it's whole hog or none."

Kerry got blindly to her feet. "How long, Dave?"

"Till your hair grows out of that blondine bleach, for one thing." *The poor little devil,* he thought. He went over to the garden door. "I'll bring your chairs in."

"Dave . . . could I tell him I'm going?"

He shook his head. "He'll find out—if he's still interested after Miss Reeves answers his calls. Why you wanted to remind him of her—"

"Because I'm not allowed to give anybody the other number, and I couldn't say I didn't have a telephone, could I? He knows I'm not a tramp."

"He did while he was here. When he gets home it'll be easy to forget. I don't know his family, but I know plenty like 'em."

"If you'd just let me tell him . . ."

"Listen, sugar." His voice was gentler again. "What good's it going to do to tell him? You told me once your family raised hell when you decided you'd be a policewoman. What do you think he and his family are going to do? You say it's prejudice. Okay. You've never run into the real old-time prejudice we got here in Baltimore."

"I can't help that. I'm not ashamed of my job. I'm proud of it. My parents may not like my job but they wouldn't think much of me if I quit it now. They're Quaker stock. They don't go back on their spoken word."

"I'm just telling you. You say to him, Look, sweetie, I'm not a female sitter, I'm a female cop, and all you'll see of him is the rubber on his heels—down the back steps over the fence through the alley up to the Belvedere bar to celebrate a narrow squeak. You're butting your head against a stone wall, sugar. But if you're crazy enough to stick at your job, start packing. And give me a key so I can check your tape. If any of Solly's crowd leaves a name we'll be pretty sure they haven't figured you. You're driving, aren't you? Got a gun?"

She nodded, blind again.

"Who's going to water the garden for you?"

"There's a colored child—"

"Well, you won't be needing any for a couple of days." Sergeant Trumper looked out at the sky. "You better get going before it breaks loose up there."

The sky was black, the wind whipping, tearing the branches of the mimosa tree, when she carried the last bag out across her garden to her car in the alley garage. But the storm didn't break until she was ten miles out on the Philadelphia road. She pulled off, the rain too dense a curtain to see through, already blind with her own tears, Dave Trumper's last words still in her ears, as they'd be there again, harder even to hear and as true then as they were now.

He'd gone to the door and stopped, looking back at her. "It isn't always so easy to be a good cop, is it, Kerry?"

5

It was eight-thirty Monday morning when Johnny Brayton shifted a garbage can in the alley back of Park and stepped up on the slatted rat-proof stand to look over the split cedar fence into Kerry's garden.

It was his second try. The first was round two o'clock. He'd called her again, half a dozen times, leaving messages in the twelve seconds allowed him, but she hadn't called back, and at last he'd got out of bed and gone over to her alley, to see the dark windows tightly closed. They still were now, and in the morning light at half-past eight the empty garden was more disturbing. The white gravel under her tree was littered with leaves and branches whipped off by the wind, a pot of pink geraniums that had been on the window sill blown off and shattered under it. He could see the venetian blinds tightly shut and the windows locked.

He got down and pushed the garbage can back into place. He could ask her landlady. Some new-born discretion stopped him, as it had stopped him on his way to Central Headquarters the day before. It fell short of that now. A few minutes before nine o'clock he was walking into the offices on the sixth floor of the brick building at Fallsway and Fayette Streets and directly to the desk where Sergeant Trumper was glancing over the Sunday arrest sheet, his hat still on his head.

"I'm John Brayton, Sergeant Trumper."

There was no evidence on Trumper's face that he'd ever seen him before or that the name Brayton had any meaning.

"I'm here to find out what happened to a girl named Reeves," Johnny said evenly.

"Oh yeah." Trumper took off his hat. "You're one of Grimes'—"

"She disappeared after I saw you in front of her house." Johnny went on doggedly. "She hasn't been home since. I want to know what you've done with her. It's a personal matter. Nothing to do with the firm of—"

"I'll bet it hasn't." Trumper fixed bleak unfriendly eyes on him. "Grimes is too old a hand to put one of Solly's outfit on the spot. I'll sure take your word for that. And I'll give you my word, Mr. Brayton. We're not holding Reeves or any of the rest of the girls you got off yesterday morning. That's a plain honest fact."

He leaned forward. "Something else maybe you haven't thought of. Lottery's big business, and dirty business. You let somebody in it get the idea Grimes' office is moving heaven and hell to get that girl away from the police, they're going to figure it's because she knows too much.—If I had any personal interest in her, it'd scare me, and I'm not kidding."

He leaned back, pulled his desk drawer open and brought out a newspaper clipping. "This is the Sunpaper's report of a Grand Jurors Association meeting. Says 170 sitters have left town since the grand jury investigation began." He tossed it back into the drawer. "What Reeves did, probably. Skipped till the heat's off. They don't stay away long if they've got connections here. So why don't you simmer down, Mr. Brayton? She'll be back, I expect." He put his hat on again. "Anything else I can do for you this morning?"

Even at that and against his own better judgment, Johnny Brayton did a tour of The Block and associated areas that night, sicker and more thankful he didn't find her the farther he went down the scale. It was safe enough. The places were all dark, the one-third candle power at floor level required by law not often observed. Nobody could have recognized him even if they knew he was in Grimes' office. Then at three o'clock in the morning he was waked from a nightmare sleep when the phone rang and he listened to the eerie voice of a woman whispering over the line.—She was safe, she'd be back sometime. It relieved his despair in one way while deepening it in another. But at least she'd bothered to get a message to him.

Then there was the daily grind at the offices of Dewar, Cadbury and Grimes, anodyne or anaesthesia, whichever it was, until he was put on FTC reports and worked nights as well as days. One thing he had, her voice on the telephone. Until it was disconnected on Monday of the third week she'd been away. It was six o'clock when he got home from the office and called, and he hurried over, his heart in the pit, expecting to find her name gone from the mail box and a For Rent sign out. Instead he saw a colored girl of about ten, watering her garden, chanting a count of twenty with the hose on each plant.

"Hi," Johnny said, over the fence.

"Hi," the child said. "She's not home yet, if you're hunting her. I'm in charge till she comes."

"You wouldn't like to let me know when she does come, would you?"

The girl grinned, rolling bright brown eyes. "What for? Is it ro-mance?"

Romance sweetened with a small down payment closed a deal. Not galvanic action on the part of the white knight on a white charger, but assurance of some kind. It paid off the night of his brother Pug's birthday party when Kerry had been gone five weeks minus two days.

"Johnny." Old Horace met him at the door. "There's a child in the kitchen—"

He stood gaping as Johnny bolted past him. The child was there. "Tomorrow evening. She phoned Mumma to open the windows and start the refrigerator."

It was a reprieve so radiant that not even the prospect of Camilla Anne could dim it as Johnny went up the stairs three at a time, whistling as he showered and got himself into a dinner jacket, remembering too late he hadn't got a present. Even the aubusson carpet in the gold-and-white front parlor looked brighter as he crossed it. They were all gathered in the back parlor, his father, the charming host even to his own family, taking the martini pitcher around. *Except to Gran.* Strictly a bourbon and water man. She was sitting erect and stately, her blue-white hair immaculately coiffed, a sapphire-and-diamond dog collar glinting above her lowcut blue evening gown. His step was blithe as he approached the double doors and caught the almost imperceptible break, infinitely small, in the conversation, a kind of wary hush quickly covered.

"Hi, Johnny."

"Hi," Johnny said. "Hi, Gran." He went over to her and bent to kiss her cheek. He'd seen her eyes narrow as they'd fixed on him, so he was not surprised to find it cool to the touch. "You look very handsome this evening, ma'am."

Camilla Anne trapped that one and whipped it to second. "Grandmother's the most handsome and distinguished-looking older woman in Baltimore, *I* think."

His sister Meg's eye met Johnny's.

"Gran still likes a little water with her bourbon, Cam," Camilla Anne's husband Dr. Pierce Brayton Jr. said.

"At my age you take it any way you can get it, Pug," his grandmother said dryly. "—Thank you, dear," she added to Camilla Anne.

Johnny went to kiss his mother. Her cheek was softly warm. "Hello, love." She was sitting in the fireside chair, a needlepoint tapestry resting in her lap. She smiled up at him and took his hand affectionately in hers.

"Where's Lolly?"

"Visiting Camp Dix. Extra liberty this weekend."

"Rather extraordinary." He heard his father's silken voice. "It's taken two world wars to make camp following respectable."

Johnny stiffened with sudden rage. His mother's hand tightened on his. "She's staying with friends of mine on the post, if any of you are alarmed," she said tranquilly.

"You've always had a peculiar sympathy for the military, Margaret," Dr. Brayton remarked.

It sounded pleasant, but somehow, Johnny realized, it wasn't. Perhaps it was his mother's silence, or the sharp contraction he saw in his grandmother's eyes, that made it seem so. It was the nearest he'd ever heard to the slightly mocking amusement in his father's voice when he was speaking to their mother. Or perhaps it was because he was turning to Johnny that the familiar tone had crept in.

"Good evening, Counsellor. A martini?"

"Thank you, sir."

God, how I hate him.

He took the glass and turned to his brother. "Skoal. Many happy returns. I'll owe you a present."

"No gift shoppies over on Park, I guess." His sister Meg's husband, Joe, a nice uncomplicated red-headed lad who worked in his uncle's insurance business, grinned cheerfully at him. "I got a friend says you haunt the alleys looking for the blonde—"

"May I have a touch more bourbon, Pierce?" Mrs. Summerfield's voice broke the abyss of silence. Joe reddened and looked

43

blankly at Meg, her head bent to count the stitches in the child's sweater she was knitting.

Light if light were needed illumined Johnny Brayton's mind. *Nobody's told old Joe. The conspiracy of silence has left him out.* The conspiracy of silence. Nobody, not even Camilla Anne, had said a word to him since the Sunday crisis. But it was obvious there'd been plenty of discussion when he wasn't around. He could see it in the way his sister's head was bent over her knitting and the sharp warning in Pug's eyes as he looked at Camilla Anne. His grandmother was going calmly on.

"—Your lady from Texas, Pierce," she was saying. "What's happened to her project? Margaret tells me she's been in town again."

"I told you she'd been and gone a dozen times, Mother," Margaret Brayton said without looking up from her needlepoint.

"Mrs. Richwitch, you mean?"

Johnny glanced at his brother. The offensive edge to his voice as he'd asked that was surprising. He and Meg were the two who'd learned quickest that silence was the best defense against their father's subtle torture.

"Ristwich is the name." Dr. Brayton corrected him without amusement or mockery. "But I'm afraid you have a right to resent her activities, Pug. It's too bad she had to publicize her plans for the Hopkins. She seems to have a sense of proprietorship that would be offensive to any self-respecting institution. So nothing's happened. I'm still hopeful we can work it out. If we can't, I'm wasting a good deal of time."

He paused a moment. "Her other idea, to endow a project of mine, is definitely out. I wouldn't consider moving it West." He looked over at his wife. "I also regard my present marriage as completely permanent. Not soluble, even in *aqua regis*, if I may put it that way. Not for all the oil of Araby."

In spite of himself, Johnny Brayton was moved by an aspect of his father he had never known to exist. He looked at his mother, expecting to see a quiet smile in her dark eyes, accepting the tribute.

But she wasn't smiling. She wasn't even looking at him. Her head was bent over her work as if she hadn't heard or didn't know it was her he was speaking to. For once Johnny was grateful to Camilla Anne.

"I think that's just the sweetest thing! Mother! You're blushing! You're actually blushing! It's simply divine!"

44

But she isn't blushing. Johnny felt a cold hand closing, tightening everything inside him. He was the only one who wasn't delighted, the only one who saw her hand quiver as she folded the needlepoint, her dark head still bent over it.

"Why don't we all go in?" She looked up then, her face ivory clear, serenely exquisite. "Take your glass with you, Mother, and anyone else, if you wish."

They followed her across the hall into the dining room, Johnny last. His heart was numb. It was strange none of the rest had seen. Stranger that he'd never until then seen the significance of her turning on him, hellfire blazing, the Sunday afternoon he'd knocked at her door. *Father always knocks.* He'd come that close to it but had left it there. *It was because I knocked. She thought it was him. That's why she turned on me.*

He stopped in the dining room doorway, a kind of semi-paralysis creeping over him, as he remembered the blazing fury. *She hates him. My God, she hates the living hell out of him. Our serene and lovely Ma . . .*

He watched her take her place at the head of the table, all her graceful warmth intact again, or seemingly so in the softer lights of the candles burning in the tall silver candelabra at each end of the table. And suddenly Johnny's mind was moving again, his eyes moving from her to the elaborate silver epergne on the Empire plateau in the center of the long mahogany table, filled with flowers, the dangling crystal cups in silver baskets filled with bunches of purple grapes. He looked at it, seeing it for the first time. It had always been there, always filled, even when he and Lolly were the only ones left at home. It was only when his father was away that it was moved off, over to the sideboard. *It's a screen. It's so she can sit at the end and not have to look at him. Night after night. My God, how awful . . .*

Something moved then, uneasily chill, in a corner of his mind as his father's words came back to him . . . *Regard my present marriage as completely permanent. Not soluble even in* aqua regis . . .

What did he mean? *It was corn. Pure corn. That's not his stuff. What was he doing? He's trapped her. He was serving notice she can't get away.*

Johnny Brayton put his hand up and rubbed his brow to try to clear his head, like a sleepwalker painfully awaking. He glanced at his mother again. For an instant there was a shadow on her face of heart-breaking hopelessness, gone so quickly he wasn't sure he hadn't dreamed it. He shook his head sharply. *I'm nuts. I must be. Nobody could live like that. She'd die if she did. Die or commit murder . . . one of the two.*

He glanced down at the end of the table toward his father, and found himself looking instead into the bitter old eyes rivetted on him. Mrs. Summerfield did not return his smile, and the glint in her eye was as hard as the glint from the sapphires and diamonds round her neck.

6

"Just wanted to see if you'd changed your mind, Officer."

Dave Trumper came through the arch into the living room and turned back to Kerry, something almost like warmth in the silent reappraisal he was giving her. The blonde pony pigtail was gone. The blue-black sheen of her cap of short-cropped curls and the glossy black of her unplucked brows made her blue eyes a deeper more velvet blue and gave her skin a softer glow.

She smiled and shook her head. "I haven't changed it."

"Not when the guy's begging you to marry him?"

Her cheeks turned a deeper rose as she went out to the kitchen to bring in the coffee she'd put on as soon as she brought her bags in round four o'clock, knowing he'd be coming, and for what purpose.

"Is there a new assignment?" She let the other question go.

"The Coral Seas. We've got a tip it's being used for a narcotics drop for runners from South America. Three ships due the middle of next week. You'll start tomorrow night. If you're still with us."

"I'm still with you. I said a year, Dave."

"That was before Brayton proposed via tape recorder.—And I guess I better tell you what I did."

If it had been anybody else she would have thought he was embarrassed. "What did you do, Dave?"

"Well, he came down to see me."

Kerry laughed with sudden amusement. "Just tell me."

He gave her a dour grin. "I thought I'd scared him. I didn't want him hunting you. But he was downtown, combing the joints. I had my wife call him, cloak and dagger stuff, three a.m. She told him you were okay, out of town till the heat was off, and you'd let him know when you got back. So it's up to you." He grinned again. "I'm doing my best for you, sugar. My advice is same as before. The Coral Seas is a client of theirs. And like I told you—"

"I know. When he finds out I'm a policewoman—"

"That's right. Most people think policewomen go round in uniform and flat-heeled shoes, tough old biddies. Or they get 'em mixed up with the crossing guards helping kids get home from school. Nobody'd think you got on your working clothes right now." He glanced at her cobalt-blue checked wool suit and high-heeled blue pumps with something like approval. "Okay, lady. Call me up when you change your mind."

Kerry picked up her bags to take them on in to her bedroom. She put her overnight case on the chest of drawers, her eyes and lips suddenly soft as she opened it. It was a trick job with a false bottom her brothers had given her as a big joke. And not as funny as they'd thought. She released the hidden catch to lift the leather-lined inset, and took out the only paper she'd carried that indicated she was other than Kitty Kelly, an out-of-work hostess from a Miami cocktail lounge. It was the strangest love letter a girl ever got, in two typed paragraphs under a Baltimore Police Department letterhead, a transcript the Inspector's secretary had sent her while they were still checking the tape-recorded calls. The date at the top was September 17th. Below it were the two messages she knew by heart.

"Kerry," the first one said, "how can I ask a voice on a tape recording that's pretending it's another girl to marry me? But I need you, Kerry. I love you so much. You've got to quit this lousy job and marry me. We'll go some place else and start from scratch. I'm going nuts without you, Kerry."

The second said, "Mr. Brayton, Miss O'Keefe. Your voice is all I've got, Kerry. Please come back. You're all my life. We'll work things out. I'm asking you again—will you marry me, Kerry? I never knew what it meant to be in love before. Please come back."

She bent her head, transmuting the cold type into the velvet rose-colored warmth that came into her heart every time she read it. Then she slipped the sheet back. She was closing the case when she heard the rap on the door. She glanced in the mirror, smiling at herself. Trumper again, back to see if she'd changed her mind. She knew what he was doing, actually—needling her, not to make her quit her job but to keep her from doing it. It was a Trumper technique she'd seen work many times.

"So you can just wait, my love," she thought. She went leisurely to the closet and put her bag in, came back to the mirror, fluffed her blue-black curls and renewed her lipstick. Then she went out across the living room without haste, still amused, looked through the one-way glass to see how patiently he was waiting, and saw a dark-grey flannel shoulder turning dispiritedly to go.

"Oh!" Her hand flashed to the door as her heart caught breathlessly.

Johnny Brayton turned back, his face lighting for an instant before it went blank, totally blank.

Oh . . . I'd forgotten. He thinks I'm a blonde . . .

"I'm so sorry. I thought Miss O'Keefe—"

He broke off, his eyes opening incredulously. "—Kerry. Oh, Kerry!"

He didn't touch her. The picture he'd always had of himself seeing her again, crushing her to him, was like so many other pictures of journeys ending in lovers' meetings. Not the way it was in fact. He stood looking at her, not moving, until she stepped back into the little foyer. He came in then and went slowly into the living room. She closed the door and came in after him. He was looking around him at the curtains and walls.

"That's what I've been wondering about. The colors. The dusty blues and dusty pinks. They didn't go with the yellow hair." He went slowly to her. "You're beautiful, Kerry," he said gravely. "Very beautiful. I love you. Even more than I thought I did." He put his arms out to her. She came softly into them and he drew her to him, not hungrily but softly tender. "I've missed you, Kerry," he whispered, the world dissolving in its twilight gold.

Until around one o'clock when he was at the door, starting to leave.

"—Tomorrow, Kerry. Let's go down to the shore and have dinner—"

"I can't, Johnny!" She tried to make her voice sound casual. "I'm hunting a job. I think I know where I can get one."

He was staring at her, not believing.

"My God, Kerry! You *can't!* You haven't seen the papers. There's a clean-up drive on all those filthy holes. Do you want them to drag you to jail again, for the love of God? You just don't understand! You don't realize what the hell you're doing!"

He was shouting at her then, saying bitterly angry things he didn't mean, goading her finally beyond endurance.

"Stop it! Just stop it!" She blazed up suddenly, lashing back at him, her cheeks burning, blue eyes as black as pitch. "You tell me you'll marry me. On what? You've already said your take-home pay is $40.56 a week. You've said Mr. Grimes only takes people with families to feed and clothe them. Apprentice lawyers in Baltimore aren't paid enough to live on. So what am I to do? Quit my job and get one in a department store to pay the rent and help feed us? Would that be respectable enough to suit you?"

She burst into tears then. "Oh, Johnny, I'm sorry! I didn't mean it. But if you think I'm so horrible, just go away. Go away and leave me alone. It's your family you love, it isn't me!"

He was still sick, but part of it was the sickness of his own defeat. What she'd said was true, and the irony of it was especially bitter. If she were any one of a dozen other girls he could think of there wouldn't be any problem of take-home pay. His grandmother would subsidize him, as she did Pug doing his internship and his sister, Meg, not lavishly but enough to pay the rent, keep a car and produce their young. It was the first time in Johnny Brayton's life that he'd come smack up against the economic facts of it.

He put his arms around her, holding her tight, waiting for the storm of tears to be over. "I don't think you're horrible, Kerry. And it's not because I love my family better . ."

"I'm sorry. I didn't mean it. I understand all that—"

"But the rest of it is true. I shouldn't have asked you to marry me when I can't support you. But I can go somewhere else. Grimes'll be glad—"

"No, you can't," she said quickly. "He took you for a year. You can't just get up and say you've changed your mind."

She brushed the tears out of her eyes. "I know it all seems so horrible to you, Johnny. But it isn't, really. Men don't make passes at me. Even in the Mimosa Club I had a lot fewer than I've had at cocktail parties or dinner next to some pillar of society. But it isn't that even. You'll just have to take me as I am. If you can't bear it—"

"If I have to bear it, I'll have to, Kerry. Until I can do something. I can't live without you. It's been hell while you were gone."

They made it up then. It was an uneasy truce, a kind of conspiracy of silence of their own. She didn't tell him where she was working, he didn't ask. He hurried up to her apartment for a few minutes after the office whenever he could get away, before the six o'clock deadline she set for them. On Sundays the whole day and the whole evening was theirs. The rest of the time he worked like a lead dog in an Arctic sledge. He wasn't happy but it was better than nothing, and made him work harder than he'd known he had it in him to work. And the fact that he wasn't walking on air as he'd done the night of Pug's party saved him even though he wasn't aware of it. His grandmother, watching him, watching and waiting, held her hand.

And because his mother was as quietly serene as she'd ever been, the night of Pug's party passed out of his mind, something he'd dreamed. Or perhaps it was Mrs. Richwitch, coming back and forth with such increasing regularity, her car and her chauffeur calling for his father, so that he was almost never home when Johnny was, that made the house seem more peaceful than it had ever been. Until the week before Christmas, when reaching for the stars he'd caught a shining handful only to look behind him into the naked face of his own fear.

At one-thirty a. m. his phone rang. He sat bolt upright in bed, his stomach turning over, the barred gate at the Pine Street Station before his eyes again, and reached for the phone, heart-sick, expecting to hear Mr. Grimes.

"Johnny!" It was Kerry O'Keefe, her voice urgent.

"What's—where are you, Kerry?"

"Don't, Johnny . . I'm all right. I wanted to call you right away so you wouldn't worry if you heard it on the radio. There was a raid. Three of us got away. I'm not in jail, I'll be home in five minutes. So go back to sleep, darling. You'll see it in the paper."

He saw it in the morning, a late flash on the back page. "Rackets Squad Raid On The Coral Seas."

"Police raided the Coral Seas Club early this morning. A large quantity of uncut heroin was found in the possession of two men being held at Central Station.

"Rackets Division spokesmen said they believe the club has been used as a narcotics drop for supplies coming in through the Port

51

of Baltimore for some time. Officers cleared the club management of any complicity. FBI agents working with the Rackets Division were present at the raid."

Johnny Brayton was sick, also sore. He was more so as he read the chatty article on the same page, with a picture of Major-General Robert Wood Preston. The title was "Tubby Preston Omits The Brass."

"Out at Friends School yesterday he was plain old Tubby on his annual visit to his home town. With a twinkle in his blue eyes he admits he thought the cavalry was still the place to ride a horse when he quit school three weeks before graduation to join up. He didn't find any hayburners, but there were plenty of tanks to take apart. He went on to learn about mechanized warfare, and learned so much that at forty-eight he's one of the youngest major-generals in (continued on page 22)"

Johnny didn't bother to turn inside to page 22. The contrast between the raid, with Kerry O'Keefe getting away just in time not to be hauled off to jail, and the general, a friend of his family, the guest of honor at a dinner at his grandmother's two nights earlier, was a kind of last straw.

Another came when the phone rang a minute later.

"Johnny . . Nelson Grimes." Mr. Grimes was very cheerful. "We've got some more girls at Pine Street. Drop around and—"

"Sorry." Johnny cut in curtly. "Get somebody else. I didn't go into the law to foul its skirts on a pack of jackals."

He heard himself, appalled, and heard the appalled and also dumbfounded silence thundering in his ear. *My God.* He took a deep breath.

"Sorry, sir. If it'll embarrass you to fire me, I'm glad to resign."

"—Now, Johnny." Mr. Grimes, when he recovered, was smoother than owl's grease. "That . . ah, that's the spirit I like to see. Ah . . never beat about the bush. I'll send Dakers. You come have lunch with me today. We've got old Parsons here. He's very pleased with your job on the FTC reports. One o'clock, Crooked Lane Club."

Johnny put the phone down, still shaken. Then he thought, *Well, I'll be damned.* He grinned suddenly, ate his breakfast and set out, a free man . . which no doubt had a great deal to do with that part of the rest of his day that ended abruptly and frighteningly at seven-forty-five o'clock.

52

At five-fifteen he was at Kerry's apartment. "Kerry! We're set!" He grabbed her in his arms, swinging her off the floor.

She stared breathlessly at him as he let her down. "I . . thought you'd be—I mean, I've been dreading—"

"Listen, girl. The worm turned. And **Mr.** Grimes invited me to lunch."

Kerry blinked. "Is that such an honor—"

"Hush and listen. Mr. Parsons was there. Senior partner of our correspondents in San Francisco. When Grimes left he said what about coming to the Coast when my year's up? How much was I getting? When I told him he stared at me. He'll start me at seventy-five hundred."

"Oh, Johnny!"

"He's going to write Grimes a letter but I'm not to tell him till later."

He took her in his arms again, his face grave. "Will you marry me, Kerry? In July? Promise me, Kerry. You do love me, don't you?"

"I promise you, Johnny. I do love you—very much."

The golden peace was there again, until he released her and said, "What did happen last night?"

"Oh, Johnny, don't let's start all that again. I don't want to talk about it. And you're going to be furious . . I'm going home for—"

"Till the heat's off."

"That's right! What am I supposed to do—starve till July?"

"I'm sorry." He took her face in his hands. "I didn't mean it. It's . . just the way any guy would feel. I love you so much. You're not leaving tonight?"

She shook her head. "Tomorrow."

"Then we can celebrate." He bounced back among the stars. "There's a place called the Fiesole. I saw their card on my mother's desk. I've got to go home—I want to tell Ma about the job. I'll get the car and—"

"I'll take a taxi and meet you there. I know where it is.—Now please, Johnny—don't start getting sore again. It's just some arrangements I've got to make. And I won't go if every other minute—"

"Sorry, sweet." He kissed her again. "Seven-thirty, as close as you can make it."

Crossing Mt. Vernon Place he quickened his buoyant strides.

"Hi, Mrs. Remstad." The blonde lady next door was coming

down her brownstone steps. He greeted her warmly, in love with all the world. "I haven't seen you for ages. You been away?"

"Yes. But I came back."

He stopped short. "Hey, what's the matter?" In the glow from the flood lights on the Monument her face looked old and washed-out, and her voice sounded dead, all the lilting warmth gone from it. "You haven't been sick, have you?"

"No. Not sick. I just don't have the heart to go any place. Like on a cruise, I mean. But you look like you got pink clouds to walk on, Johnny."

"I have, Mrs. Remstad." Johnny laughed. "She's just said she'd marry me. Just a few minutes ago."

He saw her jaw drop and her eyes open wide. "But Johnny . . your family. What's your family going to say?"

If Mrs. Inga Remstad's jaw had dropped, Johnny Brayton's dropped farther. She saw it and flushed scarlet.

"Oh, I wouldn't have said that for anything, Johnny. I . . I don't mean to butt in on your business. But . . I take walks at night, when I can't sleep. I've seen you with her, over on Park, Sunday nights. And I've seen her come out alone. She's an entertainer some place, isn't she? I can always tell 'em. I used to have an act myself once."

She was embarrassed, shifting her feet, her eyes fixed past him.

"That's why I figured your family wouldn't like it. Specially your father in that fancy car."

Johnny looked around. It was there, Mrs. Richwitch's chauffeur huddled at the wheel. He hadn't noticed it till then, and he started to move on, to avoid another meeting like the last one. But Mrs. Remstad didn't move.

"I was surprised myself, because when I saw her with you she looked just like . . like one of your own friends."

You're always seen, love.

"And I . . I wanted to talk to you. Johnny. You're like I was, sort of. We had a farm, in northern Minnesota. We had all sorts of stuff to eat, wild ducks, geese, deer in winter, all the fish we wanted and stuff we grew. Everything but money. Any money my father had he hid. Under a slab of stone in the root cellar. He didn't trust banks. Then when my mother died and he married again it was a hard life—too hard for me. So a Wild West show came through and they let the locals show off and the man said I could come with them. That's how I got in the show business. I was pretty good, too."

With her pride a little of Mrs. Remstad's gloss came back.

"But what I'm saying is, it was in the flush days. This fella and me in my act was making money hand over foot. They'd throw it at you, the stage covered like winter oats. Everybody was in the market, except me. I kept mine in my sock, like Pa. Then when the bust came, this broker was running around like he had fits, saying My God, now's the time to get rich—if you had any dough. Me, I had it. I just kept enough so if I had another accident, because this jerk I had the act with went off his nut once and shot me and blew his brains out. We had a sort of take-off on a Western."

Mrs. Remstad glanced up at the Braytons' door and lowered her voice.

"To make a long story short, what I'm getting at is if you want to marry this girl and they don't like it and you need any money, I got it and I'd be glad to let you have it. I know young lawyers don't make anything. I staked too many of 'em. That's why I say you're like I was. You got everything as long's you stay home, but they won't give you the dough to marry on if they don't like it. And I'd be proud to help you. You're the only one's been decent to me. You sent me postcards from camp one summer. I guess you've forgot, but I never have. And a May basket once."

Did I? He'd completely forgotten. Small crumbs of bread cast on the waters of a lonely life.

"Thanks, Mrs. Remstad. Thanks a lot. But we're all set now. I'm going to get a better job."

"Oh, that's fine, Johnny. But don't you let anybody talk you out of it. You just marry her and don't say a thing. Specially to your parents. But I didn't mean to keep you this long. It's just that I . . I got no more use for all the dough I got. Well, 'night, Johnny. You go easy but you stick to it."

Johnny let himself into the house. As he shut the door old Horace came in at the back in his Sunday suit.

"I didn't 'spect you home, Johnny. Lolly's having dinner out an' the Doctor's just getting ready to go."

"Where's Ma?"

"She didn't say. She just left."

Even though it was on her desk Johnny had seen the Fiesole card, it would never in the world have occurred to him that that would be the place she'd left for. It was off Thames Street in the heart of Little Italy, the part of Baltimore known as Old Town, there before Baltimore Town was founded. Outside it was strident neon, inside it was still divided into the small rooms of the pre-Revolutionary house it was. There was a not unpleasant aroma of oil and garlic, and laughter coming from a bar in the front room. Kerry was already there. How long she'd been there he never asked her.

The moment he slipped into the seat across from her, his back to the thin plywood partition between the booths, he froze rigid.

"—Crazy to go on this way. Come with me now, Megsie."

He'd heard that, the man's voice deep and vaguely familiar, as he sat down. The name meant nothing to him. Only a very few of Margaret Brayton's oldest childhood friends still called her that. But then he heard his mother's voice.

"Not now. As soon as Lolly's settled. It isn't long. And I know I'm crazy, Tubby."

Johnny sat numb, unable to move, realizing in a half-stunned way that the man was General Preston. Kerry's dark head was bent over the menu as she tried to read it in the candle light.

"There's always been a Mrs. Ristwich of some sort in his life. I don't know why this one's so terrifying. Or why I should hate him so for what he's doing to the poor creature. It's so utterly fantastic, the years I've kept from . . from *killing* him, for the way he's tortured my children—that sort of psychological vivisection—that now I could really do it for the way he's treating her. It's so wicked —and so utterly incredible that I should care. I'd have gone mad if I hadn't had you to write to and talk to. I think I—"

Johnny was aware out of a benumbed fog that Kerry had raised her head from the menu and that her eyes, velvet-black in the heart-shaped whiteness of her face in the candle light, were searching his, deeply distressed. Then he saw her reach quickly for her bag and gloves and pick up her coat. She slipped out of the booth and went to the door, waiting there for him.

"—Your overcoat." It was she who went back and got it.

"You change your mind?" The waitress had come then.

"Just going to the bar," Kerry said.

They went out into the street, Johnny moving blindly, knowing something had to be said, not knowing what to say. He heard her then, casual and matter-of-fact.

56

"I was afraid you'd got a shock of some kind," she said quietly. "I thought I'd better get you out, if they were friends of yours. What about Gino's? It's just around the block."

He was grateful, warmly and intensely grateful. But he couldn't tell then or any time the rest of the evening whether she knew it was his mother. Or whether she'd heard them. Or what she'd heard sitting there before he came.

In February, only four months and three days left till July, Kerry was back. If the joy of having her was racked by the agony of her job, Johnny Brayton's own job didn't give him much leisure to worry, and because there was hope it was no longer a grind. A working agreement to keep the peace gave them Sundays together and anytime he could drop in between five and the six o'clock deadline. When he couldn't and was working late she'd drive up to Mt. Vernon Place after she got off. He'd meet her down on the other side of the Monument, across from the Peabody Institute, drive home with her to put her car in the alley garage, wait till he saw her lights go on and walk back home through the silent streets. It was always his Kerry, not Miss Reeves. She had a bottle of flower mist and cotton in the glove compartment, so the make-up was gone, her hair combed back down to its glossy close-fitting cap again.

It was also in the glove compartment that he found her gun one day. It was a Sunday toward the end of April. They were out in the Valley eating a picnic lunch in a field under an oak tree and he'd opened the compartment to find some cigarettes. Her heart sank as he came back with it in his hand, his jaw hard.

"Kerry—what's this?"

"That? Why, that's a gun, Johnny." She kept her voice light, determined not to lose her own temper. "The permit's in my bag if you'd like to see it."

"Do you know how to use it?"

She took it and released the safety. "See that splotch of fungus on the oak? The top one in the center?"

The gun cracked and the grey-green dust splattered.

He looked at her oddly. "Where'd you learn to shoot, pardner?"

"My father and brothers. Tin cans on stumps. Then at school." She didn't say the school was the Police Academy or mention the target range at Central Headquarters.

"My mother's the only other gal I know that could have hit that bull's-eye that neat."

I've got to be more careful. It was excitement that made her forget to take it out of the compartment the night before. For the last two weeks she'd been working with Sergeant Burns of the New York Racket Squad, Dave Trumper behind the scenes, at a place called the Hay Ride Club, tipped off that a character badly wanted in New York and elsewhere was holed in there. Last night she'd caught the first sign that the tip might be right. There was always excitement, mounting tension, among all of them when it seemed likely they were closing in on any job. And it was that that made her neglect to look through the one-way disk, three days later, before she opened her door.

That was a Wednesday. Johnny had been and gone and she was hurrying to get dressed and do her makeup before Sergeant Burns came to pick her up. They had bracketed their man, by a simple thing, his habit of eating sour rye bread sprinkled with carroway seeds and his addiction to a brand of expensive Scotch whiskey far different from that dispensed to its regular clients by the Hay Ride Club. All they had to find out was who the midnight snack was taken to.

"Maybe tonight," Kerry said to her unrecognizable self in the mirror. "But just calm down, Officer O'Keefe." She put on some extra rouge, tightening the screw of one dime-store earring as she heard the rap at the door. She glanced at her watch. It was early but Burns was probably as tense as she was, even if he didn't show it. She ran out, putting on the other earring as she went, dropped it as she got to the door and stooped down to retrieve it with one hand as she opened the door with the other.

"You're early—"

As she caught the fragrance of Parma violets she stopped short and looked up quickly. A woman's feet, elegantly shod, were what she saw first. It was a lifetime, her heart still as a stone, before she got herself unsteadily erect to see the handsome figure in a grey suit and silver-blue mink stole with the violets held by a diamond

59

cluster, the blue-white hair under a small close-fitting hat of blue silk violets, the determined jaw, patrician nose, and the sharp old eyes, cold grey as a shark's, that were fixed on her.

"Miss O'Keefe? I'm Mrs. John Summerfield. You know my grandson, I believe. I wonder if you'd allow me to come in a few moments. Unless it will make you late for your work, of course."

There are moments too awful to do anything but rise to them face to face.

"Please come in, Mrs. Summerfield." Where her voice came from and how it managed to sound as steady as it did, she never knew. "Sit down, won't you?"

She saw the old eyes take complete inventory of the room without an apparent movement of the regal head, and return to her, moving very deliberately, beginning at her gold sandals, up the tawdry cheapness of the beaded evening dress, reaching her face, ending on the single dime-store earring dangling against her jaw. Kerry stood quietly, her own face as expressionless as the stony face examining her.

"I've been anxious to meet you, Miss O'Keefe. I've had such conflicting reports about you. Originally you were a . . a blonde."

Mrs. Summerfield sat down, majestically erect, the soft fragrance of the violets stirring the air as she moved. Kerry was aware of her eyes doing another detailed appraisal of the room.

"You rent your apartment furnished, I presume."

"No," Kerry said. "Everything's mine. Including the paint."

"Then perhaps I've been misled, Miss O'Keefe."

Mrs. Summerfield was no less forbidding, but in some way less openly offensive. "Perhaps it's your . ." Her eyes moved to the beaded dress again, up to the mascara'd lashes, meeting Kerry's, the Medusa steadiness unchanged as she hesitated. "Your present—"

"Get-up, I believe is the word, Mrs. Summerfield." Kerry suppressed an almost irresistible desire to laugh, and saw the shark's-eyes dart at her.

"Thank you. I see now that we understand each other, Miss O'Keefe. So I'm sure you'll understand my concern for my grandson, and understand why I felt it necessary to have a private investigator supply me with some information about you."

For the first time Kerry's eyes wavered. If they'd found out she was a policewoman it could wreck the Hay Ride job.

As Mrs. Summerfield watched her there was a glint of satisfaction in her own eyes. "During the time you were employed at the Coral Seas Club," she added. "And what concerns me is what possible interest you can have in my grandson. You don't by any chance think he can . ."

She moved her gloved hand, not sure how to say it.

" . . Raise your standard of living . . let's say? Because I can assure you, my dear child, that that's a forlorn hope. It'll be a good many years before he can feed and clothe himself. And I should very much regret having to change the provisions I've made for him. It's conceivable, of course, that you've fallen in love with him. In that case I can't believe you'd deliberately destroy his chances of advancement. You must realize how far apart your worlds are. I should imagine it must cause you as much embarrassment as it does him, not to be able to invite you into his home, to meet his family and his friends. If he's ashamed of you now, Miss O'Keefe, when he's apparently fascinated by you, it's hardly likely he won't suffer far more acutely at a later date. I'm thinking of your happiness as well as his."

"Thank you, Mrs. Summerfield." Kerry had relaxed again. Either the private detective hadn't found out she was a policewoman or had kept his mouth shut not to jeopardize his relations with Headquarters.

"You've never been abroad, have you, Miss O'Keefe?" Mrs. Summerfield was quite pleasant.

"No, I never have."

"From the pictures on your walls, I'd judge you might find a few years in France and Italy very interesting. If it were arranged so you could live in reasonable comfort—even in luxury, Miss O'Keefe, I'm sure you—"

"I'm sorry, Mrs. Summerfield." Kerry rose abruptly.

"It's a little absurd to pretend you're sensitive, Miss O'Keefe," Mrs. Summerfield said easily. "Not with the evidence I have of your . . professional activities."

She got to her feet. "Women have to be practical, my dear child. In a currency that has nothing to do with moonlight and roses. Think it over, Miss O'Keefe. And if you should prefer something more bizarre than a trip abroad, as you easily may considering your present choice of occupation, it can be arranged. Life in Baltimore is not that, I'm afraid."

"On the contrary, Mrs. Summerfield," Kerry said. "I think it's exceedingly bizarre. Like your being here now for example. And I hope you'll forgive me if I find it offensive as well as bizarre. So if you'll excuse me . . "

She went to the door.

There were few times in Mrs. Summerfield's life when she was speechless. And then not for long.

"The truth's frequently offensive, my dear." She followed Kerry and stopped in the doorway. "But I'm not trying to offend you. I'm merely asking you to consult your own interest as well as my grandson's. All for love or the world well lost is very fine indeed until there are bills to pay and your clothes get seedy and your former friends avoid you. Think it over. It's purely a business proposition. My number's in the phone book. I shall be at home until five o'clock tomorrow evening. I shall expect to hear from you before then. I shall be most reluctant to take any further step."

Kerry closed the door and stood for an instant, waiting for some kind of reaction, of anger, shame, remorse, something. There was nothing. She had no feeling of any kind. It was not until she got home that night, the lingering fragrance of the Parma violets still in the room, and looked at herself in the mirror, that the reaction came. She put her head down, hot with shame. *How horrible. How horrible she must think I am. How could she help it! But it would have been the same thing if she'd known I was a policewoman.*

I ought to tell him, she thought. But when Johnny came for a few minutes around five-thirty the next night she didn't tell him, or tell him that Mrs. Summerfield had given her till then to make up her mind.

So Johnny Brayton went whistling up the brownstone steps at five minutes past six without warning.

"Hi, Johnny dear." Camilla Anne greeted him gaily from the front parlor. She was holding one end of a rope covered with laurel leaves, Horace holding the other, fixing it across the open double doors of the gold-and-white room.

He stopped. "Hi. What goes on?"

"Pilgrimage, darling. You know. House and Garden tour. Annual event. I promised Mother if she'd open again I'd do the work and be hostess-in-chief. I expected Lolly'd help, but she's scooted off again. And Grandmother's upstairs. You'd better take her a spot of bourbon. There's no admittance here."

"Gran can have my bottle."

He took the steps three at a time before she could decide she needed more help.

"Hi, Gran." He met her at the top of the staircase. "What about a quick snort with me on the third floor?"

She looked at him, not offering her cheek, not smiling. "No thank you, Johnny." She pulled on her gloves. "I'm taking Camilla Anne home for dinner now. Your mother's in her room. She'd like to see you, I believe."

He looked at her, surprised but not alarmed. She was crotchety at times. "Okay, lady. May I assist you down the stairs first, ma'am?"

"No, Johnny."

He waited nevertheless till she was safely down, turned blithely to his mother's door and opened it. "Hi, Ma." He took a buoyant step into her sitting room and stopped, his feet frozen into the pile of the eggshell carpet. "Mother!"

She was sitting erect by the table in front of the window, her body rigid, her eyes with great deep circles under them, wells of agony in the deadly pallor of her face.

He sprang across the rug toward her, his heart curdled with fear. "Ma . . what's the matter? For God's sake, what is it?"

When he was almost to her she rose quickly, her body taut, her eyes on him compelling him to stop. She moved her hand, flicking it back to the table, to the white square of paper lying there. She flicked it forward at him.

"—Is this true, Johnny? Is this the girl you go to see? Is this the girl you've fallen in love with?"

Her voice, not raised, was coming quietly from the depths of hell.

He stared at her, his hand moving in a slow-motion arc to take the glossy print she held face up in her hand. Her face was so ghastly that it held him in a Medusa grip as he took the picture, moved his eyes down then, and froze again in the sudden depths of a hell all his own. It was Kerry. Kerry coming out of the Coral Seas Club, the name spangled over the cut-out, by the door just behind her, of a larger than life-size almost nude stripper, holding a filmy black petticoat in one hand and a glass of champagne bubbling in the other. And Kerry . . He closed his eyes, sicker than he'd ever been.

"Is it true . . or isn't it, Johnny." His mother's voice was deadly still.

"It . . is and it isn't, Mother. This isn't what she's—"

"Please, Johnny." She put her hand up quickly. "Please don't. Are you . . are you living with her?"

"No! I'm not living with her! I'm going to—"

"You are going to marry her?"

"Yes. I am."

"Good." Her eyes were bright, deadly bright. "That's all, Johnny. There's only one other thing. Never bring her here. Never let me see her. Go now. That's all."

"But Mother—"

"I said go, Johnny." Her voice was beginning to break as he moved backwards. "—Oh God, I could kill him. I could kill him!" She stumbled back into her chair, her head on her arms on the table, her body shaking.

"Mother . . " He started back, but she flashed up, her eyes blazing.

"Go, I said! Go, Johnny! Leave me alone! And take that thing." She thrust her hand out at the picture fallen face up on the floor, the larger than life-size stripper obscenely vivid. "Take it away. I can't bear it. My Johnny! My son! Go now, please. Go away, love."

He bent down and picked it up, crushing it in his hand. "Please, Mother—"

"No, Johnny." She'd drawn herself together again, her voice serene, her face still ghastly. "Go now. And close the door if you will, please. Tell Horace I won't be down for dinner. I'm not at home if anybody calls. Thank you, love."

He closed the door and stood in the empty hall. There was no sound anywhere except his Aunt Elizabeth Brayton's perpetual television.

"My God, she could die there and nobody'd ever know it," he thought with an irrelevance that was the measure of his shock. "—No, I guess not." He saw Horace trudging up the back stairs with her supper tray.

He trudged on up himself and met the old man in the third floor hall.

"I won't be home for dinner," he said. "You'd better send my mother a tray—a little later, not right now. Is my father home?"

64

"No, he gone out. The Texas lady, she back again, I'm 'fraid."
He peered at Johnny through his gold-rimmed spectacles. "You in
trouble of some sort, Johnny?"

"No."

"Well, don' mind. It's jus' your grandmother. I knew she was
up to somethin', the way she high-horsed it in here today. She
makes life misery for your Ma, poor soul. You sure you don' want
somethin' to eat."

"Quite sure, Horace. I'll be leaving in a few minutes. If I don't
see my mother before I go, will you tell her? I'll call you tomorrow
and tell you where I am."

"Now, Johnny . . "

"Sorry, Horace. The time has come. I'll see you."

He went into his own room and shut the door, still in shock,
nine-tenths of him not functioning, and sat down at his desk, looking straight ahead of him, seeing nothing but the ghastly pallor of
his mother's face, feeling nothing but that he'd come to the end of
an era and the book was closed. He put his hand in his pocket
then, took out the crumpled glossy sheet, smoothed it gently flat on
the desk, tore the stripper off and held his lighter to the paper until
she folded into black carbon and dropped into the waste basket.
Then he bent his head and touched his lips softly to Kerry's face
on the cool paper, seeing it not as it looked there but as he knew
it was.

When he raised his head he folded the strip of glossy paper carefully and put it in his billfold, took out the money in the other
side of it and counted it. It wasn't difficult. He had twenty-six dollars, and what little change there was in his pocket. He put it back
and looked around the room. There was nothing of his there that
had any sale value. Everything there that he could presumably
pawn was what his grandmother or his mother had given him, not
his now. He reached for a pack of cigarettes in the carton on the
desk and took his hand back. He hadn't bought it. It was there,
always replenished by Horace, like the bar over by the window
he'd so blithely offered his grandmother a snort from. Nothing in
the room was really his own. When he'd told Kerry his $40.56 a
week took care of his clothes and his car and lunches he meant
it might take care of them. Actually, he had his clothes. All he'd
bought was a few shirts and a tie or two. His car his mother had

given him as a present when he passed his bar exams and most of his lunches came in on his club bills that his grandmother paid.

You brought nothing into this world, you take nothing out of it.

He didn't mean to be irreverent. It was merely a fact, in the kind of death he was dying. The taste of the bitter hemlock of his dependency on the old woman who'd put Kerry's picture in his mother's hands was the bitter taste of his mangled pride. If he hadn't been a fool it wouldn't have happened. He could see now that they'd left his mother out of the conspiracy of silence. It was literally true that Camilla Anne had told her he'd met an old school friend, of course at his grandmother's direction. His mother hadn't known. She'd known there was a girl, but she'd never question the kind of girl . .

He closed his eyes and bent his head again. He could see his grandmother bringing the horrible picture out. It was before Christmas that Kerry was at the Coral Seas. That was how long she'd been watching and waiting.

He started to push his chair back and get up when he saw the envelope propped against the row of law books at the back of the desk, "Johnny" written across it. The handwriting was his father's. He got up without taking it and went over to the closet to get out a suitcase. He thought then *I might as well get the works,* went back, picked up the envelope and opened it. Inside was a leaf torn from a pad. *Memorandum from Dr. Brayton* was printed at the top. The memorandum from Dr. Brayton said: "Johnny, I hear you're causing the ladies of the family some concern. Have breakfast with me in my study if you will. I'm sure we can find a civilized way to manage, to the satisfaction of all parties. I've had a good deal of experience in these matters.—P. B."

There's always been a Mrs. Ristwich of one sort or another in his life. He could hear his mother at the Fiesole again.

"—I doubt if you've had any experience at all in this matter, sir." He touched his lighter to a corner of the note and dropped it onto the carbonized stripper. "—The hell with you, Memorandum from Dr. Brayton." He went on with his packing, taking as little as possible, a half-empty tube of toothpaste he had to hunt a cap for instead of a new one Horace had put there.

His mother's door was locked when he went downstairs. He'd known it would be, and slipped the note he'd written her under it. "My dearest Ma, —She's not like that. I tried to tell you about her the Sunday I met her. I'd like to tell you, whenever you'll listen. I love you, Ma.—Johnny."

He went down the stairway through the silent hall. The place was full of flower arrangements, the doors all barred with laurel-covered ropes to keep the feet of the unchosen from sacred carpets and their hands from bric-a-brac.

8

Maybe if I've got a dollar I can come in and look around some day. His grin was lopsided as he went out and stood at the top of the brownstone steps. Just where he was going he had no idea. The Stafford and the Belvedere were the only hotels he'd ever stayed at, when the house was closed in the summer. Both of them were out if he wanted a roof for more than a couple of nights running. But what he wanted most was to see Kerry. He went down the steps. If he could get over her garden fence he could wait there till she got home. He crossed the street to cut over the gardens toward Cathedral.

Behind him he heard a window go up suddenly. "—Johnny! Johnny!"

He looked around and up. There was no light on in Mrs. Remstad's second floor front, but he could see her blonde head in the glow from the flood-lit Monument and the lamps in the plaza filtering through the young spring green of the trees.

"—Wait a minute!" she called urgently.

She disappeared and he saw her hall lights come on. But a session with Mrs. Remstad was nothing he wanted. He started on to the gardens, and stopped, the picture of her sitting at the window in the lonely dark there in his mind. *So damned many lonely people in the world.* His own loneliness, in the sense that until he saw Kerry he was very much alone, made him aware of a universal truth he hadn't given much thought to before. He put his suitcase on the ground and waited. She came out the front door, a fur coat thrown on over some kind of flowing peignoir, her pink satin mules clacking down the steps. She looked around anxiously until she saw him, across the pavement, and hurried down, stopping for a car to pass before she crossed. The headlights catching her face, its rosy makeup gone, her bright hair pulled to a hasty bun on the nape of her neck, made her look older than he'd ever thought her, and in an odd way sort of raddled.

"You're not leaving, Johnny . . ?"

She caught his arm.

"I'm leaving."

"Oh, no . . that's crazy." Her grip tightened. "Come on over and sit down a minute." She went through the bushes to a bench on the sunken walk around the interior gardens of the plaza and sat down, pulling her coat around her, sticking her feet in the fancy mules back under the seat. "What've they done to you, Johnny?"

She was so distressed, so whole-heartedly on his side, that it was easy to unburden. *Commensurate with proper dignity of course,* Johnny Brayton thought as he heard himself telling her, a little stiffly, careful not to overstate his case.

"My grandmother showed my mother a picture of Kerry coming out of the Coral Seas. My mother blew her top. Naturally. It's all my fault. If I'd come clean when it all started, none of it would have happened."

"That was the place they raided," Mrs. Remstad said. "She's not a stripper. You can tell the way they walk, even when they got their clothes on. I could tell she wasn't a high-class entertainer. What is she, one of these sitters they got the heat on in the clean-up drive they making all the stink about?"

Johnny Brayton stiffened, and relaxed.

"That's it," he said calmly. "But she's my girl. I don't give a damn what she does."

"That's the stuff, Johnny!" said Mrs. Remstad.

He was aware again that when she was talking about show business she was likely to lapse into a rudimentary speech she didn't use when she was being the proper householder on Mt. Vernon Place.

"—But you're just like 'em. You got pride. That's your trouble. That's why you're clearing out. I offered you the dough. You could of married her and they'd of all been behind you like a fire wall, like it or hate it. But you were too proud to take my dough. Listen, Johnny. You aren't cuttin' your own throat, walkin' out. It's the girl's throat."

"I don't know how you figure that, Mrs. Remstad."

"Okay, get sore at me."

The voice is the voice of Mrs. Remstad, Johnny thought suddenly, but the tone is the tone of Mrs. John R. Summerfield. The Colonel's lady and Judy O'Grady . .

Mrs. Remstad's face was set, not rosy-soft but the face of the daughter of the hard-bitten winters on the north Minnesota farm and the Swedish immigrant who'd hid his money under the slab in the root cellar. But her speech was nearer what she'd picked up.

"—You walk out. How long is it before some reporter's going to get hold of it? This clean-up on The Block's news. The Braytons are news. Put the two of you together, it's real news."

She broke off, looking at him intently. "Where'd your grandmother get the picture?" she asked abruptly.

"She must have had a detective. My sister-in-law knows where Kerry lives."

"Okay. So she brings out the picture. She don't bring out the picture of the girl looking like I've seen her, coming out to go to the grocery store. You bet she don't. And if she's kept her mouth shut and didn't tell your mother all this time, that means now she's come out sluggin', don't it?"

"Afraid so." His own jaw hardened.

"Okay. So she's not going to stop now. She's smart. She's got the pictures. You leave home. She feeds 'em to the papers someday. It doesn't hurt you. People just say Good old Johnny, who'd'a thought it, ha ha. But they don't say that about the girl. Even if you married her, you'd always be watching over your shoulder, ready to clip some guy making a pass at her, figuring that's what he had in mind even if she was Mrs. Johnny Brayton. You see, Johnny. You see what I mean."

Johnny Brayton nodded slowly. "I see." He hadn't thought of it that way. When he did, he could see his friends, clapping him on the shoulder in the gents' room. Good old Johnny. How's it going, Johnny, boy. He could see the picture of Kerry with the cut-out of the nude stripper with the black petticoat in her hand, alongside one of him, taken preferably in one of his younger, more earnest moments.

"So you just sleep on it." Mrs. Remstad put her hand on his arm. "Put your pride in your pocket, honey. She's just gettin' you out on a limb. I betcha any dough at any odds. Come on, Johnny."

70

She picked up his suitcase before he knew she was doing it and was clacking across the street to his own steps when he caught up with her.

"It don't do any good to go off half-cocked, Johnny. Like me. I keep figurin' why should I sit here on this fancy street, nobody speaking to me, when I should go places and do things? What the hell do I get? It's a laugh. But I guess it wears you down, living here. My heart don't seem to be in it, havin' a good time. 'Bye, Johnny. Just take it easy."

Put your pride in your pocket, honey. He put it there and walked back up the steps. As he got to the door it opened.

"Evenin', Mr. Johnny," Horace said. "You take your bag up and I'll fix you somethin' to eat in the kitchen. There's plenty of fried chicken."

The familiar formula that had greeted him coming home from school or visits as long as he could remember relieved him of any ignominy. One part of it was missing—"Your Ma's sure goin' to be mighty glad to see you, Johnny. 'Deed an' she is, boy."—and he felt the hollow place it left. But when he passed her door the other side of the picture flashed suddenly into his mind. *My God, of course she's shocked. How couldn't she be?* If he'd been frozen sick himself, how could she, knowing nothing, coming cold on the obscene cutout, how should she be anything but brutally, horribly, unbearably shocked? *But she'll listen to me. She's always listened.* When he went to sleep, feeling better now he'd seen it wasn't all as lost as it had seemed before, the only hurdle he really had was the Memorandum from Dr. Brayton.

It was bleakly in his mind the first thing in the morning. But as he was tying his tie he learned that the age of miracles hasn't passed, as commonly supposed. Also that the toad though venomous can yet wear a precious jewel in her hair. With his coffee came another Memorandum from Dr. Brayton folded on the tray.

"Johnny—I forgot the Garden Tour. C.A. asked me to be out early. It seems my study is to be on view. May we breakfast another time?—P.B."

"We may indeed, sir." Johnny glanced at the clock and reached for the phone. He dialled Kerry's unlisted number.

"Hi, Kerry. Sorry to wake you—"

"Oh, Johnny, I'm so glad you did." Her voice always came wide-awake and fresh as dawn. "I've got a long and bitter day—" She

71

broke off, laughing. "What I mean is, I've got to shop. Shoes and things."

His always instant alarm at any change in her routine wiped out the pleasure of hearing her voice. "You're not—"

"No. No, precious." She laughed gaily. "Everything's beautiful. It's just that I'm frantically busy. I was going to call you. I won't be able to see you today or tomorrow . . but next week, Johnny? I'm taking the whole week off to get a little springtime and fresh air. I'll see you every minute you can spare. Is that agreeable to you, Mr. Brayton?"

He put the phone down, the gaiety of her voice still vibrating through him. *What if I'd seen her? What if I'd told her?* In his mind's eye he could see Mrs. Remstad, a blessing in disguise, a guardian angel in clacking mules. He collected his briefcase and went whistling out the door and downstairs, stopping at his mother's door. Camilla Anne was just going to his father's study.

"She's gone, dear. To Gibson Island, for the day—to get the house ready. Lolly's going to use it for a honeymoon cottage. Just think, her wedding's less than a month away . . invitations out. Or have you noticed, darling?"

It was a crack, but who cared, with the promised week so blithe a thing? He smiled happily at Camilla Anne and went on downstairs. It was the last time he was to smile at her, and the promised week was to be a living hell.

Kerry O'Keefe put her own phone down and hurried barefoot to the kitchen to start coffee, her eyes dancing.

What if I'd told him? It was the nearest thing to a bad slip she'd made for a long time. Unless he'd think the Baltimore City Police had gone stark raving mad, assigning a female sitter to escort the Women's League for Municipal Improvement on a House and Garden Tour.

It was a crazy deal anyway. She could still hear Dave Trumper, as grim about it as she was herself.

"So that's the way it is, Exhibit A," he said, heavy with disgust. "They represent twenty-five districts out of the forty-eight states. This Mrs. Parker's the head girl of the outfit. She heard the dean of your college on Careers for Women in the Modern Municipality, for God's sake. Our Miss O'Keefe's a policewoman in Baltimore, says the dean. So you're tapped by personal request to the Commissioner himself. And we all figured it's easier to let you go than try to explain. Nobody from the Hay Ride's out looking at Chippendale rugs and vases. It sounds crazy right at this point, but they figured the angles and this looks the safest."

"But I don't even know which houses are open, Dave."

"With these babes you don't have to know from nothing, sugar."

"And twenty-five of them." Kerry's heart sank lower.

"Plus one from Texas along for the ride. You meet 'em at nine-thirty a.m. They got their own bus. And you can't spread your gospel about The Lady Cops Your Daughter's Career. They been told they're not to mention you being a lady cop. We figured a little cloak and dagger'd seal their lips. The security angle, that they understand."

And it hadn't been as grim as Kerry expected it to be. At the famous gold bathtub at Evergreen she finally relaxed and began to enjoy herself. Mrs. Parker the head girl was a nice and capable woman, and all of them seemed to be walking encyclopedias of period furniture, china, glass, flowers and trees. All of them except the lady along for the ride.

There's bound to be a poison pup, Kerry thought tolerantly, giving as wide a berth as possible to this one as she gave each successive hostess a full resumé of her life and times, particularly of the fabulous collections owned by some woman named Alice Rich, boiling in oil down Texas way. Or so Kerry gathered from the farthest distance possible, fascinated with a Baltimore that was the farthest distance possible from the one she best knew.

"You've been most helpful, Miss O'Keefe," Mrs. Parker said round four o'clock when they were on their way down St. Paul Street back to town. "I wonder if you're up to just one more? Or are you dead on your feet, poor child?"

No bat's wing fanned Kerry's smiling face, no icy premonitory shiver chilled her spine. "Oh no. I've had a delightful day. I'd love to see another one."

"Well, I'm certainly glad," said the poison pup, with a touch of rancor in her voice. "Because I talked to Alice Ristwich last night and she said we simply had to see Dr. Brayton's house if we didn't see a single other one."

No premonitory chill. Nothing but an instantaneous plunge into the deepest pit. Kerry sat stunned, unable to speak, hardly able to breathe.

"You can relax," Mrs. Parker said. "I merely thought we wouldn't want to impose on Miss O'Keefe if she was tired. She's not as used to this sort of thing as we are." She turned to Kerry. "So many of us have know patients of Dr. Brayton. We'd have been sorry to miss his house."

Oh, no. What can I do? Kerry closed her eyes. *What if his grandmother's there? Even if she doesn't recognize me* . . But it wasn't that. It was the tacit unspoken understanding she and Johnny Brayton had that as long as she was a sitter she couldn't be asked into the house. Now she was crashing in . . It would have been horrible enough before his grandmother's visit. It had a special kind of ignominy now she'd been told she was not of their birth, not of their breed.

I've got to do something. A sudden hope dawned on her as the bus turned into the narrow crowded street on the north side of the plaza, and died as suddenly as it swerved around the west end of the gardens, and two cars pulled out from in front of the brownstone mansion and the bus driver swung deftly into their place. There was little chance of her losing herself now. Still less when Mrs. Parker said, "You take the tickets, dear."

Kerry took them, her feet and hands numb as she mounted the steps to the open door.

"These ladies are from the League for Municipal Improvement meeting in Washington." She heard herself introducing them as she'd done in each house. Each time before she'd introduced Mrs. Parker as their leader, but she didn't have a chance this time. The poison pup had steamed ahead of everybody. Kerry heard her.

"My great friend Alice Ristwich said we must be sure to come," she was saying brightly.

Kerry heard a voice not bright but formally gracious.

"My father-in-law is devoted to Mrs. Ristwich. I'm Mrs. Pierce Brayton Jr."

Camilla Anne, that Johnny doesn't like. Kerry was still at the ticket table by the door. She slipped over to get as far in the corner as she could while the rest gathered in the double door of the front parlor. She heard Camilla Anne's voice muffled by the pounding of the blood in her own ears, and turned back to the front door to breathe the fresh cool air.

"—Can anybody get in?"

A large blonde woman in a green dress and mink stole had come up the steps.

"Anybody's who's got a dollar." The nice girl taking tickets laughed, and so did the blonde woman. As she went in, Kerry heard a sharp break for an instant in the flow of Camilla Anne Brayton's discussion of the Aubusson carpet. It went on again, but it was definitely cooler.

"It's surprising the different kinds of people interested in the houses, isn't it?" the nice girl said to Kerry. "I'm Polly Putnam. You're from the Central Committee, aren't you?"

But before Kerry could answer Polly Putnam's face had lighted and she got quickly to her feet. "Oh, hello, Mrs. Brayton! We've had streams of people. Lunch was divine."

Kerry caught her breath at the sight of the woman coming up the steps. *Oh . . she is beautiful.* Her face was very pale, her dark eyes somehow poignantly sad, until she stopped just inside the door and smiled at Polly. And smiled at Kerry O'Keefe.

"I'm glad," she said. "You precious lambs, you both look exhausted." She was still in the doorway. "Polly, would you think I was a dog if I just slipped around the back way upstairs? I'm not up to seeing many people." She moved back out, smiling at them again. "You're angels to help out. Thank you so much, girls."

Kerry's heart sank lower. Not denying she was a helper made her even more of an imposter. The girl at the table leaned forward then. "Look . . the rest of the hostesses are out in the kitchen with their shoes off having a drink. Why don't you slip out for a slug? You look bushed."

Camilla Anne was dog-tired. She gave up and moved over to the stairs. "—I'll be right here if you have any questions." She wanted to slip off her shoes for a minute, but Mrs. Richwitch's friend was right there with her, more interested in telling her about her own and Mrs. Richwitch's antiques than she was in looking at the Braytons'. But there was always one or two on every tour. Camilla Anne fixed a glassy smile on her face, closed her ears and let her mind roam.

There's Mother leaving, sneaking around back. I hope she didn't see that awful Mrs. Remstad. She's just being offensive, trailing her minks in here. But a dollar's a dollar. I wonder who that pretty girl is Polly's talking to. She must be from the Committee. Somebody I ought to know. Her face looks familiar. I've seen her somewhere. She tried to catch Kerry's eye to smile at her but couldn't.

75

She turned to Mrs. Richwitch's friend, breaking in on her steady flow. "I'm so stupid today," she said. "I know that girl but I can't think of her name. The dark-haired girl going out the door, that the Committee sent around with you. It's so silly of me."

The woman looked around. "Oh, you mean Carrie O'Keefe."

Camilla Anne's eyes opened slowly wider, her hand closed on the ormolu bannister. *The pictures. Grandmother's pictures.*

"—She's not from any committee I know of. She's a policewoman."

Then, as Camilla Anne flashed around, staring blankly at her, the woman's hand shot to her mouth. "Oh dear! I wasn't supposed to . . we were told we weren't to breathe a word—"

"Did . . did you say a *policewoman?*" Camilla Anne's face was as blank as her voice still was.

The woman nodded quickly. "—Sssh!" she said. But because Mrs. Parker was still at a distance and young Mrs. Brayton was so distinctly astonished, she brightened at once. "You'd never in the world have thought it, would you. I mean, looking at her, you wouldn't. Would you?"

Young Mrs. Brayton's brows arched. "I certainly wouldn't." Then her face broke into a happy smile of real delight. "Never in the world. And thanks . . it was really sweet of you to tell me."

She turned to the ladies straggling toward them. "Shall we go up now? I do want you to see Dr. Brayton's study."

She was bright as dawn, her feet like feathers floating up the stairs, and very cordial. Cordial even to the large blonde woman coming down as they came up.

"You people are too slow for me," Mrs. Remstad said. "Chippendale looks the same as a park bench to me, I guess." But she was so good-natured about it that the ladies all laughed, Camilla Anne even more delightedly than the rest.

"Young Mrs. Brayton was perfectly enchanting, when she got her second wind," Mrs. Parker said to Kerry O'Keefe waiting alone in the bus.

It was the next night that was the night of May 1st.

Johnny Brayton, late from the office, let himself in the front door and paused for an instant. The heavy clouds gathering in a chill drizzle sent lengthening shadows through the open rooms. The house was curiously still, or the quality of its silence curious. He put his hat on the table, only home for a moment to pick up some papers to take back to the office library, and stopped again, listening. The voice he heard seemed to be his father's, speaking in a musical cadence, richly vibrant, as if reading something or reciting. It came, or seemed to come, from the Common Room, a place where his father never went. He was always, for as long as Johnny could remember, closed up in his study on the second floor whenever he was home. *I must be nuts,* Johnny thought. Deeply puzzled, he went quietly along to the foot of the stairs. A narrow fraction of light showed along the edge of the Common Room door. He listened again.

> Call her once before you go.
> Call once yet.
> In a voice that she will know:
> "Margaret! Margaret!"

Something more chilling than the rain crept uneasily down his spine.

> Children's voices should be dear
> (Call once more) to a mother's ear:
> Children's voices, wild with pain.
> Surely she will come again.

He went quietly on up the stairs then. But the chill sharpened. He was more deeply perplexed when he looked in at the open door of his mother's room and saw her hat and furs, gloves and bag lying on a chair. It was strange she'd be down there listening to him reading her love poems, feeling about him the way there was no possible doubt she did feel. But it wasn't any of his business. He went on upstairs. As he started to collect his papers he remembered suddenly the night of Pug's birthday. *I regard my present marriage as completely permanent. . . Not soluble even in* aqua regis . . and the utter hopelessness on his mother's face that brief moment at the dinner table.

He went back into the hall, listening again. All he could hear was the sounds from the TV set in the front room. He went quietly down the stairs, his feet silent on the marble treads. *I'll act as if I'd just come in.* At the bottom he stopped, listening to the strangely thrilling, almost hypnotic voice.

> . . dwells a loved one,
> But cruel is she.
> She left lonely for ever
> The kings of the sea.

There was a long pause. Then something like a torn sob broke the silence, and he heard his father's voice again: "—Margaret! Margaret!"

Johnny went noiselessly across the hall and switched on the lights. "Hi . . anybody home?"

There was the sharp movement of a chair and the Common Room door was torn open. His mother came running, swaying as she ran, her face, terror-drawn, deathly pale.

"Johnny . . " She seemed about to faint as she reached him, clinging to him, her heart pounding, her body cold, shaking like a dead branch in a freezing wind. There was no sign of his father. It was almost as if a disembodied voice had done the reading.

"Hi, Ma. Let's have a drink upstairs." He made his voice cheerfully casual.

Her steps were so faltering that he would have carried her except that he was afraid his father would come out and see him. Inside her room he did pick her up, brushed her things off the chaise longue and laid her down, cold and pale but not shaking any more except for an occasional convulsive tremor. Her head lay back against the lace pillows, her eyes closed. He sat by her holding her freezing hands.

"What is it, Ma?"

She shook her head back and forth. "Nothing. Nothing, love."

"He . . was reading to you, wasn't he?"

"A poem he used to read to me a long time ago." Her voice was hardly audible. "Before we were married. And when I tried to leave him, after Meg was born. And again . . after Lolly. I . . I don't know why, but it . . it hypnotizes me. It breaks my heart. It . . it's like Svengali. I'm lost. It leaves me—"

"But . . why should it, Ma?" Johnny said gently. The poem had come back to him. He remembered the poignant picture of the forsaken father and the children calling to their mother named Margaret—and the nightmares he'd had years ago fearing their mother named Margaret might somehow forsake them. Two other lines came into his mind that were and weren't like his small sister Lolly:

> For the cold strange eyes of a little Mermaiden
> And the gleam of her golden hair.

"—Maybe then, but not now. The Merman's plenty able to take care of himself. The Merchildren are all grown up."

"I know." A convulsive tremor went through her again. "But he wants me to go abroad with him . . he won't give me a divorce without—"

She drew her breath in quickly, breaking off. "Oh, I'm sorry. I shouldn't have said that. Forget it, darling."

She moved her head back and forth on the pillows, brushing her hand slowly across her eyes, opening them at last.

"Johnny," she said softly, "I was cruel to you the other night. Forgive me. I should have known your grandmother by this time. If you love that girl, she can't be what the picture says she is. It was just that I couldn't stand—" She closed her eyes again for an instant. "But never mind. Sometime we'll . . talk about it. Not now, sweet. And you must bring her to see me. But go now, Johnny. You're working downtown tonight, aren't you?"

She sat up, trying to smile. "You'll have to eat out. I let the servants go. Camilla Anne and the Garden Tour yesterday exhausted them."

She saw him hesitate. "Go along, dear. I'll be all right. Your father's dining out. All I want to do is go to bed and go to sleep. You go back to work. Don't worry." She smiled then. "I've . . got my courage back now. Goodnight, love."

He waited a moment, watching her, then went out, closing the door softly. But he didn't go back to the office library. He got some food out of the icebox, fried chicken and salad, and went up to his room. He was there working when Kerry called him around ten-thirty. She was half-crying. He was frantic for a few moments until he finally made out what she was saying. Or part of it. Then he was angry because it had something to do with Camilla Anne. He understood finally that in some way or other Camilla Anne had wrecked a job of Kerry's and Kerry was on her way uptown and would meet him in the usual place across from the Peabody.

His first anger at Camilla Anne was tempered, on further thought, in spite of whatever it was had happened. Kerry's losing her job couldn't distress him less. It was okay with him even with Camilla Anne as the agent. With his mother on his side now they could work it out, not have to wait for the year to be over. No more night spots, no more delay. He waited a little while to give her time to get uptown, got his raincoat and hat and went down the stairs, his heart buoyant. There was a light now under his father's study door. He tried his mother's door, found it locked and went on, out the front door.

He glanced up to wave a cheerful salute to Mrs. Remstad at her front window. While nothing Camilla Anne ever did was agreeable to him, sometimes, through no fault of hers, the results were fine. Just fine. He felt a little like a dog nevertheless, which may have been why he did not see the famous horseman riding his cold pale horse up the brownstone steps, passing him, mounting the curving marble stairs to the second floor where Dr. Pierce Brayton was waiting for him not knowing he was waiting . . not suspecting that he would look up from his desk to see a familiar face he would not recognize as the face of sudden death.

10

The place Kerry usually parked in, across from the Peabody Conservatory of Music, was taken and she drove on across Charles Street to a space reserved for a women's club west of the Monument, across the plaza from the Braytons' house.

She saw Johnny come out and down the steps, very blithe, not waltzing precisely but not laden with care of any kind, from the way he turned and waved cheerfully up at the window of the house next door. She couldn't see his friend Mrs. Remstad he'd talked about, because of the leafing trees, but she could see Johnny very plainly in the white glow diffused from the flood-lit Monument. She sounded her horn as he headed for Charles Street, but he was in much too great spirits to hear it.

But of course why shouldn't he be? She'd assumed Camilla Anne had told him she was a policewoman, but it was obvious now he thought it was the sitter's job she'd meant. Reaching forward to start the car she caught a glimpse of herself in the windshield mirror, her make-up a grisly mess, streaked with tears and smudged where she'd dabbed at her eyes to wipe them. She got the cotton and lotion out of her glove compartment quickly and swabbed her face clean, putting on her own rose-red lipstick, and combed her short curls neatly in place again. She was ready to start around after Johnny when she heard the shot.

She looked down at the clock on the dash automatically, opened her door and got out in the rain, her foot hardly firm on the wet pavement when she heard the second shot. It was not as loud, the central crack not as sharp, but it was a revolver shot nevertheless and from the same direction as the first. Both were from inside a house. She knew that from the overtone, a muffled reverberation.

She looked quickly up and down the houses on either side of the central garden, empty now in the chilling rain, then around to see if the post officer had heard the shots and was coming. No policeman was in sight. The reports seemed to have come from the other side of the street and from somewhere above the first floor level. The budded trees hid most of her view if anybody was opening an upstairs window. She waited, listening intently, but there was nothing, no confusion, no door burst open, no car stopping. The only sound was from a dance orchestra somewhere and a high soprano giving voice at the Peabody. No pedestrians were wandering around in the rain, chilling to Kerry herself in the trench coat one of the detectives had thrown around her as they pushed her out of the Hay Ride Club as the near-riot broke loose. She'd been running for her car when she heard the crash of shots down there, and there'd been shouting and confusion. Here she heard nothing at all. Nothing but silence and the swish of cars on the wet pavement round the Monument, and the sound of music in the dripping air.

She got back in her car and checked the time. It was eighteen minutes to eleven when she'd looked at the clock on the dash. She'd been out of the car when the second came. They weren't fired in rapid succession, at least five or six seconds between them, not crack-crack as they'd come at the Hay Ride Club. She sat there restlessly, watching for the post officer or a police car, no idea now of driving around for Johnny. Her job was to stay until an officer came into sight, to see that nobody came running, or walking, from the scene of an accident—or a crime. She watched the minute hand of the clock move. One minute, two, three. It was moving to the seventh minute when she saw a door burst open. The Braytons' door. She stiffened sharply, opened her door and was out again. A woman in a bathrobe was running down the steps, waving her arms, looking frantically up and down the street. Kerry was running instantly, through the rain, across the gardens, pulling the belt of her trench coat tighter as she ran.

The woman was not Mrs. Brayton. *It must be his aunt Elizabeth. My aunt's not bats precisely, just a gently harmless addict to the dope dispensed via her TV set on the third floor.* That flashed through her mind as she reached the sidewalk and heard a voice calling down from the second floor window of the other brownstone house adjoining.

"—What's happened, Miss Brayton? Do you want me to call for help? But there's a policeman coming."

Kerry saw the post officer, running from Charles Street. She stopped on the steps till he came up.

"I'm Policewoman O'Keefe. Assigned to Rackets. Inspector—"

"My brother's shot himself." Miss Elizabeth Brayton was suddenly calm. "I think it's most peculiar I don't hear any sirens. On television when the police come there are always sirens."

The post officer's eyes rested steadily for an instant on Kerry's face. "Look, get this balmy dame inside. I'm O'Brien. Here comes Garrett. I'll leave him here at the door. Get her in and stand by."

"Their son's down by the Peabody. Can you send somebody for him?"

Maybe he could get one of the people beginning to gather out of nowhere, hanging curiously around the bottom step. The woman next door was still leaning out of her window, but she was as silent as the ones on the sidewalk.

"Don't you think it's odd about the sirens?" Miss Brayton asked as they headed quickly for the curving stairs. "And odd about my brother." She gathered her robe and nightdress around her knees and streaked up to the second floor. She stopped there and moved her hand out toward the door of the front room to the left.

"You'll find him there," she said, with gentle composure. "Excuse me now, please. When the program's finished, I'll dress and come down. If I'm to be grilled with the rest."

She faded quickly up to the third floor where the voice of television was murmuring steadily on.

Kerry went across the hall. The door of the study was open, the smell of burnt powder drawn out by the draft from the downstairs door. She saw Mrs. Brayton first. She was sitting in a chair by the fireplace, her back to the window, her hands folded in her lap. She was still dressed, in a soft sea-green wool suit, her face, ivory pale, as calm as the depths of the quiet sea, her eyes fixed on some scene infinitely sad, infinitely remote. No tears, no despair. Nothing but sadness. She was facing the desk set diagonally in the wide angle of the fireplace wall and the inner partition, but she was not seeing the terrible figure lying across it.

83

Kerry saw it now. The body of a man with silver hair, sprawled forward on the desk, the left side of his head blooming horribly in crimson death. His left hand was flung out in front of him across the desk, the pen set tipped sideways. A revolver lay to his left on the floor, as it flung reflexively from a lifeless hand to skid across the polished surface of the desk to the floor. His right hand was buried under him.

Kerry O'Keefe stood for an awful instant before she closed her eyes, fighting down the nausea, struggling to keep from fainting. Then she made herself move across the room, forcing her voice steady.

"I'm a police officer, Mrs. Brayton." Then, because she was also a woman, she said, "Your son will be here in just a moment."

"Oh, no!"

The instant alarm in Margaret Brayton's voice was so startling that Kerry unconsciously moved back a step.

". . . Unless the police have called him," Mrs. Brayton added quietly. "He's working downtown tonight."

Was that the first thing that disturbed her? She was to ask that many times, desperately wondering if it hadn't been for that she wouldn't have been watching Johnny Brayton and his mother a moment later as intently as she was. But if it hadn't disturbed her it would have been so natural to say "No, I saw him leave the house." She didn't say it. Then, hearing Post Officer O'Brien running up the stairs she went quickly out into the hall.

"Don't you think it would be a good idea to check the back doors?"

He looked surprised but nodded at once. "You stand by. I'll take any statements. Homicide's on the way. Garrett's at the front door. He's sent a guy to look for Brayton."

Kerry went back into the study. She folded the sleeves of her trench coat back more neatly and tightened the belt, feeling strangely self-conscious, dressed like that in the room with death. Mrs. Brayton had slipped back into her silent land. The room was silent as the grave it was.

It's a beautiful room. Kerry's mind moved with her eyes searchingly around it. The marble fireplace with its shining andirons where a fire had died was flanked with bookcases from the floor to the carved cornice, the four-foot sections divided with fluted

84

pilasters of polished pine, satin-sheened and dark with age. The heavy cherry damask curtains were drawn in sculptured folds over the two broad windows looking down on the gardens of Mt. Vernon Place. A great velvet-piled oriental carpet stretched from wall to wall. Over the mantels and on tables were photographs signed by the world's distinguished great. Her eyes, travelling from where Dr. Brayton's head would have been as he sat at his desk, saw the nose of the bullet buried in the broad grey back of a book in the shelves against the inside partition wall. She stood there silently until Officer O'Brien came in.

"All locked," he said curtly. "Chain bolted on the inside." He gave an instinctive start as he saw the figure on the desk, and came forward a little to look more closely.

He turned then. "My God, Mrs. Brayton." He was deeply moved. "Why . . . why would he do it, ma'am? He always seemed so . . ."

"I know, Tom."

Margaret Brayton closed her eyes an instant. "I . . . I was in my sitting room at the back on the other side of the house. I heard something. It sounded like a shot. But I thought it must have been a truck backfiring. The walls of these old places are so thick and the doors were all closed. It wasn't till I went in my bedroom, in the front of the house, just across the hall, that it seemed to me I smelled burnt powder."

She let her head rest back.

"I came out in the hall. I could definitely smell it then. I knocked at my husband's door. Then I opened it and saw him. It . . . was so awful I couldn't believe it. It seemed to me like hours before I could move . . . get the phone to call the police."

"And Miss Brayton. Did you call her?"

"No. I didn't call her. She came down, just a few moments ago, to go to the icebox to get something to eat. I'm afraid we forgot her, today. The servants are out. She smelled the powder and came in, and started running, out into the street hunting a policeman. I couldn't make her understand I'd called them. She tends to be a little . . . a little fey, you know."

"I know, ma'am." O'Brien was looking at the gun on the floor. "Was the . . . the Doctor was left-handed, was he?"

His voice sounded to Kerry O'Keefe as if he were doubting the angels.

"Yes. He was."

Kerry saw his relief. She hesitated an instant. *Did you say you heard one shot?* She started to ask that, but O'Brien interrupted her at the sound of many feet in the hall below.

"You'd best go to your room, ma'am. They'll talk to you in there." He was pathetically anxious to save her all he could.

"Thank you, Tom."

She rose and started for the door, but before she reached it the room seemed suddenly swarming with men. But men silently making way for her. Men used to death but never used to it. And then came the instant that Kerry O'Keefe would never forget. As Mrs. Brayton reached the door, Johnny Brayton was in it. Kerry in the trench coat pushed off behind the detectives was invisible to him, but she could see him, see his face, see the stunned horror on it as he saw his father, and see, in the split fraction of an instant, the greater horror as his eyes moved to his mother. It was only a tiny fragment of time before he reached his arms out, protectively drawing her into the hall.

"Come away, Ma. Come away."

Kerry stood, her heart frozen, her hands clenched tight at her sides, not daring to breathe, her eyes closed then, not daring to look at the faces of the men around her . . . waiting. Surely one of them had seen what she had seen. Johnny Brayton's face when he looked from the body of his father to his mother. The second dawn of horror, the deeper horror, freezing his soul. As if he had shouted it, aloud, with all his strength. *Ma, you killed him. How could you do it, Ma!*

She opened her eyes then, very slowly, and looked around her, hardly believing what she saw and heard. Every man setting about his own job. None of them had seen. She let her breath out painfully and edged back against the wall out of the way, shaking, still freezing cold.

It's only because I know him so well. Because I know every expression. Every movement of his face. I read his eyes without his having to speak.

She heard him almost instantly in the hall again, and one of the detectives.

"I'd stay out if I were you, Mr. Brayton. Not very pretty to see. We'll talk to you in a minute. Maybe you can tell us why he did it. He was left-handed, wasn't he?"

"That's right."

She could hear the agony behind his voice, knew he did not dare ask the question torturing him.

"We'll check on the gun, but there's not much question about what happened. You go on with your mother, son."

Kerry leaned against the wall.

She watched the flashbulbs, saw the swift routine. *This is the time to tell them.* But she didn't speak. She saw the Medical Examiner, a very young man, and heard his technical phrases that added up to a single bullet fired at close contact, entering the left temple, going through the brain and out the right temple, death instant and forever. She saw the detective examining the gun.

"Get the bullet out of the book there, Bill. Check the gun. One chamber empty."

I've got to tell them there were two shots. As soon as they've finished. But suddenly they were finished.

"Send him over to City Hospital. Tell the son he can have the body first thing in the morning."

The Medical Examiner said that on his way out. The camera and fingerprint men were closing their bags, Detective-Sergeant Horner was waiting, the men with the stretcher were coming in. Kerry turned her face to the window. When she turned back, only she and Officer O'Brien were left in the room.

"You'll make your report separately, I guess. It's a shame. She's such a nice lady. I'll go in while they talk to her. You want to come?"

Kerry shook her head. She was alone then in an empty room. It seemed more terribly empty than any room she'd ever been in.

You didn't tell them. You were afraid to tell them. Because it's his mother. You're withholding information.—I'll tell them tomorrow.—Tomorrow'll be too late You've forgot you're a policewoman.

Suddenly she was hearing Camilla Anne's high-pitched laughter

again at the Hay Ride Club. *Is there a policewoman in the house?*
It was in that instant she made her first decision.

She went swiftly over to the door, closed it and came back to
the desk. She pulled the phone forward and dialled.

"—Is Sergeant Trumper around anywhere? It's Kerry O'Keefe.
Get him for me, can you?"

She waited, her body taut, her face white.

"—Dave. Listen. I'm at the Braytons'. Dr. Brayton's dead. Shot.
They've taken him to City Hospital. Could you get hold of Dr.
Fisher or Dr. Freimuth?"

"Both out of town, attending a meeting."

She didn't realize how long her silence was until she heard him
speak again, very deliberately. "—What's the deal, Kerry?"

"It's just . . . just if one of the senior men . . . I mean, Dr. Brayton's so well known, and . . ."

There was an instant's sharp silence at Trumper's end. "Okay,
Kerry."

She put the phone down and held onto the desk, steadying her
knees, swallowing the painful lump in her throat. *If they see him
and say it's suicide* . . . She let it go there. She'd done her duty.

Or had she?

It was done enough to dull her own conscience. Or so she tried
to make herself believe, until at six the next day Dave Trumper
came, on Rackets business, as impassive as ever. No mention of the
Brayton suicide announced over the radio the night before, and
implied if not stated in the morning paper. It wasn't till he was
leaving that he stopped and looked at her, a long moment, before
he opened the door.

"—It's not always so easy to be a good cop, is it, Kerry?"

He went out then, but not, she knew, before he saw the sick
pallor that blanched her cheeks and saw her eyes move away to
keep from meeting his.

From then until six o'clock the next evening was a thousand hours, each dragging its leaden sleepless feet through her heart and through her mind, each longer than the one before it. She hadn't heard from Johnny, and she'd tried to tell herself it was perfectly reasonable. Whether the suddenly guarded accounts in the Saturday evening and Sunday morning papers were guarded out of deference to Dr. Brayton or because the police were guarded, she didn't know. Like Johnny, she didn't dare to ask. But wherever she turned she could see Trumper's impassive face, hear his impassive voice. *It's not always so easy* ...

At six o'clock Sunday evening she dialled John Brayton's number, her heart constricting as tightly as her throat when she heard his voice.

"It's Kerry, Johnny."

There was silence, sharp and cold, then his voice, cold too and colder as it went on.

"Policewoman O'Keefe, you mean, don't you? I'm afraid—"

"Oh, Johnny, please don't! I've got to see you. It's hideously important. Please come!"

She put the phone down before he could answer and buried her head in the bed pillows, beating her fists in agony.

Maybe he won't come. It was almost a prayer, hoping he wouldn't. But he came, at nearly ten o'clock, when each of them was worn taut with separate and personal despair.

He came as a stranger, someone she'd never met before.

"I'm sorry I couldn't make it sooner. There seems to be some kind of mystery, the way they're holding my father's body. I've got to get back. If you have anything to say—"

She flushed hotly. "I'll say it as quickly as I can then." It was easier than she'd thought, now it was a stranger she was speaking to. Or it was easier until she was actually saying it. "It's about . . . Friday night. I was across the street, waiting for you. I . . . I heard the shots.—There were two shots, Johnny. Not one."

He stood motionless, staring at her. His face, at first grey-white as he heard and understood what she said, flushed a dark angry red.

"What the hell are you talking about?" he demanded harshly. "—There was one shot. One and one only. There couldn't be—"

"I'm sorry." Her voice was still steady. "There were two. I heard one, and then I heard the second." Then, seeing him, seeing the grey horror seep back into his eyes, her voice broke, torn by her own special agony. "Oh, Johnny . . . I'm so sorry! I didn't tell the police. I've tried not to. But I've got to tell them, Johnny! I can't keep quiet, I couldn't live with myself if I just kept quiet! I've tried, I swear I've tried. But I can't do it any longer. I've got to tell them. But I had to tell you first—"

"—Tell me first . . ." He looked at her silently for an instant, his voice terrible then in its bitter irony. "You're telling me first that you're branding my mother as a murderer?"

"I'm not! I'm not! All I'm saying is I heard two shots!"

Their voices were like frayed ropes pulled beyond their strength, tearing apart. Johnny Brayton no longer made any attempt to control himself.

"It is my mother! You know she was alone in the house. You know she hated my father. You know it because I've been in love with you and told you all about my family . . . not knowing you were a police spy, thinking you were the girl I loved. Even when I thought you were a sitter I loved you. But you weren't. You were a policewoman. My God, if I'd known that! You have to tell me first . . . after you've spied on my mother to crucify her!"

"Stop it, Johnny! Stop it! I haven't said a word about your mother!"

"And you didn't send O'Brien tearing through the house, checking back doors, to see there was nobody else—"

"Stop it! Stop and listen! It's you that's accusing your mother. I'm not! Let me tell you what happened—"

"I don't want to know what happened. All I want is out, now and forever. Go to your police. Tell them everything I've ever told you. Tell them I had to wait for the dumb cop on the corner to tell me it was Policewoman O'Keefe told him to be sure nobody was in the house, nobody but my mother.—Kerry O'Keefe, the tramp I got out of jail, that broke my heart, that I kept begging on my knees to marry me and give it up. And all the time you were laughing, talking about big kettles and little kettles, laughing behind my back, waiting, just waiting for the chance to tear my heart out. You don't know my mother. You've never even seen her—"

"Oh, Johnny, stop it! Can't you see what you're doing? It's you that thinks she killed your father! I don't . . . all I know is what I heard! Just let me tell you about Friday—"

"The hell with Friday. Tell the police, don't tell me."

He pulled himself together, his jaw hard, his eyes furious, his voice scathing with contempt.

"Tell them I think my mother's a murderer. I should have cut my tongue out before I spoke her name to you. Where's your tape recorder? It'll back you up. You're a policewoman . . . do your duty and be damned with it. And the next poor sucker that wants to marry you, just tell him he's welcome to you. Thank God I got my neck out of the noose in time. Goodbye. You're free, Officer O'Keefe. Free as the wind. I wish I'd rotted in hell before the day I ever met you!"

She heard the door slam and his steps pounding down the hall. The outer door slammed. She sat there on the sofa, her heart too numb to feel. It was there she woke the next morning, cold and miserably spent, to crawl wretchedly through the hours until she went down to Central Police Station at eight o'clock, to crawl back home again. She was there, the last rays of the sun creeping like living fingers through the slats of the venetian blinds, when the phone rang. She dragged herself slowly into the bedroom and picked it up.

"Kerry?" It was Dave Trumper. "Better sit down, Kerry. I've got tough news."

Her heart soared like a lark rising to the sun. Tough news for Trumper had always meant the collapse of a case, a whole fine theory vanished into non-existent air. She waited, standing erect, her eyes bright, lips parted, breathless, for him to go on.

"You caught the perfect murder, Kerry. Not suicide. Murder that so damn near worked it makes me sick. If you hadn't heard that second shot it would have worked."

Kerry sat slowly down on the side of the bed.

"And as you're the first officer on the scene of the crime you report in at nine, the Inspector's office.—Try to get some sleep, Kerry . . . it's tough on you now but it's going to be a hell of a lot tougher before it's through."

At nine o'clock Tuesday morning she was in the small sound-proofed room with burnt sienna curtains on the fifth floor of Central Police Headquarters. At ten-thirty the Inspector of the Rackets Division came back from the conference in the Commissioner's room on the fourth floor. It was a summit conference, the Commissioner, the Chief Inspector and the heads of the Detective and Rackets Divisions listening intently to the autopsy report brought up from the Morgue on the waterfront by the toxicologist from the Chief Medical Examiner's Office.

"So what we've got is the perfect murder that missed by a hair," the Commissioner said, summing it up. "Like the Grammer case. Sheer chance, or the grace of God . . . but we had a police officer at the right place at the right time. We know what looked like suicide was not suicide. It's impossible that Pierce Brayton could have fired the gun that killed him. That seems to be all we know. Take it from there, gentlemen. Rackets should stay with it on special assignment, working with Homicide. You people cracked the Grammer case. I guess this one won't throw you."

As the Inspector came in and sat down behind his desk he gave Kerry a brief appraising glance. She was pale, her blue eyes a dull grey.

"Well, there's no evidence of any second shot, Kerry. There's one contact wound, one bullet track through his brain, one exit wound, one bullet nose buried in a book on a direct line level with his head as he sat there, one empty chamber. That's the story."

"You think I just dreamed it."

"I'm talking about evidence." The Inspector of the Rackets Division was a lawyer as well as a policeman. "If we can't prove it to the court or jury beyond a reasonable doubt, it's still the perfect murder as far as the law's concerned. I'm talking about the gun the Crime Lab. says is the one that killed him. What we've got so far looks like conclusive evidence pointing two ways in opposite directions."

He glanced up at Dave Trumper coming in.

"Contact wounds are conclusive evidence of suicide. Nobody's going to sit motionless and let somebody jam a gun right against his head and not even jerk while it's being fired. That's why this was written off with no question . . . until you stuck your nose in it. Then they make every test in the book. They come up with conclusive evidence Dr. Brayton never fired that gun. Or any other, but that one for sure. It hadn't been cleaned since all six chambers had been fired the last time. But his hands were antiseptically clean. No trace of nitrates or nitrites, Doc says. And it's a sure thing he didn't wear gloves and take 'em off. So, it looks to me like there's got to be this second shot that you say you heard."

"—That I *did* hear."

"Take it easy, sugar," Trumper said.

"What I'm saying is, the evidence of the gun says there was only the one shot. But with the evidence of his hands, it doesn't make sense. But unless we can prove there was a second shot, we're leaving a big loophole for reasonable doubt. So that's where we start. Special assignment, Trump. You and Kerry."

"Looks to me like Kerry's done her job," Trumper said impassively. "And one thing's sure. Nobody else on Mt. Vernon Place heard a second shot. Nobody heard from nothing. Caspari combed the street yesterday afternoon. Not even in the house next door. The two old girls who're tenants on the third floor were dead to the world. Didn't hear a thing. A couple of empty sherry bottles gives 'em pretty good backing. The office on the first floor was closed. Woman named Remstad owns the house, lives on the second floor, and she clammed up. Caspari said he didn't know whether she didn't like him or didn't like cops. So I went to see what I could get out of her. It's cops, period. Chiefly Officer O'Keefe."

He glanced at her as he went on.

"Mrs. Remstad likes John Brayton—he speaks to her on the street. She offered him money to get married on, and she's burned up now the girl turns out to be a cop, not a sitter. That's the only reason she talked to me at all. She'd just found it out last night. And she didn't like me either."

He gave them a dour grin.

"I was tryin' to be sociable. She's got a collection of little china animals—pigs, cows, chickens and stuff—in book cases both sides of the fireplace. I picked one up. It didn't pick—glued down. She said, 'See, that's so people can't walk off with 'em. The cheap ones

94

are over there by the windows. It's okay if you stick one of them in your pocket.'

"So all I got was she saw John Brayton leave the house and saw Miss Brayton come out waving her hands. In between, she was out in back in her kitchen, and she was eating and getting herself some beer when she heard a sound. It could have been a truck or could have been her TV. She had it on at this same Western Miss Elizabeth Brayton was looking at."

The Inspector shook his head. "No second—"

"Inspector, she heard a sound, period. And if Dr. Brayton killed himself or somebody killed him it's okay with her. She said, 'You can't expect me to weep any salt tears.' She's lived in that house right smack up against the Braytons' twenty-seven years and John Brayton's the only one ever gave her the time of day. She'll neither help 'em nor hinder 'em, she says. They mind their business, she minds hers.

"But one thing I got, I didn't expect. There's a woman whose car came for Dr. Brayton all the time. It's got gold-plated fittings, leopard-skin upholstery and a Texas license plate. It's the first we've heard about—"

"That's Mrs. Ristwich's," Kerry said quietly. "She's a patient of Dr. Brayton's. An oil widow."

The Inspector and Trumper looked at her and briefly at each other.

"Homicide's checking," Trumper went on. "And one other thing. Last night they had a whole flock of lawyers out at the Braytons' place. One of the Homicide boys walked past a huddle of 'em on the sidewalk afterwards. Heard one say something about holding off a while. He said, 'Getting Enoch Chew's like pleading Guilty before she's accused.' "

"Who's Enoch Chew?" Kerry asked, when neither of them said any more for a moment.

"He's the top trial lawyer in these parts, sugar," Trumper said. "—A trial lawyer they're talking about . . . before they've got the body back."

Kerry flushed, the tears springing out along her lashes before she looked quickly away from the two dispassionate faces turned toward her.

Trumper looked down at the Inspector's desk. "You got O'Brien's report there?" he asked without any apparent connection.

95

The Inspector riffled through the dozen or so reports in front of him, the bare beginning that would add up until they made an immense black-jacketed volume containing every item of information, relevant or not, that came to hand. He handed Trumper Post Officer O'Brien's, laboriously hand-written and turned in Saturday morning.

"Listen to this." Trumper read it.

"Ordered to investigate report of suicide phoned in from Brayton residence, West Mt. Vernon Place, Friday, May 1, 11:24 p.m. Found Policewoman O'Keefe on premises with Miss Elizabeth Brayton. Miss Brayton said, My brother's shot himself. Informed by Officer O'Keefe that John Brayton, the son, was in the vicinity. A crowd was collecting. Instructed Officer O'Keefe to proceed inside with the sister Miss Brayton and go to scene. Waited for Patrolman Garrett. Instructed him to stay at door and send for John Brayton if possible. Proceeded to second floor. Officer O'Keefe said an inspection of premises should be made. Instructed her to remain on situs and did so. Found all cellar windows locked and barred, doors locked and chain-bolted on inside. Checked first floor. Kitchen and pantry doors to back porch bolted likewise. Windows secure. Second floor, right rear sitting room locked. Entered through right front bedroom and bath. Noted sitting room fireplace full of burned papers, ashes cold. Center room front piled with boxes and wedding presents, otherwise empty. Third floor check found Miss Elizabeth Brayton watching TV in front right bedroom. Rear right bedroom occupied by John Brayton recently occupied. Law book open page 811. Meat of half apple showing tooth marks still fresh, not turned brown. Checked closets and bathrooms each floor. Checked attic."

Trumper tossed it back. "We're talking about you, sugar," he said bleakly. He turned to the Inspector. "Everything O'Brien did of any importance he did on account of Officer O'Keefe told him to. He was thorough, but it was O'Keefe's idea. Maybe you lawyers can twist things around and keep Kerry off the stand—if we get to trial. Regulations say the first uniformed officer on the scene joins Homicide till the investigation's complete, and that's O'Brien, policewomen not being in uniform. Or maybe you can stretch the rule about a cop not making an arrest in his own or his family's quarrels. I don't know. But I know if you put O'Brien on the stand instead of Kerry, he's so honest he's going to say it wasn't me, it was Officer O'Keefe. She ordered the premises searched . . . and by doing that she put the noose around Mrs. Brayton's neck. Because that's sure where it is."

Kerry O'Keefe closed her eyes. *Oh, Johnny . . . I'm sorry. I'm so sorry . . .*

Trumper motioned down at the reports on the desk.

"That's the trouble with those things. They're just a bunch of observed facts. They don't say what's the feeling you had when you observed them. You don't have to be in that house five minutes to see John Brayton thinks his mother did it. Those things don't tell the impression you get when the kid sister they call Lolly gets back from some place down south and jolts to a stop in her mother's sitting room, and nearly faints when her mother introduces Caspari and me."

The Inspector made no comment. He was sitting, his chair tilted back, his hands clasped behind his head, his glasses on the desk, staring abstractedly into space.

"Those shots," he said abruptly. "Kerry. You're sure—"

"Oh, I'm absolutely sure! And I wish all of you people would just stop nagging me! I wish to heaven I'd never—"

"Take it easy," Trumper said. "If you say you heard, you damn well did. Nobody doubts your word. We're just trying to figure. And nobody's going to beat your brains out, Kerry. You better get out of this. Go on upstairs. There's plenty of work on my desk. Get going, Officer."

He held the door open as she went blindly through.

"The poor little devil."

The Inspector nodded. "If we have to put her on the stand and they get Enoch Chew, he'll tear her to ribbons. But if there's an out I don't see it. What do you think about her?"

Trumper was silent a moment.

"The big deal she and this Brayton boy had's all smashed to hell. She's in ribbons now. She knows she's the one that nailed the killing on his mother. I don't think she'd leak to help him . . . but I wouldn't stake a case on it. She's like the rest of us. She's human. Why not send her to Pine Street on regular duty?"

"Wilmington wants to borrow a girl. Why don't I send her there? We'll know she's safe."

Trumper nodded. "Hold off till the four-thirty shift leaves. There's a waitress from a pizza joint on Thames Street saw the Braytons' pictures in the paper, says she recognizes Mrs. Brayton and her son.

They were both there, the son with a girl. She's got quite a story, if true. If it was Brayton, the girl'd be Kerry. But Caspari wants to keep this waitress under wraps for a surprise witness, if she's dependable, so he wants to see if she can pick Kerry out of a bunch of other girls piling out of the elevator going home tonight."

"Then ship her off first thing in the morning." The Inspector tilted his chair back again, staring off into space.

"Trump," he said, "if it wasn't suicide, it's *got* to be two shots. Whether anybody heard 'em or not. If suicide's out, it's murder. If it's murder, there's got to be two shots. Not one."

Trumper got to his feet. "You're the boss. You figure it. I'm going." He grinned at him from the door. "Tell me when I get back, will you?"

As he closed the door he heard the desk chair shoved forward. He didn't see the excitement with which the Inspector reached for the phone to dial the City Morgue.

"—Doc? Listen, Doc . . ."

So Kerry O'Keefe read in a Wilmington paper that Miss Laura (Lolly) Brayton's wedding had been called off and presents returned. The Braytons' social connections made it front page news.

It was there she read that Mrs. Brayton had been arrested and charged with murder and that she had refused to take a lie-detector test.

It was three days later that she saw the headline: Grand Jury Indicts Widow In Doctor's Murder.

Four days before the trial was opened she got her orders to return to Baltimore.

John Brayton sat beside his mother in the courtroom, Enoch Chew on the other side of him, his head bowed, listening, hardly hearing the words being read.

"The Jurors of the State of Maryland for the body of Baltimore City, do on their oath present that Margaret Summerfield Brayton, late of said county, on the first day of May at the county aforesaid, feloniously, wilfully and of deliberately premeditated malice aforethought, did kill and murder Pierce Brayton, contrary to the form of the Act of Assembly in such case made and provided, and against the peace, government and dignity of the state."

"How say you, Are you guilty of the matter wherein you stand indicted or not guilty?"

"—I am not guilty."

His mother's voice was quiet but distinctly clear, her face as he looked up at her tranquil, serenely lovely.

"Don't Johnny. Don't worry, sweet," she whispered, kissing him goodbye as the matron came to take her back to the Pine Street Station to the narrow room on the second floor. He could only close his eyes and thank God she wasn't down in the cell block behind the silvered gates that tore him with rage every time he went there to take fresh clothes or went with Enoch Chew when he talked to her, and had to relive that Sunday morning with Joe Anselo and the girl in the red dress.

As he was reliving now the night his grandmother's lawyers brought Enoch Chew to the house, the night of the day his mother was arrested, charged with murder. An old-established extremely conservative firm that handles estates and taxes, and on occasion when they were forced to it a very quiet divorce, never before faced with a murder, they were nervous and unhappy, personally as friends as well as professionally.

"We want this handled as discreetly as possible. Nothing flamboyant, old man. Try to keep it from becoming a cause celebre."

"It's that already. You gentlemen don't read the out-of-town papers?"

Enoch Chew was a large genial man with a handsome grizzled mane and comfortable paunch, a trial lawyer whose tears came easy and expensive, whose voice could be a lion's roar or a kitten's purr with equal facility as occasion demanded.

"I'm sorry I wasn't brought in sooner. From what I've read and what you've told me I wonder if a plea of Not Guilty is really advisable?"

"My daughter says she is not guilty, Mr. Chew." Mrs. Summerfield fixed bitter indomitable eyes on him. "Therefore she is not. It's preposterous on the face of it. When the invitations to her daughter's wedding were already in the mail. No woman would commit murder three weeks before her daughter's marriage."

Chew smiled. "Feminine reasoning isn't necessarily specious," he observed pleasantly. "We should have some ladies on the jury, I expect."

"And if it hadn't been for my grandson taking up with that jailbird my daughter would never have been put in this position. Never. It's pure, unmitigated spite."

Johnny saw Enoch Chew's eyes move to him, going over him in minute appraisal.

"If we ask Mr. Grimes to lend him to us for the defense table it will probably be a great comfort to his mother," he said easily. "I'm sure it can be arranged. And as we haven't much time, perhaps he and I could have a chat. In private, if you don't mind. And if it's convenient perhaps you'd wait, Mrs. Summerfield, and give me a lift home."

In private the genial mask was gone, sharp intelligence there in its place. "I want to know everything you can tell me about her—this girl, Brayton."

"Let's keep her out of it, sir." Johnny's jaw hardened. "She's not a jailbird. I don't want to drag her—"

"Your mother's charged with murder, Johnny." Chew shifted

into paternal kindliness. "She says she isn't guilty. At this time, I'll be frank to say to you, I see no way of proving it. But, if your personal feelings—"

Johnny flushed. "It's common decency, sir—"

"In a murder trial, Johnny, there's no decency of any kind. It's this girl or your mother. Take your choice. All I want from you is the plain basic facts. Where you met her and how." *The rest I can get from that old rogue your grandmother and this sister-in-law I've heard about.*

Johnny Brayton put his head in his hands. In his pocket was the telegram his mother had slipped there for him to send just as the police arrived.

"Don't worry. Don't come. It's what we feared. Pray for me, is all I ask."

It was to Major-General Robert W. Preston.

While in the small sound-proofed office on the fifth floor, Dave Trumper had just come back from a final check with Homicide officers at the office of Alec Dobson, Assistant State's Attorney in charge of the prosecution.

"He's crazy," he said, staring grimly at the smoke curling round the tip of his cigarette. "He's opening with Kerry. Maybe he's got to do it that way to establish the second shot. Maybe he's got to do it that way. It scares the hell out of me. He thinks she's safe. He thinks the Braytons won't want Johnny's past with a female sitter he picked up at the jailhouse aired in public. He thinks the family lawyers will ride herd on Enoch Chew."

He got up and stuck his cigarette in the aspidistra pot.

"So what did they hire him for?—If there was just some way out of putting her on the stand at all. But I guess it's glamor. The prettiest cop on the force to offset Mrs. Brayton who's sure an angel to look at. Throwing Kerry to the wolves. It makes me sick. Like that night she was jailed.—In fact this whole case worries me. I keep waking up at night with a feeling we've been flimflammed. When we open up the package that's got the thousand-dollar bills in it, we're going to find a stack of oblong pieces cut out of last week's News-Post. I don't buy this Ristwich dame, myself."

"Nobody did till Caspari turned up with that note Mrs. Brayton wrote her husband," the Inspector said. "But it's out of our hands now. Go on home, Trump, and get some sleep."

The State of Maryland *vs.* Brayton opened in Part II of the Criminal Court of Baltimore City on the last Tuesday in June, before Judge Sansbury, brought on from the Eastern Shore when the regular judges had disqualified themselves on grounds of social contact and personal friendship with the defendant and her family.

If it seemed to the crowds packing the public benches that Enoch Chew had lost his old fire, it was a relief to Alec Dobson, backing up his belief that the Brayton family, sitting staunchly together in the front bench nearest the defense table, would play it down as much as possible. And so he thought until Friday morning when Enoch Chew accepted the last four names presented for the jury at once and without any of the tedious wrangle that had occupied the three preceding days, the panel was sworn in and Alec Dobson was opening for the State at twenty minutes past eleven. As Chew's great forte was the drama of his openers, he made his own short and severely factual, closing it with the noon recess. When court reconvened at two o'clock and Enoch Chew rose easily to his feet, it was too late for the prosecution to change tactics.

"Ladies and Gentlemen of the honorable jury—I am not going to weary you with discursive prose. I ask you only to look at the lady who sits here, the defendant in this case, and to watch her during the unhappy days that must come to her. The human face is the external image of the human heart and the human soul. If there is guilt in either, it is there reflected. I ask you to watch for it here in hers. For try as it will, and by its very nature must, and with every means, fair and foul, it has in its ever-growing, its frighteningly increasing power over us, the State through its prosecutors here will never alter, never change the transparent innocence of this woman's face, in this lovely mirror of her heart and mind. A terrible charge has been brought against her. It has neither truth nor substance. The truth and the substance are the quiet plea she made here when this charge was made, the question asked 'how say you, are you Guilty or Not Guilty?' She said, 'I am Not Guilty.' Ladies and gentlemen of the jury, *that* is the truth."

There was a flicker in his eyes meeting his old friend Alec Dobson's as he sat calmly down beside John Brayton at the defense table, aware of the sudden flurry at the table for the prosecution and the sudden flurry at the press table. He was aware also of the startled silence, equally sudden, along his own table. His brothers for the defense probably thought he'd taken their injunction "Nothing flamboyant, old man," too literally, not knowing that his whole strategy, the only real hope he had for the defense, was to get the girl O'Keefe on the stand with time left for him to cross-examine her, to tear every shred of credibility and respectability from her, before the weekend recess.

He glanced without seeming to at the three women he'd got on the jury. Two were mothers of unmarried sons, one the mother of a son married and divorced whose lips had tightened at the mention of her son's ex-wife. None of them had daughters. With fifty-four hours in possession of their minds before court reconvened on Monday, the dragon-seeds of Kerry O'Keefe, the cell-block pickup, scheming to marry another mother's son, embittered when she was thwarted, would have plenty of time for sprouting. Female tenacity would keep them watered to produce that reasonable doubt which was the most Enoch Chew hoped for. He had won verdicts before with such strategy in more hopeless cases with less to go on.

He leaned back, smiling a little, as the Assistant State's Attorney rose and came forward.

"Police Officer O'Keefe."

Kerry heard her name and heard Dave Trumper sitting beside her whisper "Take it easy, girl." She had never been on a witness stand before. She rose, her feet moving the rest of her in a kind of paralysis as she came forward, unconscious of the audible gasp that went throught the packed benches.

Enoch Chew was conscious of it, in the benches and in the jury box, even on the bench as Judge Sansbury's eyes opened with surprise an instant before they swept over the room, silencing it. But none of that was as important to Chew as what happened at that instant to John Brayton sitting beside him. It was the first time he'd seen her since the Sunday night in May two months ago. Presumably he hated her. But for a tortured instant his eyes met hers, suddenly pleading, as she stood, her hand on the Bible to be sworn in, torture in her own eyes, her hand trembling, her face suddenly pale.

Enoch Chew had himself been startled. It was the first time he'd seen Kerry O'Keefe except in the pictures Mrs. Summerfield had and a casual glimpse of her head bent down, shoulders drooping, behind the prosecutor's table. He was not prepared for the girl he now saw, recovering her poise, clean and fresh, her voice and chin steady as she sat down, folding her hands in her lap, crossing her slender ankles in high-heeled blue pumps. She was nothing whatever like the girl either Mrs. Summerfield or the sister-in-law had described to him.

Sensing the atmosphere of the courtroom—hers, all hers—and hearing the satisfied note in the prosecutor's voice, slow anger burned inside him. *This will take a miracle,* he thought.

"You are a member of the Baltimore City Police force, are you not, Officer O'Keefe?"

"Yes, sir."

"On the night of Friday, May 1st, you had reason to be in your car on West Mt. Vernon Place. Officially or not?"

"Not officially, sir."

"Will you tell us what happened while you were there, Officer O'Keefe."

She told it, simply and briefly, only the occasional dark arrow of pain in her blue eyes, the quiver of a raw-touched nerve at the corner of her mouth and the unconscious quickening of the pulse in her throat betraying her.

Enoch Chew, leaning forward intently, felt a nudge at his elbow, glanced sharply around and saw the note slipped covertly down from the other end of the defense table. He opened it and read it.

"She's going to hang us. For God's sake do something."

He crushed the note savagely, his face unchanging, and jammed it into his pocket. Now they were telling him. A cold fury settled in the pit of his stomach. If they hadn't lied to him, if they'd given him an honest picture of the girl . . . He looked at the clock. She was finished, but Dobson was trying to keep her on the stand. He couldn't keep her there much longer. Judge Sansbury had already started to tug irritably at his gown. Then abruptly it was over. The State's Attorney moved back, leaving her there for the defense.

Enoch Chew glanced at the clock again. There was an hour left. It was all he needed. He rose and came forward, genial and benign, smiling at the girl there on the stand.

Kerry O'Keefe watched Enoch Chew moving toward her, his smile kindly, full of paternal benevolence. A sudden panic, almost like the panic she'd felt the night the cell block gate clanged shut behind her, froze her heart, constricting her throat. She heard Dave Trumper then, clearing his throat, and braced herself as she'd done at the sound of his voice through the silvered gates.

She wasn't aware of John Brayton then, but Enoch Chew was aware of him. It would take a miracle, he'd thought. A minor miracle had happened, when he'd least expected it. John Brayton had forgotten the jury, the judge and the crowded benches, even his mother sitting beside him. He was conscious of no one but the girl on the stand, the girl who'd betrayed them, his burning eyes fixed steadily on her, no longer tortured but bitterly hostile. If he stayed that way until Enoch Chew could point up the relationship between the defendant's son and the defendant's accuser, it was all he asked.

"I know how hard this is for you, so I'll be as brief as possible, Miss O'Keefe," he said kindly. "And it *is* Miss O'Keefe, isn't it? Miss Kerry O'Keefe? Not *Mrs.* O'Keefe?"

"Yes, sir."

"And not Policewoman O'Keefe. Mr. John Brayton never called you Officer O'Keefe, did he?"

Kerry flushed sharply. "He didn't—"

"Now let's not have a sparring match, Miss O'Keefe." Chew smiled, amused at her warmth. "Just a simple yes or no, my child. We'll both be through a great deal quicker. Did he or did he not?"

"He did not."

"Thank you. Now how old are you, Miss O'Keefe?"

"I'll be twenty-three next month."

"And this . . this odd profession of yours. Just how long have you been a member of it, Miss O'Keefe?"

"Two years and three months, sir."

Her color heightened again. She remembered she'd been warned not to let him make her angry.

"So that we can assume, in spite of very charming appearances to the contrary, that you've what is commonly called 'been around' long enough so that my questions won't offend your sense of delicacy, as they might have done two years and three months ago, perhaps. And by the way, before we proceed let's get one thing cleared up, if you please. —These good people." He waved casually back toward the State's Attorney's table. "Have they made you any promise, pursuant to your appearance in this courtroom?"

"No, sir."

"Nor the police? The Rackets Division or the Detective Bureau? You're a very ambitious young lady, I take it. They haven't promised you a promotion, have they?"

"Certainly not."

"Then you're here entirely because of your own animosity toward the defendant?"

"That's false." Kerry flushed hotly. She saw the State's Attorney getting quickly to his feet.

"Then I withdraw it, for the moment," Enoch Chew said blandly.

He paused to let the receptive silence deepen before he asked the question that would force the State's Attorney to object and give him his one chance to destroy this girl—destroy her before she destroyed them. He shot it bluntly at her.

"How long have you been intimate with John Brayton, Miss Kerry O'Keefe?"

Alec Dobson rose without haste. "I object, as irrelevant, immaterial, and designed only to mislead the jury, your honor," he said casually. He knew now the ordeal Kerry O'Keefe had ahead of her, and that his only course was to play it down, to keep Chew from dramatizing her vulnerability. He managed to sound a little bored. "And in case my distinguished friend here has not had time to read his brief with his accustomed care and assiduity, I would like to point out, to both him and the ladies and gentlemen of the honorable jury, that however earnestly, and with whatever exercise of his deservedly famous—I had almost said, infamous—histrionic talent, my learned friend seeks to make it appear to the contrary, Mr. John Brayton is not on trial before this court. His capacity here is that of a junior member of a very brilliant, I might almost say ostentatious, display of legal talent with which the defense seeks to confuse and overpower us. Mr. John Brayton is not on trial before this court. Let me remind you of that again, as I shall, I am afraid, be forced to do more than once in the course of my distinguished friend's forensic legerdemain."

Enoch Chew smiled, bowing slightly.

"My friend from the State flatters me, your honor," he said suavely. "I am perfectly aware that Mr. John Brayton is not on trial. I would not for the world do him the dishonor of so imply-ing. But Mr. John Brayton's beloved mother is on trial here, ac-cused of the most terrible crime that one human being can commit against another. And without the intimate relationship existing be-tween this young woman and John Brayton, this gracious and lovely lady would never have been dragged here to suffer this despair, and this humiliation. And certainly my friend for the State cannot be so blinded and befuddled by the charm and beauty of his own witness to have forgotten in less than half an hour that it was he, not I, who introduced Mr. John Brayton's name into this case . . not directly and honorably, but indirectly, seeking to evade the truth and its consequences . . when he asked this witness if she was in Mt. Vernon Place the night of May 1st on official business or busi-ness that was not official."

He smiled with friendly irony.

"I do not wonder that the State's Attorney passed so quickly on, evading the question What was your unofficial business there? Because her business there was John Brayton. I can well believe that my distinguished friend has spent many a sleepless night pray-ing for some miraculous dispensation that would allow him to escape from bringing John Brayton's name to this child's lips. But no such prayer was answered, no such miraculous dispensation granted him. Without the intimate relationship between this wit-ness and John Brayton, this girl would never have been in Mt. Vernon Place in front of the Brayton house that Friday night. And none of us—this Court, this jury—would be here now. Because it was this girl who first cried Murder when there was no murder—and is no murder, and no murder case, nothing but a sickening farce, a palpable and putrescent example of police persecution of a very old and very distinguished Baltimore family—originated, and abetted, and pursued, by this girl, with malice, conscious or unconscious—"

Judge Sansbury's gavel came down the third time too sharp and too loud for Enoch Chew to continue to ignore it.

"The jury will disregard counsel's animadversions against the Baltimore police." Judge Sansbury's tone was even. "Counsel will also restrain his enthusiasm unless he wishes to find himself in contempt of this Court. Overruled, Mr. Dobson. Proceed, Mr. Chew."

"With the Court's permission," Enoch Chew said, quietly and very gravely, "—I wish it stipulated that I am not impugning the conscious veracity of this witness. I am not now, or at any time, whatever my distinguished friend for the State may try to insinuate to the contrary, —I am not, I repeat, trying to tell you that this charming girl in her simple delphinium blue cotton suit, white blouse with the simple strand of pearls at her lovely throat, is deliberately lying, or indeed that she can be said to be lying at all, in the truly ethical sense of that word. I would be a fool to try to tell you so. Her complete honesty is so palpably written in those delphinium blue eyes and on that broad clear brow . . No one can sit here and look at that white heart-shaped face and trembling young mouth and not be deeply moved at the heartbreak she is so valiantly trying to conceal. This slender dark-haired girl, this mere child who walks, an unsullied flower, through all the murk and evil of a great city, among the lowest of the low, this child is not lying. I know that. I stipulate it. She *believes* what she has told you."

He turned to thrust an angry forefinger at the State's Attorney.

"I doubt if even my sly and subtle friend of the prosecution has been able to make her distort or change or add or subtract one tittle or one iota in the extraordinary and fantastic story she has told you. And I am not questioning her intimacy with John Brayton with the purpose of degrading her in the eyes—"

"Oh, your honor—I must really object!"

"I should have thought you must have done so considerably earlier, Mr. Dobson." Judge Sansbury's voice was tart. "This Court has no desire to interfere with counsel. It recognizes certain bizarre and in its experience entirely unprecedented elements in the case before it. For that reason it will allow unusual latitude to the counsel for the defense—and expect him not to abuse it. It also expects the State's Attorney to afford this witness all the protection at his disposal. If necessary it will recess the Court to make it clear to counsel on both sides. Objection sustained. Proceed, Mr. Chew."

"I'm afraid I've forgotten my own question." Enoch Chew turned to the court stenographer with a deprecatory shrug.

"Refresh counsel's memory, please," Judge Sansbury ordered acidly.

The stenographer read mechanically. "How long have you been intimate with John Brayton, Miss Kerry O'Keefe?"

"—Or, if the word 'intimate' embarrasses you, my child, I shall be happy to put it in more euphemistic terms. How long have you known John Brayton?"

"About a year."

"You do know him."

"Yes, sir."

"Point him out to me, please."

He paused as she bent forward. "Oh, I'm so sorry—I'm obstructing your view." He moved aside. "You can see him now? Point him out, please."

She raised her hand, pointing, her head bending in a frail unhappy arc for an instant before she drew herself quietly erect again. Enoch Chew, aware of the jury's quickening excitement, was motionless, watching the whole focus of attention shift, alternating between the white face of the girl and the face of the young man, relentlessly carved in stone. He was offering them their choice between the two . . for in spite of the State's Attorney he had succeeded in putting John Brayton on trial before that Court. It was no longer the State of Maryland *versus* Brayton. It was John Brayton *versus* O'Keefe . . and Enoch Chew's only hope was to keep it that way.

"And you say you've known him about a year?"

"Yes, sir."

"Do you recall the precise date you met him?"

"Yes, sir."

"It was Sunday morning the 25th of July of last year, was it not?"

"Yes, sir."

"In another courtroom?"

"Yes."

"—Objection. It's quite immaterial where these young people

met. It's murder, not romance, that concerns us here, your honor."

"On the contrary." Enoch Chew spoke sharply. "We are very much concerned with this romance—if that's what we should call it. My friend for the State has tried to delude us into the belief that this young lady is nothing but a police officer—a disinterested observer who found herself unofficially in Mt. Vernon Place.— That she just happened to be in Mt. Vernon place the night of May 1st . . and just happened to hear, that night, what no one else heard, or could have heard. But she is not an observer. She is a participant, greatly interested, highly prejudiced, intensely hostile to the Brayton family. Her first meeting, and all her subsequent meetings with John Brayton—where she met him, what she was doing when she met him—these are the root and branch of that hostility and that resentment and prejudice. They are the sole and direct reason for her presence in Mt. Vernon Place that night of May 1st, and the one clear and valid reason for her extraordinary conduct in the days following . . culminating in the fantastic testimony she has given here today."

Judge Sansbury had leaned forward, with a puzzled frown. "The Court regards these as very serious charges, if true," he said slowly. "It overrules your objection for the present, Mr. Dobson. Counsel may proceed, bearing that in mind."

Enoch Chew turned to the white-faced girl on the stand.

"You met John Brayton in another courtroom, Miss O'Keefe?"

"Yes, sir."

"In the Women's Court at the Pine Street Police Station?"

"Yes."

"The morning after the raid on the Mimosa Club in what is known in Baltimore City as 'The Block'?"

"Yes, sir."

"Do you know The Block, Miss O'Keefe?"

"Yes."

"Fairly intimately, would you say?"

"Fairly, yes."

"You've worked there, have you not?"

"Yes."

"You were working there the night of July 24th?"

"Yes, sir."

"At the Mimosa Club?"

"Yes."

"You were arrested there and taken to the Pine Street Police Station? The Women's Police Station?"

"Yes, sir."

"And spent the night in a cell there?"

"Yes."

"And were fined ten dollars and costs in the Court there the next morning? For disorderly conduct?"

"Yes."

"And Mr. John Brayton came there?"

"Yes."

"As the legal representative of the proprietors of the Mimosa Club, to pay the fines for the entertainers who were taken in the raid?"

"Yes, sir."

"And he paid yours?"

"Yes."

"Was your hair black at that time, Miss O'Keefe?"

"No, sir."

"Was it blonde? Bleached blonde?"

"It was bleached blonde."

"These blue-black feather-cut curls you have now. Are they the product of the dye-pot too?"

"No, sir."

"They are your own?"

"Yes."

"And did you have on this delphinium blue cotton suit and demure white blouse and simple strand of pearls that morning, Miss O'Keefe?"

"No, sir."

"But you had some clothes on. What were they?"

"I had on a red evening dress."

"Surely you didn't leave the Pine Street Police Station on Sunday morning in a red evening dress, did you, Miss O'Keefe?"

"I had a jacket."

"Whose jacket?"

"John Brayton's."

"He loaned you his grey and white cotton seersucker jacket?"

"Yes."

"You'd known him before, Miss O'Keefe?"

"No, sir."

"You had just met him that morning, in the courtroom?"

"Yes."

"You did meet him, did you?"

"Yes, sir."

"Who introduced you, Miss O'Keefe? Now please, my dear child, don't look surprised. The customary way of meeting a young man is to be introduced to him. You say you met him. Who introduced you?"

"Nobody."

"So you didn't meet him. You picked him up—or he picked you up . . whichever way it was. It was a pickup . . was it not?"

"If you want to call it that."

"It's not what I want to call it. It's what it was. If a young woman of your age knows The Block she should certainly—I would have presumed—have some knowledge of basic popular semantics. You know what semantics is? Or do you?"

"It's the science of the meaning of words, isn't it, sir?"

"I'm asking the questions, Miss O'Keefe. I'm just an ignorant trial lawyer, my child. I've never even been arrested for disorderly conduct, or had to borrow a jacket to leave the Police Court in on a Sunday morning. But let's get on. You allowed yourself to be picked up and loaned John Brayton's seersucker jacket. Did you just walk off with his jacket?"

"No, sir."

"No. He went to your apartment with you, did he not?"

"Yes."

"Is that a customary procedure in your . . profession, Miss O'Keefe?"

"No."

"Speak up, my child. Remember, we do not have the fantastically developed sense of hearing that the State's Attorney would have us believe you are endowed with. Is it customary for you to take men from the Police Court home to your apartment?"

"I didn't *take* him home. I didn't want him there."

"No. Because you knew this was his first case . . as you told him. You were only twenty-two years old, but you were familiar with courtrooms. He was not. I suggest, Miss O'Keefe, that you thought he was a struggling young lawyer not worth your while until you found out he was a member of a distinguished Baltimore family. That's the truth, isn't it, Miss O'Keefe?"

"No. It is not."

"But you say you didn't take him home and you didn't want him there. After that you let him come back, didn't you? He did come back, did he not?"

"Yes, sir."

"Frequently. Very frequently, in fact. That's true, isn't it?"

" . . Yes."

"To your apartment? After you knew who his family were?"

"Yes."

"And he saw you at other places?"

"Yes."

"Very well, Miss O'Keefe. You're familiar with The Block, you said."

"Yes, sir."

"You've heard it compared with the old Barbary Coast and other such places of so-called entertainment, have you not?"

"Yes, sir."

"Then you know what a 'sitter' is, I presume. I don't mean a baby sitter. I mean what's called a female sitter in night spots, like the Mimosa Club and the Coral Seas. You do know?"

"Yes."

"A sitter is an alluring young lady who sits at a table and entices men to buy refreshments, liquid and otherwise, is she not?"

"Yes, sir."

"And Article 25, Section 175 of the Maryland Code makes it unlawful for the proprietor, lessee or manager of any place of entertainment to employ or allow a female sitter in his establishment. That's correct, is it not?"

"I'm not a lawyer, sir. You know the Maryland Code better than I do."

"But I've never been a female sitter, and you have, haven't you, Miss O'Keefe? Weren't you one the night the Mimosa Club was raided?"

"I was acting as one."

"As a sitter? What I mean is, you were a sitter, not a stripper, which I believe is the other category of entertainers in the night spots on The Block? You were a sitter, not a stripper. Also at a place called the Coral Seas Club. Now let me show you this."

He went back to the defense table and took a photograph out of his briefcase.

"—Oh, no, please!" Margaret Brayton started up from her chair beside Johnny. "Oh, please don't!"

Judge Sansbury rapped sharply, a court officer moved quickly forward. But Johnny had drawn his mother back into the chair. There were white ridges standing out along his jaw. This was the fine hand of his grandmother, sitting rigidly there in the front bench behind him. He hadn't known, but he should have known. He sat there sick, his hand tight on his mother's arm, as Enoch Chew went deliberately back to Kerry.

"You heard the protest drawn from the lips of the lovely lady sitting here charged with a terrible crime against the father of her children. You heard her cry 'Oh no! Please don't!' . . trying even in this hour of her own agony to save you, the girl who first cried Murder against her. Because she's seen this foul thing.—A photograph of the girl who was trying to marry her son." He thrust it at her. "It is your picture, is it not, Miss O'Keefe?"

Kerry's hand trembled as she took it, her eyes moving down to it. She started violently, the color draining from her face.

"It is your picture, is it not?"

"Yes."

"Thank you. I'd like this marked and entered as evidence. And I should like the ladies and gentlemen of the jury to see it at this time."

Chew watched the jury as each of them looked at the enlarged photograph of Kerry leaving the Coral Seas, the already larger-than-life cut-out of the stripper, her black petticoat in one hand, the bubbling glass of champagne in the other, the back drop for the girl who bore little or no resemblance to the girl sitting pale and shaken on the witness stand.

How horrible. Oh, how horrible. Kerry closed her eyes, trying to keep down the faintness that blurred the faces of the packed benches, except the Braytons' . . Mrs. Summerfield, sitting rigidly erect in the front row, Pug Brayton by her, the small dark girl she knew must be Lolly. Next to her was an empty seat where Miss Elizabeth Brayton had been, beyond that the other sister and her husband. Only Camilla Anne had not appeared.

"And now may I ask you, Miss O'Keefe . . this extraordinary profession you've chosen. You did choose it, did you not?"

"Yes, sir."

"Deliberately, of your own free will and volition, as we say?"

"Yes."

"And you've been to college. You are in fact a college graduate, are you not?"

"Yes, sir."

"So you had many other opportunities to make a living?"

"I didn't want any other—"

"No. You enjoy this sort of thing." Enoch Chew motioned toward the photograph going its second round of the jury box. "And your parents, Miss O'Keefe? I presume you have parents."

"Yes. I have."

"Do they approve of your traipsing along the streets, an agent provocateur, luring men—"

"That's not true—"

"Then I withdraw it, Miss O'Keefe. We have the photograph in evidence for any conclusion that may be drawn. Do your parents approve?"

"No, sir."

"They disapprove."

"They don't like my job, if that's what you mean, Mr. Chew."

"It's precisely what I mean, young lady." His voice and manner changed, no longer benign and benevolently paternal.

"And John Brayton, who loaned you his seersucker jacket—did he approve?"

"No."

"He disapproved?"

"He disapproved of my being a sitter. He didn't—"

"He disapproved strongly of your being a sitter, didn't he, Miss O'Keefe?"

"Yes."

"Did he buy you refreshments at these establishments?"

"He never came to them when I was there."

"Because you didn't want him to waste his money?"

"Because I didn't want him to come . . . period."

"I'm sure you didn't, Miss O'Keefe. But in spite of all this, he offered to marry you, did he not?"

"He asked me to marry him."

"—And his family were opposed . . . were they not?"

"I was told so."

"And you resented it—did you not?"

"No."

"You were pleased about it?"

"No. Of course not."

"But you didn't resent it?"

"No."

"Please . . . my dear child." Enoch Chew shook his head patiently. "Your friends the police, and my friend the distinguished gentleman for the State, must have instructed you not to try to evade the truth, when the truth is as patently obvious as it is right now. Are you asking this jury of highly perceptive men and women whose experience with the world is far more profound than yours —if not so bizarre—are you asking them to look at your flushed cheeks and smoldering blue eyes and believe that you didn't resent, and resent intensely, the Brayton family's antagonism to your marriage with their son?"

"I didn't resent their not liking my sitting job. I didn't expect them to like it."

"That's not what I'm asking you about, Miss O'Keefe. Let's see if we can approach this in a different way. John Brayton proposed marriage to you? Is that correct?"

"Yes."

"And you accepted him?"

"Yes."

"—Did you, or didn't you? I must ask you to speak up, Miss

O'Keefe. None of us here have the extraordinary powers of hearing that you are pretending to be endowed with. None of us are able to hear through stone walls. We're just ordinary mortals. So bear with us, please, Miss O'Keefe.—In spite of the Brayton family's opposition, you did accept their son's proposal of marriage?"

"I didn't think about his family when I accepted him."

"But would it have made any difference in your answer?"

"Probably not."

"And when you did learn they were vigorously opposed, you didn't offer to break your engagement . . . did you?"

"No. I didn't."

"Because you wanted to marry John Brayton, didn't you?"

"—Yes."

"Louder, please, Miss O'Keefe. You did want to marry him?"

"Yes."

"And when a member of the Brayton family came to see you, and saw you, not this demure little lady the police are trying to put forward to beguile and deceive us, but as you are in this photograph we have of you in your working clothes—may I say—this distinguished elderly lady imploring you not to ruin her grandson's life, you told her she was offensive. Do you recall that, Miss O'Keefe? 'Offensive' was the word you used?"

"It was offensive, to be—"

"I'm sure you so regarded it, Miss O'Keefe. That's my sole reason for bringing the matter up. You found it deeply offensive. And on the night of Friday, May 1st, when another member of the Brayton family saw you, you were at another one of these establishments, were you not?"

"Yes. I was."

"A female sitter, again . . . except that you were standing, Miss O'Keefe—leaning over the bar, were you not?"

"That's right." Kerry's eyes had begun to smolder again.

"And you were furious, weren't you?"

"Yes, I was. But not—"

"You were in a blazing fury. You stormed out into the street and called John Brayton, demanded he meet you, got in your car and drove to West Mt. Vernon Place. That's a fact, is it not?"

"I left the club. I didn't storm, because—"

"Because you regard yourself as a well-bred young lady . . . just as good as the Braytons. And these parents of yours, Miss O'Keefe . . . Are they employed?"

"I'd like to leave my parents out of this, Mr. Chew. They have nothing to do—"

"You mean you're ashamed of them, Miss O'Keefe? Or don't you want them to be ashamed of you?"

"It's neither—"

"Just as you were grossly offended at being told the truth, that John Brayton was ashamed of you, ashamed to take you to his home to meet his parents. But you were running to tell him about the member of his family finding you at the bar at the Hay Ride Club. Did you tell him about his grandmother's visit to you?"

"No, I didn't."

"You kept that to yourself. But the second time, when another member of the family had tracked you down, you were in such a blazing fury you couldn't be as discreet as you'd been the first time. This was maddening—"

"It was my job. It had nothing to do with me personally. It was the job we—"

"You didn't care about John Brayton or his family . . . just your job. Is that it?"

"That's not true. I—"

"You did care about him."

"Of course I did."

"You were determined to marry him, in fact, weren't you? Or did you think you were in love with him?"

"I . . . knew I was."

"Very deeply in love, weren't you, in your fashion. And you still are, aren't you, Kerry?—But strike that out, please. I have no wish to cause you pain. I'm merely trying to show the honorable Court and this honorable jury that you were not a calm, dispassionate observer on that Friday night of May the first in Mt. Vernon Place. I suggest that you were, on the contrary, passionately not calm, Miss O'Keefe—so emotionally overwrought, so overstimulated, that you did not in point of fact hear any second shot. I suggest that its only existence was actually in your own fevered mind."

"That's not true."

"I ask you to think carefully when you say so, Miss O'Keefe. I would like to spare you the other alternative. The infinitely blacker alternative that I would earnestly beg you not to force upon us. I would most earnestly beg you to let us believe that that second shot was the product of an overwrought imagination. That, we could understand. All of us, none of us denying the cross of human frailty each of us bears, all of us could understand, and deeply sympathize. But if that second shot was not the product of your distress and unhappiness of that night, if you did not invent it, that night of May the first, Kerry O'Keefe, you did then invent it in the days following . . . invent it deliberately, with malice aforethought, to defame and to injure the people you believed had injured you. There is no other alternative. I ask you again, earnestly, and with all the gravity I am capable of, my child, to tell us the truth. . . . The second shot that only you claim to have heard, that you invented on the night of May the first. It was that night you invented it, was it not? A simple Yes or a simple No is all I want."

"No."

"Then you invented it four days later, deliberately and maliciously?"

"No. That's not true."

"Then I withdraw one of those qualifications. It was not deliberate and malicious. It was the product of another passionate upheaval. Because I shall suggest to you that there was another. But I shall let that rest for the moment. Let us go back to Mt. Vernon Place. You had stormed out of the Hay Ride Club. You called John Brayton. You were weeping, because—you say—your job there was ruined by a member of his family. You asked him to meet you. You didn't ask him to come to you. You got into your car and went to him. Did you go to his house and ring the doorbell, Miss O'Keefe?"

"No."

"You stayed in your car?"

"Yes."

"Parked in front of his house?"

"No."

"Where did you park?"

"Across the plaza. On the other side, going west."

"Why did you do that? You were engaged to marry him. Why didn't you go to his house and ring his door bell?"

"Because I didn't want to see him in his house."

"You preferred to see him outside, in the rain. It was raining, and miserably raw, that Friday night, wasn't it, Miss O'Keefe?"

"Yes."

"Had you ever been in his house, Miss O'Keefe?"

"—Yes."

"Speak up, please. It isn't raining in this room, nor is Friday night traffic swishing back and forth here. Nor am I asking you to make yourself audible through thick brown stone masonry, Miss O'Keefe. But I must ask you to speak audibly enough for the ladies and gentlemen of the jury to hear you. And if at any time my questions are too painful for you to answer, please tell me so, my child. I will be happy to withdraw them.—You had been to the Brayton house in Mt. Vernon Place?"

"Yes, sir."

"You had been there. How many times, Miss O'Keefe?"

"Once."

"Just one time? And you had known John Brayton for nine months and eighteen days? How long had you been engaged to marry him?"

". . . About four months."

"Speak up, please. You must remember when he proposed to you . . . when was it?"

"In September."

"So you'd been engaged to him for eight months—not four."

"No. I didn't . . . I didn't accept him until Christmas."

"Why not? Weren't you in love with him? Or did it take you that long to find out what a very substantial catch you'd managed to make for yourself? Or what was the reason?"

"It was my job."

"Because he didn't like it?"

"Partly."

"But nevertheless you had become engaged to him at Christmas. Were you taken to his house at that time?"

"No."

"Because he was ashamed to take you there. But they couldn't keep you out. Not Miss O'Keefe. You went there anyway. When was that?"

"It was the Maryland House and Garden Pilgrimage, April 30th."

"Please don't try to hide your embarrassment, Miss O'Keefe. It does you honor. Unless of course you neglected to pay the one dollar admission. You surely didn't go in without a ticket, did you, my dear?"

"I had a ticket."

"So that the one time you entered the Brayton house was when it was opened for the general public with other distinguished mansions in Baltimore, and in Maryland, for the benefit of the Hammond-Harwood House in Annapolis. And did you make your presence known to any member of the Brayton family, or any of the hostesses assisting them?"

"No, sir."

"You just handed in your ticket and slipped in, and pried around in a house you had never been invited to. And you were very pleased with yourself, weren't you, Miss O'Keefe?"

"No."

"No. You were ashamed, really, weren't you? Most unhappy.—Or were you happy?"

"I wasn't."

"And you hated yourself, and you hated the Braytons—did you not?"

"No. I didn't."

"Oh, come, my dear child. If you had a mirror in front of you at this moment, you could see what all of us here can plainly see. Your burning blue eyes and burning cheeks tell the truth your lips are trying to deny. But I don't want to distress you. Whatever impulse made you commit such a shameful breach of good manners, most of us can still understand how you might be intensely curious about the home of the man you were engaged to. But let's get on. —The very next day you were across the plaza from the Braytons' brownstone mansion the raw and rainy night of May first—waiting for John Brayton. What time did you get there?"

"Before ten-thirty."

"Was he standing there eagerly in the rain, waiting for you, Miss O'Keefe?"

"I got there quicker than I thought I would."

"And you saw him come out of the house, some time later?"

"About five minutes later."

"And did you sound your horn?"

"Yes. But he didn't hear me."

"He has only ordinary hearing.—Or was there considerable traffic?"

"There was some traffic on Charles Street. It was raining."

"And what did he do?"

"He went toward the Washington Monument. I usually parked down across from the Peabody Institute, toward St. Paul Street."

"So you were in the habit of meeting in Mt. Vernon Place."

"At times, yes."

"Many times?"

"A good many."

"Why, Miss O'Keefe?"

"Because he worked all day, and it was late when I got off—too late for him to come to my apartment."

"So you met in the street."

"We met in my car."

"But you didn't follow him down there, that night of May the first."

"No. I remembered I still had my makeup on—"

"And you didn't want him to see you that way, so you just let him go hunting in the rain."

"I was going to pick him up as soon as I was through."

"You'd found a place to park right across the plaza from his house?"

"There's a club there with a reserved entrance."

"So you were breaking a police regulation. But we'll let that go. You were taking off your makeup. John Brayton had gone down the street hunting for you. And you say you heard a sound."

"I said I heard a shot."

"There was no doubt in your mind that it was a shot, not a car backfiring?"

"None at all."

"You're familiar with guns, Miss O'Keefe? Are you an expert?"

"I'm not an expert, but I know a shot when I hear it."

"So you heard a shot. And there was no question in your mind that it was a shot."

"That's correct."

"Could you tell where this presumed shot came from, Miss O'Keefe?"

"Not exactly."

"What do you mean by 'not exactly'?"

"I mean I could tell it came from inside a building. It wasn't in the street. It was muffled."

"What did you do, Miss O'Keefe?"

"I opened the car door to get out."

"Why did you do that?"

"Because I expected to see somebody come out, or call for help, or something, and I expected to see the post officer—"

"—Post officer. That's what vulgarians like myself would call the cop on the beat, is it not, Miss O'Keefe?"

"Yes, sir."

"Thank you. I'm sure the jury don't mind being called vulgarians either. But you didn't see anyone come out or call for help, did you?"

"Not then."

"And somewhere in here is where you pretend to have heard this second shot. Was it like the first?"

"Not exactly."

"It was different?"

"Yes."

"How long after you heard the first sound that you instantly identified as a shot—how long after that did it take your overwrought mind to determine you heard another sound? How long was that?"

"Several seconds. I can't say exactly how many."

"And you weren't really sure you'd heard it at all, were you, Miss O'Keefe? Because you didn't say so, did you? But let me go back. You've heard a shot. You've opened your car door and got out in the rain. Is that correct?"

"Yes, sir."

"Now then, Miss O'Keefe. I want not what you thought you may have heard but what you did. You got back in your car, didn't you?"

"Yes."

"Why?"

"Because I didn't want to stand in the pouring rain."

"Now come, please. Don't let's get in a temper. I suggest the reason you got back in your car is that you weren't sure you had even, in actuality, heard one shot—much less an echo of it, reverberating through the brownstone mansion, which I suggest—if there is one tittle or iota of substance of any kind behind this fantastic auditory dream of yours—is the one obvious and reasonable explanation for it. —An echo, a reverberation. I suggest you thought you'd made a mistake and that's why you got back in your car. Because you didn't know the shot came from the Brayton house at that time. Did you?"

"No. I didn't."

"So you weren't very much interested, really, were you, Miss O'Keefe?"

"I was interested."

"But you weren't rushing up and down avidly yelling Murder, were you? You were sitting in your car taking off your makeup, waiting to read the Riot Act to John Brayton. Were you or were you not sitting in your car, Miss O'Keefe? Answer my question."

"I was."

"And you sat there for how long?"

"It was eighteen minutes to eleven when I heard the first shot—"

"And you were worried about John Brayton's not coming."

"No. I wasn't."

"Why not?"

"I thought he'd run into a friend and stopped to talk, or something else had held him up. I knew he'd find me."

"And then you saw something, Miss O'Keefe. What did you see?"

"I saw the Braytons' door open and a woman in a robe run out onto the porch and look up and down the street."

"And what did you do?"

"I got out and ran across the garden."

"Toward John Brayton's house."

"Yes."

"And you saw the post officer coming."

"Yes. He was running up from Charles Street."

"But you got to the house ahead of him?"

"A little ahead of him."

"It was his job, not yours. You were unofficial. Why were you there?"

"I thought there'd been an accident, and thought I could help."

"But you didn't wait to be invited to help."

"No, sir."

"And you didn't have to pay a dollar admission this time you thrust your way into the Brayton house. You hotfooted it in there and bolted up the stairs."

"Miss Brayton went up with me. That's where the smell of gun smoke was coming from."

"And you burst into a room. It was a library, wasn't it?"

"I didn't burst. It was a library."

"And you found a body there, Miss O'Keefe?"

"Yes, sir."

"Did you touch it?"

"No."

"Did the post officer touch it?"

"No."

"—Because there was no need to touch it to see that the terrible tragedy was complete . . . that death was there, beyond human power to assuage. Death was all too horribly evident, was it not, Miss O'Keefe?"

"Yes."

"And you stood there, in awed silence, didn't you?"

". . . Yes."

"You didn't jump up and down at once and shout Murder, did you?"

"No."

"Or did you go quickly over to the post officer and whisper 'This is not suicide, it's murder'?"

"No."

"Or did you say so to Lieutenant Caspari of the Homicide Squad when they got there?"

"No."

"Or to the Medical Examiner?"

"No."

"No. You didn't, Miss O'Keefe. You didn't open your mouth or utter a word—because you could see for yourself the terrible truth. Now then, Miss O'Keefe. You've told the State's Attorney the deceased was not alone in the room. There was someone else there."

"Yes."

"A lady."

"Yes."

"What was she doing, Miss O'Keefe?"

"Just . . . sitting there."

"Did you know her?"

"I knew who she was."

"You knew she was John Brayton's mother, Miss O'Keefe?"

"Yes."

"You'd seen her, the gracious hostess in her lovely home, the day you'd paid the dollar, had you not?"

"I saw her then."

"Had you seen her at any other time? When you didn't have to pay a dollar for the privilege?"

". . . No."

"But you see her now."

"Yes."

"Then point her out to me, Miss O'Keefe.—Point her out, I say. Or if you can't raise your eyes to meet the eyes of this gentle lady, this lovely woman who's looking at you, not bitterly, not in anger, but with pity in her heart, pity not for herself but for you, Miss O'Keefe . . . if you can't make yourself raise your eyes, just raise your hand to point to her, sitting quietly, serenely facing this terrible ordeal that you alone, Miss O'Keefe, have forced on her.— The lady who cried 'Oh, no, please!' when those of us who are trying to save her from the hideous charge you and you alone have forced against her, when we brought forward the picture of you so the jury could see you as the Brayton family saw you, and be able to see for themselves the reason the Braytons didn't want you in their family—which you so bitterly resented."

"I didn't—"

"I suggest that you did, Miss O'Keefe. Bitterly resented it. And, now, you say you wanted to marry John Brayton. You are engaged to him, I believe."

"No." Her voice was like wet silk being torn in shreds.

"You are not engaged to him. Did you break it, finally?"

"He . . . he broke it."

"John Brayton broke it. Not you. When, Miss O'Keefe? What date?"

"The third of May."

"The third of May. That would be Sunday, would it not? And did this happen in the morning, or at night?"

"At night."

"Late?"

"Yes."

"After midnight, perhaps?"

"Earlier, I think. I don't know."

"But you do know what happened at eight o'clock the morning of the next day—Monday the fourth of May, do you not, Miss O'Keefe?"

"Yes."

"You went to Central Police Headquarters on Fallsway at eight o'clock. You didn't go to the Detective Bureau. You went to the Chief of the Rackets Division.—*And that's when you cried Murder for the first time....* That Monday morning—not Friday night, not Saturday, not Sunday, but Monday morning—that's the first time you even so much as whispered, or in any way intimated, to any member of the Baltimore City Police, that you had heard, or thought or dreamed you'd heard, any echo, or any reverberation, of that single shot you heard in the night. Not until John Brayton broke his engagement with you ... not until then, Miss O'Keefe, did you unsheath those terrible claws to rend the family that had rejected you."

Out of the corner of his eye Enoch Chew saw Judge Sansbury's gavel raised for the final lurch of the minute hand on the face of the courtroom clock.

"That's the black alternative I suggest you've given us here ... the black, pitch-foul alternative. Your pound of flesh, Miss O'Keefe ... a mother's head for the heart of the girl her son rejected."

The gavel came down. "The members of the jury will go to their homes and avoid any discussion of this case until Monday at ten o'clock when this Court reconvenes. Counsel will see me at once in my chambers. Court is adjourned."

In the rising clatter of the packed courtroom Kerry O'Keefe was the only one who did not move. She sat motionless in the witness stand for an instant before she slumped forward. Dave Trumper caught her as she fell.

"Police Witness Faints On Stand."

Kerry saw the headline on her landlady's extra on the hall table an hour later as she got to her apartment. Under it was the photograph of her coming out of the Coral Seas. "Defense Accuses Rackets Girl Of Bias When Family Sought To Prevent Marriage To Son."

She went slowly along the hall to her door, holding the knob, her forehead pressed hard against the cool wood of the door frame, steadying herself an instant before she opened the door and went blindly on into the room. She stumbled forward and slipped to the floor, burying her head in the cushions of the sofa.

Oh, I wish I could die. I wish I could die. She whispered it softly to the empty room.

Monday morning in the Criminal Court of Baltimore City.

Judge Sansbury touched his gavel to the bench and leaned forward.

"Before you proceed, Mr. Dobson. The Court wishes to call attention to the fact that there are no privileged members of the public here present. Anyone leaving the courtroom before noon recess will not be readmitted."

A girl society reporter slipping into her place at the press table hastily scribbled a note to the reporter next to her.

"That's for balmy Miss Elizabeth Brayton. It's not the john, it's the TV set at Mike's Bar. What's the betting?"

"Eight on Johnny gets you five," said the note handed back to her. "Pending agonizing reappraisal after O'Keefe's redirect. Postponed at the moment for the Morgue."

It was at the conference Friday in the judge's chambers that it had been agreed to postpone the State's redirect examination of Kerry O'Keefe until the fact of murder itself had been established. "The State's first obligation is to prove unlawful killing, not to defend the character or morals of a member of the police force," Judge Sansbury had said tartly.

Slipping in late with Dave Trumper, Kerry saw, propped up near the witness stand, facing the jury, the greatly enlarged photographs of Dr. Brayton's body lying across his desk. She saw the three woman jurors sitting together in the lower row, and saw one nudge her neighbors, the three of them looking at her, their faces tight, eyes unfriendly as they followed her to the chairs against the wall behind the prosecutor's table.

Enoch Chew was finishing his cross-examination of the young assistant from the Medical Examiner's Office.

"So that you had no hesitation in telling Lieutenant Caspari to tell John Brayton they could have his father's body the first thing in the morning.—That sending it to the City Hospital was a pure formality."

"That's right, sir. But I—"

"There are not buts about it, Doctor. It's what you thought and what you said, is it not?"

"Yes, sir."

"That's all."

The toxicologist from the Chief Medical Examiner's Office followed him to the stand.

"On the 4th of May of this year, Doctor," Alec Dobson said, "you had occasion to examine the body of Dr. Pierce Brayton, whose death occurred on Friday, May the 1st. Why was there this delay?"

"The senior examiners were out of town. You've just heard that the first medical officer to see the body believed it was suicide. At the request of the police authorities, made before the body reached the City Hospital, it was transferred to the Morgue and held there for closer examination by senior examiners when they returned."

"And they informed you why the body was to be held?"

"We weren't there to be informed, sir, at that time. We were informed on Monday morning that an officer had heard two shots and that the possibility of a crime might exist."

"Did you find evidence of a second shot?"

"Not directly. By inference, we did. If I may explain, sir."

He pointed to a greatly blown-up photograph of a wound sprawling over the glossy paper.

"This is why the first medical examiner assumed that death was self-inflicted. What you see here is the annular abrasion or contusion. That is this arc of bruised skin around the bullet hole. But you can see it's separated from the edge of the hole and the bruise by a narrow band of intact skin. This lesion is caused by the sudden slapping of the skin against the gun muzzle as gases from the discharge of the bullet enter the hole and expand beneath the surface. Like a blast in a confined area. That's why you get all the blood and tissue you see.

"You can also see what we call 'sight marks.' Those are abraded points where the skin was blown against the foresight at the end of the gun barrel. Whenever they're present they're unmistakable evidence of close-contact wounds. You can see the margins here are lacerated. They were torn by the explosive escape of gases from the discharge.

"This is certain evidence that the gun was pressed firmly against the head when it was fired . . . and in the absence of other evidence, clear and certain evidence of suicide. It stands to reason no man is going to sit perfectly still while someone jams a gun against his head and fires."

He turned to another photograph.

"Here you see the nose of the bullet buried in the back of a book. You can also see that the book is on a level with the head of the person seated at the desk. The track of the bullet through the head is level, the exit wound directly opposite the wound of entrance. Decedent was known to be left-handed. All evidence pointed to a self-inflicted wound. And, as you've already heard this morning from the Crime Laboratory personnel, there was no external evidence of a second shot having been fired. There was equally no internal evidence of more than one shot."

"You are coming now to what you referred to as inference, I take it, Doctor?"

"Yes, sir. To inference established when we made exhaustive microscopic and chemical tests of the body. Particularly decedent's hands. As you've also heard from the Crime Laboratory officer, the gun that fired the one bullet that was identified as the cause of death was dirty. It had been fired, the entire six rounds, and had not been cleaned before the identified bullet was fired from it. It was therefore evident that had decedent fired the gun, which was found near his body—what might be called the murder gun—his left hand must show definite traces of the fact in the form of nitrates and more particularly nitrites, or burned powder. There was no such evidence. Decedent's hands were almost antiseptically clean, with evidence showing they had been washed with a surgical detergent very shortly before death."

"So that that constituted positive proof that death was not self-inflicted? That someone else had fired the death shot or shots? In short that it was murder? Not suicide but murder? Is that correct, Doctor?"

"Yes, sir."

"You couldn't have been mistaken?"

"If decedent had fired the gun, or even handled it, immediately before death, the laboratory tests we made would have showed it. That is not inference, sir. That is scientific fact."

"Thank you, Doctor. Now there is one more point I would like you to discuss. On Wednesday, two days after you had made these tests, you received a telephone call, did you not? Who called you and what did he say?"

"The Inspector in charge of the Rackets Division called me at my office. It was about the problem of the second shot. He asked me if it was possible for some person, whom I'll call A, presumably a friend or someone known to decedent—whom I'll call B—to fire a shot through B's head, killing him, from a distance, and then instantly come up to the body, jam the gun in the small wound already there, fire another shot that would produce the effect of annular abrasion and contusion that we see in the photograph, hastily retrieve the second bullet, reload the second chamber . . . in other words, produce the entire effect that we see here of suicide."

"What did you tell him, Doctor?"

"I told him No. It was not possible. There would be internal evidence of the second bullet. A second track through the brain. The angle of the body could not possibly be exactly restored so that the exit wound would exactly coincide with the first exit wound."

"What did he say to you?"

"He said that it had to be something of the sort. Not only had an officer heard a second shot . . . there was still the extreme unlikelihood of a man who hadn't handled a gun allowing another person to stoop down, or to sit down, beside him and put a gun directly in contact with his head. With which I agreed. He then said he would bet the sergeant in charge of the Gun Shop could work it out."

"And did you later receive another call from him and from the sergeant in charge of the Gun Shop at Central Police Headquarters?"

"Yes, sir. The next day. The sergeant at the Gun Shop had come up with the idea that a blank shell could have been fired into the existing small wound made from a distance, with the gun held against the head. I told him that we would spot that at once on examination, because a blank shell is made with black powder, which is easily detectable."

"And then, Doctor?"

"The sergeant then suggested that a blank shell not made with black powder could be contrived by removing the lead nose from a .32 caliber shell of the same type as the murder bullet, using some substance, possibly a bit of tissue, or a paste, in place of wadding, to hold the powder in place. I assured him that we were thorough and accurate in the Morgue laboratory. If there had been any foreign substance of any kind in the brain, we would have discovered it. I suggested that perhaps a wad of hair could be used, which would not be a foreign substance. This he tried. But the hair burned in a tight wad. When fired it was still so solid that it made a hole in the wood floor of the gun shop.

"But the sergeant then came up with the one substance that could successfully be substituted for wadding and that would disintegrate in such a way that we could never discover or suspect its presence in the wound."

"What was that, Doctor?"

"Blood. Blood put in place of the wadding and allowed to dry. The sergeant used his own blood. He was able successfully to fire a blank shell of the kind I've described that would leave absolutely no detectable trace and would give precisely the effect of a direct contact wound. This is why we've called this killing the almost-perfect murder."

"Thank you, Doctor."

Enoch Chew came forward as Dobson took his seat.

"Just one question, Doctor. It is quite clear there is no evidence of a second shot, is it not?"

"None whatever, sir."

"Thank you, Doctor."

Chew started to return to his table, and turned back.

"Don't you think you and the Inspector and the sergeant in charge of the Gun Shop are rather wasting your time, Doctor? With such extraordinary creative imaginations as you all appear to have, there's a far more lucrative field open to you. Murder fiction, I have in mind. You're a great loss to it, all of you. That's all, thank you."

The State's Attorney came forward again. "These photographs, Doctor. Are they creative, imaginative fiction?"

"No, sir. They are conclusive and incontrovertible evidence of murder. They are not fiction but fact, sir."

"Thank you."

He glanced around at Enoch Chew, who shook his head, smiling. He was still smiling when Kerry O'Keefe was recalled to the stand.

As she turned toward the jury the faces of the men on it were guarded, the women openly hostile. The whole atmosphere of the court room was distinctly changed. *It's as if I'm on trial, not Mrs. Brayton,* she thought. She tried not to look at Johnny Brayton seated next to his mother, Mrs. Brayton's face pale but still gravely tranquil, movingly serene. She might have come from her own home, not from the narrow barred bedroom above the cell block at Pine Street.

The Assistant State's Attorney's face was the only friendly face she saw. He came forward, smiling pleasantly at her.

"Officer O'Keefe.—Or perhaps Miss O'Keefe, as my learned friend for the defense prefers to call you . . . and as I shall call you, so there won't be any confused notion in anyone's mind that Officer O'Keefe and Miss O'Keefe are not one and the same person. There is another point that should be made equally clear. I'm afraid my distinguished friend, quite unwittingly and not with any malice, certainly, may have left the impression in some minds that there was something wilfully disreputable in your being at the night spots on The Block and elsewhere in Baltimore City."

His smile said "Absurd of course, but you never know."

"Now let's get this straight. You are a member of the Baltimore City Police Department, are you not, Miss O'Keefe?"

"Yes, sir."

"Assigned to the Rackets Division?"

"Yes, sir."

"For what would commonly be called undercover work?"

"Yes."

"And it was to conceal your identity in that capacity that you were arrested with the rest of the outfit at the Mimosa Club and spent the night with them in the Women's Jail at Pine Street Station, was it not?"

"Yes, sir."

"And you did not enjoy it, did you, Miss O'Keefe?"

"It wasn't pleasant. But it was part of my job."

"So that this disgraceful business"—Dobson smiled again—"of a young lawyer's unconsciously recognizing you as a lady and offering you his coat is not as disgraceful as it has inadvertently—I repeat —been made to seem. And what you accomplished at the Mimosa

Club was the destruction of a three-million dollar a year take-in station for the numbers racket, was it not, Miss O'Keefe?"

"I object—"

"Overruled," Judge Sansbury said curtly.

"I helped, sir. I didn't do it alone."

"But it was you, Miss O'Keefe, who spotted the existence, and the location, of this three-million dollar a year station, was it not?"

"Yes, sir."

"And at the Coral Seas Club—"

"I object, your honor." Enoch Chew was suave and patient.

"Overruled, Mr. Chew." Judge Sansbury's eyes were beginning to snap. "We listened to you at great length on the subject of these very establishments. The State has every right to clear up any possible misconceptions of the facts you brought out."

"—At the Coral Seas Club, Miss O'Keefe. Where this picture of you was taken. The papers said the police were surprised at finding that one of the customers there the night of their raid had narcotics in his possession. Is that true, Miss O'Keefe?"

"No, sir. We had been watching the place for over two months, trying to catch the man we thought was receiving narcotics there."

"And you were instrumental in the success of that operation, were you not?"

"My superior officer thought so, sir."

"And it was in the disguise of a female sitter that you were able to accomplish these things? Four men taken, with enough heroin to destroy the lives of hundreds of young people—"

"I object, your honor."

"The Court would suggest that counsel reserve his social commentary, and proceed with the facts," Judge Sansbury said evenly.

"Four men are in prison for many years each, as a direct result of your sitting at the Coral Seas Club. That's correct, is it not, Miss O'Keefe?"

"That and the work of other members of the Department."

"Your modesty does not diminish the extraordinary job you did there, Miss O'Keefe. But to go on. Let's get to the Hay Ride Club, where you were also a sitter. What was the object of your being there?"

He looked patiently round at Enoch Chew who shrugged and kept his seat.

"The police had information that an escaped prisoner wanted for killing two men in the course of an armed robbery was either hiding out there or was coming there frequently."

"You went there as a sitter, to see if you could pick up any information about him. Is that correct?"

"Yes, sir."

"And did you?"

"Yes."

"What information?"

"—I object."

Judge Sansbury looked inquiringly at Alec Dobson.

"If the Court please.—At very considerable length last Friday, my distinguished friend . . . I won't say bludgeoned, but queried, Miss O'Keefe on what he called her storming out of the Hay Ride Club, in tears of rage, because a kindly and well-meaning member of the Brayton family found her there, not sitting but at the bar. In his own well-meaning, and I'm sure kindly meant if unhappy, efforts to attribute Miss O'Keefe's perturbation on the night of May 1st to purely personal chagrin, I'm afraid my distinguished and learned friend left the impression that it was only Miss O'Keefe's job as a sitter that was involved, and that—"

"Overruled, Mr. Chew. Proceed, Mr. Dobson."

"What information did you secure, Miss O'Keefe? Please explain it to the ladies and gentlemen of the jury."

Kerry O'Keefe felt the color rise in her cheeks. The State's Attorney had moved as he spoke. She saw John Brayton unconsciously lean forward, tense, not looking at her. From here on, Kerry knew, he knew nothing . . . or knew from Camilla Anne's version of what had happened. She was telling him as well as the jury, trying also to blot his tense image from her peripheral sight.

"—Explain the situation, Miss O'Keefe, so that you can then explain what really happened to upset you."

"The gunman was Curly Boy Jackman. He was an escaped convict, wanted in New York. He was on the FBI's list of ten. A New York detective was here, working with us. He knew Jackman's habits. One of them was a fondness for dill pickles and rye bread with a lot of carroway seeds. He drank nothing but a twelve-year-old Scotch. That was how we found out he was at the Hay Ride Club. Two such snacks were brought in at about the same time every night. But we couldn't find out where they went to. On the night of April 30 I found out that they were going to a woman supposed to be one of the sitters. It was so dark there that the disguise was simple. But we couldn't take him then because we knew he'd be armed and dangerous for the people in the Club."

"All right, Miss O'Keefe. What about the night of May 1st?"

17

She saw the almost imperceptible shake of Alec Dobson's head and realized she was getting angry all over again. Her muscles had gone taut and she could feel the sudden fire burning in her eyes. She drew a deep breath, relaxing, and sat back more easily in the chair. When her voice came it was quietly restrained.

"On the night of May 1st the officers working with me were ready to take him as soon as I could spot where he was. The sandwiches had come. I was at the bar . . . that's the only truth—"

She caught Alec Dobson's eye again and broke off, pausing a moment.

"I was waiting to see the bottle of Scotch put with them and watch what table they were taken to. I was to wander over there as a signal to the officers. Then I was to get out while they moved in to surround him."

"And did you do that, Miss O'Keefe?"

"No, sir."

"Why not? Tell the ladies and gentlemen of the jury what happened."

Kerry O'Keefe drew another deep breath. *I must think of it as if it happened to somebody else, not me.* She kept her face a mask, her eyes and voice cool.

"I was at the bar. The snacks had come. The special bottle of Scotch was being brought out. Everything was ready. Then suddenly a red light flicked on just under the bar. The barman put the bottle back and somebody called out 'Six pinch bottles on the rocks.' "

"Did that have special meaning, Miss O'Keefe?"

"Yes. It meant 'Six society slummers are here. Strippers and sitters cover up.'"

Judge Sansbury rapped sharply with his gavel.

"The officers will clear the Court at any further laughter or demonstration of bad taste in this Courtroom," he said sharply.

"That was the signal that society ladies and gentlemen were about to enter, was it not, Miss O'Keefe?"

"Yes, sir."

"What happened then?—I know it's difficult for you even now to restrain your anger. But I'm sure you can if you try, Miss O'Keefe."

"What happened was that six young people, three girls and three young men, came into the room."

"What condition were they in, Miss O'Keefe? I mean, had they been drinking?"

"I object—"

"If my distinguished friend finds that an offensive term, let me put the question in another way. Did they seem happy, Miss O'Keefe?"

"Very. They were high as kites."

"I object, your Honor—"

"The witness was present, Mr. Chew," Judge Sansbury said curtly. "You've outlined in considerable detail her considerable experience in these palaces of sin. I see no reason she shouldn't be allowed to draw on that experience for the information of this Court."

Enoch Chew bowed and returned to his seat.

"What led you to believe they were high as kites, Miss O'Keefe?"

"The way they were laughing. The way they were acting. What they did. No one in his senses—"

"Let's be calm, Miss O'Keefe. I ask you this: did you recognize any of these young people?"

"I recognized one of the girls. Camilla Anne Brayton. Mrs. Pierce Brayton Jr."

"How did you recognize her?"

"I'd heard her introduce herself to a woman at the Brayton house on the Garden Tour, the day before."

Two warm spots burned on Kerry's cheeks.

"That's when you . . ." Dobson moved back to the table and consulted his notes. "I'm sorry," he said amiably. "I recall now that I got the impression that you . . . I've forgotten the precise words, but the record will show them when the ladies and gentlemen of the jury start their serious deliberation of these matters, so I won't take the time to ask to have them read now—I seem to recall that 'shameless' was one of them. A shameless breach of good manners, for you to go to the Brayton house on a Garden Tour. And that it was curiosity about a house you'd never been invited to enter, definitely excluded from, in fact. Something of that sort. Is that view of what you did correct, Miss O'Keefe?"

"No. It is not."

She looked directly at John Brayton then. But it was Enoch Chew she saw most clearly, saw the surprise flick into his eyes and the flush of suppressed rage on his face. *So he doesn't know this. Camilla Anne didn't tell him the truth about this either. And he's furious.* She saw it only for an instant, as Enoch Chew settled back, his brows raised, a little bored, somewhat amused.

"Why were you there, Miss O'Keefe?"

"I was there because the Commissioner of Police had been asked by an important organization of women, meeting in Washington, to allow me to be their official escort on the Baltimore House and Garden Tour. The women were asked not to say I was a policewoman, but we assume that one of them—not a member of the organization—did tell and that it was Mrs. Brayton Jr. she told."

"And did you pry around in the Brayton house, as I believe has been suggested, Miss O'Keefe?"

"No. I handed in the tickets, introduced the women and stayed as near the front door as I could get. I got out as quickly as I could and sat in the bus till the rest of them came out."

"Nevertheless you were upset by this incident, as my distinguished friend for the defense has so ably pointed out."

"I was indeed. I was very much upset. It was a hideous position to find myself in."

"Especially as another member of the Brayton family had already been to see you, as my learned friend has also indicated, without naming her. That was Mr. John Brayton's grandmother, was it not?"

"Yes."

"Tell the jury what happened, please, Miss O'Keefe."

"That has nothing to do with—"

"Please, Miss O'Keefe. It has been indicated that that interview was the beginning of your intense resentment of the Brayton family, which eventually led you to the monstrous iniquity of putting your duty as a police officer before your affection for a member of the family. We've heard that you told the lady she was being offensive, that you bitterly resented her coming to you."

"I thought it was offensive to be offered a trip abroad if I'd get out of Baltimore. But I didn't resent it, I understood it perfectly. I was getting ready to go to the Hay Ride Club when Mrs. Summerfield came. I looked horrible. She'd had a private detective following me. I suppose he's the one who took that photograph, so she knew I'd been acting as a sitter at the Coral Seas Club. She looked so elegant, and I looked so awful—like the photograph— that I didn't blame her at all. I was distressed and embarrassed. But I wasn't bitter. There was just nothing I could do. I couldn't explain."

"This brings up another matter, Miss O'Keefe. It's been suggested that you presumably have parents—"

"I don't want my parents—"

"And it's been implied that you're highly presumptuous in aspiring to marriage to the son of a distinguished Baltimore family. Further, that the young man was ashamed to take you to his home. In this instance I must agree with my distinguished friend for the defense and ask that you keep your temper, please, Miss O'Keefe. What do your—"

"My father's a lawyer. At present he's judge of the Circuit Court in our district. One of my brothers is a medical student, the other's a lieutenant in the Air Force, now in Africa. My mother's the . . . a gardener, cook and general housekeeper, employed at home. I'm afraid it's never occurred to the O'Keefes that we're unfit to associate with."

"Thank you, Miss O'Keefe. And this occupation of yours that my learned friend regards as so exceedingly bizarre and that your parents are opposed to. Your job as a policewoman. How did you—"

"Because I learned that young women are needed in police work, as peace officers, to help women and kids keep out of trouble, as much as to help them when they're in it."

"But of course you couldn't tell that to this lady who offered you the trip abroad. Or to John Brayton. Why not?"

"Because the law firm he's employed by represents the Mimosa and the Coral Seas Clubs. I didn't expect him not to do his duty to his employers. But I couldn't let that keep me from doing mine."

"And the Hay Ride Club, Miss O'Keefe—was that a client?"

"No. But that was too important. Only a very few people were in on that, even in the Rackets Division. There was too much at stake. It was too dangerous."

"Very well. We're back to the night of May 1st, Miss O'Keefe. You were at the bar of the Hay Ride Club, ready to give the signal to the detectives waiting to close in on one of the FBI's ten most wanted criminals. But another signal came, that six society slummers had arrived. They came in the door, and you recognized Mrs. Pierce Brayton Jr. They were high as kites, you've said. What did they do, Miss O'Keefe?"

"They stood in the doorway laughing like zaneys. There's always a hush when a crowd like that comes in one of those places. They don't belong there. They tend to act as if they're visiting the monkey house at the Zoo. These people kept on laughing and poking at each other, and then Mrs. Pierce Brayton Jr. stepped forward and said 'Is there a policewoman in the house?' She called it out the way they call for a doctor in the theater. There was a ghastly silence then, and she looked around and spotted me over at the bar, where it's reasonably light. She called out, 'Oh, Officer O'Keefe, there you are!' Then they all doubled up, shrieking with laugher. It was absolutely side-splitting."

"And you went storming out, we've been told. Jut what did you do?"

"I was too petrified to storm anywhere. I just stood there. We had six detectives in the room. Three of them moved in at once and stood around me so I wouldn't be shot. They were the ones who got me out."

"It's been suggested you were furiously angry," Alec Dobson said, very quietly. "You say you were petrified. Were you afraid of being shot?"

"I was afraid for the three nice guys, all of them with families, standing around me, protecting me. They were the ones that might be killed. And for forty other people in the room, with a hopped-up gunman somewhere there in the dark, knowing he was cornered and ready to shoot anybody that got in his way. Especially Camilla Anne Brayton and her friends there—blocking the door. It was a terrible thing."

"And this gunman got away, Miss O'Keefe?"

"Yes. He got away. He's still away. They haven't caught him. And he's robbed two banks and killed a night watchman since."

"And that night. Was anyone hurt, Miss O'Keefe?"

"Yes. An old woman who cleaned the girls' dressing room. She saw what she thought was one of them climbing out of the window. She tried to stop him, thinking one of the girls had gone crazy, and he shot her dead. That's why I was furious. That's why I was crying. She was such a pitiful old thing. There was no reason for her to die. It was a cruel, wanton thing for Camilla Anne Brayton to do . . . stupid, abysmally, criminally stupid!"

Enoch Chew sprang to his feet at the defense table, his face purple. His movement was like a starter's gun releasing the tension in the courtroom. Other men sprang up as the roar of applause rocked the room, women screamed, a woman fainted.

"Sit down, Mr. Chew!"

As Chew controlled himself and sat down the judge's gavel made itself heard. Bailiffs carried the unconscious woman out into the corridor. Kerry sat in the stand, her face pale, her eyes wide.

"This Court is not a Roman hippodrome. It is a court of law. It stands recessed for ten minutes, until an atmosphere befitting one is restored."

Judge Sansbury left the bench in a hush so profound that Enoch Chew could hear his robes swish as he went through the door. It was not only the silence that enabled him to hear. It was every nerve he had, strained to the utmost as he sat outwardly benign, watching the jury, feeling the attitude of the crowded benches. His face unchanging, he reached for a pad and scrawled a note to Johnny Brayton.

"If your sister-in-law or any of the rest of you have given me further misinformation, I must know it at once or I decline further responsibility for your mother's case."

Johnny read it, heartsick. *She lied to us too. About everything.* He could see now why Camilla Anne had lied about her part at the

Hay Ride Club. Why she'd lied about the Garden Tour, saying Kerry had come alone ... *But it's my fault. I should have listened when Kerry tried to tell me. Oh, God, take care of my mother. ...*

Enoch Chew sat there, his face placid, thinking fast. The lies he had been told by his client's family had made a fool of him and cost him the crowd and the jury. Before then, this police witness's looks and her home background had been a shock. What else he had not been told about, or had been falsely told about, he had no way of knowing. It was adequate professional justification for withdrawing. He wondered. Sitting back calmly, on the very verge of washing his hands of the whole deal, his eyes rested on the anxious faces of the other defense counsel and the lost face of the young man sitting next to him. They touched Margaret Brayton's in what could well be a farewell salute. Touched it, moved on, and moved instantly back to it, a sharp needle of light pricking in his mind.

This gentle lady, this lovely woman who's looking at you, not bitterly, not in anger, but with pity in her heart. ... His own words of Friday whipped back at him. Margaret Brayton's face was tranquil. No sign of fear, none of apathy, nothing but a deep and abiding calm was visible in it as she sat there, undismayed by anything around her. Her hands were motionless in her lap, no pulse beat quickened in her throat.

Look at her. By God. ... Chew let his chair abruptly back on its feet. *By God either she isn't guilty or she'll carry it off.* In the instant a whole new pattern of strategy flared out in his mind. *It's a chance in a thousand. They'll believe her or they'll hang her. But I'll take it. By God, I'll put her on the stand.*

He waited calmly for Kerry O'Keefe to take the stand again.

"Mr. Chew," Judge Sansbury said. "You had risen—"

"To object, your honor. But if the Court please, I wish to present no objection. I stand second to none in my applause for this young lady's impassioned anger at the stupidity and gross irresponsibility of the young people she so vividly described. It only intensifies our sympathy for the emotional turmoil she was in, sitting in her car in Mt. Vernon Place, less than an hour after that event took place."

Alec Dobson would have preferred to leave Kerry O'Keefe at her point of dramatic impact. Now he came forward again.

"Miss O'Keefe. Just why did you go out to Mt. Vernon Place after the tragic incident at the Hay Ride Club?"

Kerry raised her head, her face unconsciously softening.

"Where else would I have gone? I loved him, I thought he loved me. He was the natural one for me to turn to."

Dobson glanced at the jury. "That's all, Miss O'Keefe." He waited for her to step down. "—Call Mrs. Alice Ristwich, please."

18

The sharp flurry of interest that went through the courtroom, people craning their necks to see the fabulous widow with the fabulous fortune that the out-of-town papers had trumpeted, quieted as Mrs. Ristwich came forward. Short and plump, she was somewhere in her middle forties, with blue eyes, blonde hair discreetly tainted against the fading hand of time. Apart from the limousine, the private plane and the oil, Mrs. Ristwich was a commonplace little woman. She spoke in a soft Texas drawl and with a diffident and even ingratiating manner as she took the oath and identified herself.

It doesn't seem possible Dr. Brayton could have wanted to marry her, Kerry thought, glancing from her to Margaret Brayton.

For that was the burden of Mrs. Ristwich's testimony, convincing because it was subdued and her grief obviously real, the implication self-evident that passionate jealousy of her had made Margaret Brayton kill her husband, and at that time.

"You were in Baltimore the night of May 1st, were you not, Mrs. Ristwich? Will you tell us in your own words what happened?"

"Well, I was just so lonesome, all of a sudden, that I decided to fly to Baltimore. And if I hadn't, it wouldn't have happened, I blame myself for that. I got here around four in the evening. I wanted to surprise him, so I called the house to tell the butler to tell him I was expecting him to dinner when he came home. But *she* answered the phone instead."

"The defendant, Mrs. Margaret Brayton, answered the phone."

"Yes. And she said she'd tell him I called. Then she said, 'But would you kindly not send your car for him. He can take a taxi if he doesn't wish to drive himself.' I thought it was funny, but she sounded all right, to me."

"But Dr. Brayton did not come for dinner."

"No. He called me around half after seven and said he couldn't come. His wife was emotionally upset and he didn't dare leave her alone with the servants away."

Enoch Chew saw Mrs. Brayton close her eyes for an instant and open them calmly as Mrs. Ristwich continued.

"He said, didn't I get the letter he'd written me, and I said I must have just missed it. It was to tell me he was planning on flying down home to see me the next day, but now I was here, we'd just go together in my plane, early in the morning. So that's why, when I heard on the midnight newscast he was supposed to have killed himself, I knew it was a terrible lie.—When he had everything to live for."

"Mrs. Ristwich, I have a letter here. Will you look at it and identify it. Then I wish it marked and placed in evidence."

She put on her glasses and examined the letter. "This is it. The last letter he wrote me. April 29th."

"You've been very brave, Mrs. Ristwich. Your bringing this letter was the act of a courageous and high-minded woman. I regret that I must ask you to read it publicly here."

"I'll . . . I'll try.

"My very dear Alice,—I have a plane reservation for Sunday night May 3rd. I long to see you. I shall spend a whole week with you, to open your great heart to the future that is ours, yours with me, mine with you. Let's have no guests. I want to be alone with you. I know your impatience with the rigid restrictions of life in Baltimore. You're not spoiled, no one less, but your heart has never been disciplined to these narrow confines. We will take long rides together where we can tune our hearts to the vast creation of sky and plain and explore our glorious future, and with your heart and your clear proud vision find the way to make it ours. My love to you very simply now, my dear.—Pierce."

The courtroom was silent as her faltering voice stopped. Tears filmed the eyes of the women jurors, there was compassion on the faces of the rest, gazing at the little woman weeping on the stand. None of them looked at Margaret Brayton. Enoch Chew's eyes resting on her for an instant as he rose to cross-examine, sharpened suddenly. She was as serene as ever, but there was a curiously ironic light in her eyes, her brows almost imperceptibly raised.

He went to the witness stand.

"Mrs. Ristwich," he said briskly. "You knew Dr. Brayton's great interest in medical education, did you not?"

"Yes, sir."

"If I am not mistaken, didn't you announce a glorious plan for giving a very large sum of money to a local hospital?"

"That was my publicity agent announced it, before the details were ironed out."

"—I'm sorry. I didn't quite hear, I'm afraid. Your what?"

"I mean the public relations man in my husband's offices."

"He published them, not you? And what happened to the glorious plan?"

"It fell through."

"Because it was felt you insisted on running things? Isn't that correct?"

"Well, we were still trying to work things out, Dr. Brayton and I."

"—Which, I suggest, was the reason, and the sole reason, that Dr. Brayton was coming to spend a week with you? This glorious plan was the glorious future you were to explore under the vast creation of sky and plain, with your great heart and great vision. It—"

"No! That's false! It was—"

"So you've said, my dear lady. You've said it was marriage. But Dr. Brayton does not say so. He was not free to say so. Dr. Brayton was a married man, with a distinguished reputation, trying to salvage a vast sum for medical education. I suggest it was your glorious future as a great philanthropist he was interested in, Mrs. Ristwich, not your person, charming as it is. May I now ask who advised you to come into this Courtroom to make this utterly fantastic charge against this man's lovely wife, the mother of his four children?"

"Nobody advised me. It—"

"Thank you. I was afraid it was your publicity agent. That's all, Mrs. Ristwich."

Something Dave Trumper had said to Kerry as Court opened came into her mind. *I'm not as sold on that dame as some people.* She turned to look at him, standing against the wall under the clerestory windows. Whatever his opinion at this point, no reflection of it was visible on his face. It was set, dourly inscrutable as ever. Then she saw he was not concerned with Mrs. Ristwich. His eyes, shuttered but intensely alive, were resting on someone in the rear benches whom she couldn't see.

"—Detective-Lieutenant Caspari. Will you take the stand, please."

Lieutenant Caspari beside Kerry rose promptly. He was swarthy-cheeked, his black hair dusted with grey, a veteran police officer.

"You are a member of the Homicide Squad of the Baltimore City Police Department?"

"Correct, sir."

"On May 5th your duties took you to the Brayton residence in Mt. Vernon Place. Will you tell us what you found there?"

"I found a letter. It had been folded and placed in the back pocket of a tail coat that was hanging in the mothproof closet in the attic. A London tailor's label in the coat had the name 'Dr. Pierce Brayton' written on it."

"Is this the letter, Lieutenant Caspari?"

Dobson handed him a single sheet of blue note paper.

Enoch Chew glanced inquiringly at John Brayton, who shook his head. As he glanced then at Mrs. Brayton his spine stiffened. The blood had drained from her face, leaving the ivory pallor a ghastly grey-white. Her eyes were closed, her hands gripped the seat of her chair.

She's going to faint.

He clamped his hand on John Brayton's arm, sensing his movement almost before it was made. "Sit still, you fool!" he whispered savagely, trying to control his own tension, praying as he had seldom prayed that she'd come out of it, praying that the jury was looking at the letter and the detective on the stand and not at Margaret Brayton.

We're lost now. If she faints we're lost. Her fantastic serenity, her complete and confident tranquillity, was the whole substance he had to build on. *If the jury sees her.* . . .

But the jury had seen her. Out of the corner of his eye Chew saw one woman nudge another, saw one eye after another turned toward her.

Caspari had taken the letter. "That's it, sir. Those are my initials at the lower left-hand corner."

"I would like this letter marked and placed in evidence."

Alec Dobson handed it to the clerk and took it again.

"Is there a date on this letter, Lieutenant?"

"No, sir. But we dated it by inference, from Dr. Brayton's engagement book."

"Is this that book, Lieutenant?"

"Yes, sir."

The book was numbered and submitted in evidence, and returned to the witness.

He opened it and read: " 'March 28th. Dinner Sir Malcolm Parker. 8 p.m. Baltimore Club. White tie.' His secretary keeps this book, sir. Engagements and whether the occasion is white or black tie."

"Which means this was a formal occasion on which he wore his white tie and tail coat."

"That's correct, sir."

"And is there a later entry of that kind, calling for that costume?"

"No, sir. That's the last."

"From whom is the letter, and to whom?"

Enoch Chew glanced at Margaret Brayton again. She had not fainted but sat there, eyes closed, her head drooping, her body limp, descended into what dark valley of fear, what agony of hell, he could only guess.

"It's signed 'Margaret.' It's written to 'Pierce.' "

"Will you read the letter, please."

Caspari read:

"Dear Pierce,—I'm writing this because I'm too infuriated to trust myself to speak to you.

"The situation with Mrs. Ristwich has become intolerable. I cannot prevent you from seeing her, but I do demand that her car quit coming here to take you to her and standing by the hour at the curb in front of this house. It has become a public scandal, and is as intolerable to me as it must be to Mrs. R. if she has any sensibilities of any kind. You might treat her and your own family with at least some outward show of courtesy—until after Lolly's wedding at least. The innuendoes and raised eyebrows of our friends have become mortifying beyond my limited powers of endurance. If you can't keep that woman in Texas you can at least keep her car away from my front door. I shall go mad if it continues. I cannot bear it a great deal longer.—Margaret."

"—You have had cause to see and talk to Margaret Brayton

many times in the course of the investigation of this case, have you not, Lieutenant Caspari?"

"Yes, sir."

"Then you know her. Will you point her out, please."

Caspari raised his hand toward her. She sat there with eyes still closed, her face ghastly, writing her own death sentence on the faces of the jury turned toward her without pity or compassion.

Alec Dobson waited a long moment, and moved back to his table. It was ten minutes to twelve, and the only time in a long career that counsel for the defense failed to take advantage of an opportunity offered him. Enoch Chew shook his head.

Dobson came forward, waving Caspari off the stand. He had intended to put the waitress from the Fiesole on. It was now unnecessary.

"The State rests," he said.

Judge Sansbury's gavel came down, ending the sudden stir in the benches.

"Mr. Chew, do you wish to begin now, or will you wait until after the noon recess?"

"I shall wait, if the Court please."

"Court is adjourned."

Enoch Chew took Johnny's arm, restraining him again as the released tension filled the courtroom with a tumult of excited voices. Margaret Brayton was moving off into an anteroom, like a sleepwalker, not conscious of people or things.

"Let her rest a moment. Then we've got to see her.—We can't go on, Johnny. We're licked—"

"—Johnny."

John Brayton turned his head blindly, his brain too numb for him to recognize the voice of the woman speaking to him there, too numb to be surprised to see her. All he was conscious of was Mrs. Summerfield stiffly erect beside him, her head up, and his sister Lolly's face, tortured with despair.

"Johnny!" Mrs. Remstad said urgently. She put her hand on his arm. "Look here, Johnny. I can help."

Enoch Chew swung around. "—How can you help?"

Johnny staring at her, saw her now, her face troubled, deeply earnest.

"This is Mrs. Remstad," he said. "Our next-door—"

"I know who she is. I want to know how she can help."

"Not here," Mrs. Remstad said quickly. "Can we go some place?"

Dave Trumper out in the corridor, waiting for Kerry, saw the three of them head rapidly toward the elevator. He'd watched the State's Attorney and the police leave, unable to conceal the confidence, like a pillar of fire by night, marking their path through the crowded hall. Kerry came out alone. There was no joy in her face and none in Trumper's.

"What'll they do?" she asked quickly. "Change her plea?"

He shook his head. "I told you I had a hunch we'd been flim-flammed. That Remstad woman's been sitting in the back row like a hen on a hot griddle. She broke her neck getting up front to talk to them."

"The blonde woman? Is that Mrs. Remstad?"

She remembered seeing her at the House and Garden Tour . . . *Can anybody get in?—Anybody that's got a dollar* . . . and remembered her warm husky laughter.

"Come on, let's eat," Trumper said. "I want to get back quick. Something's cooking."

There was still the air of suppressed jubilation at the prosecutor's table when the court opened at two o'clock that afternoon; the odds at the press table, ten gets you five Brayton changes her plea, no takers.

Margaret Brayton entered the room with the matron, calm again as she took her seat. Kerry O'Keefe, watching Johnny Brayton, felt her heart rise. He walked with a surer step. His face that had been heartbreakingly haggard, was drawn still, still haggard, but the light of hope was in it. In Enoch Chew there was no apparent change until he rose to open the case for the defense. He was direct and deeply serious.

"Mrs. Inga Remstad, please."

He bowed her gravely to the stand. Mrs. Remstad's earthy flamboyance and the sparkling glint in her eyes were gone. She looked like a middle-aged woman troubled and ill at ease, except for her mouth, set tight, and a sullen determination in the look she gave the court and jury as she took her oath and sat bolt upright, waiting.

"What is your occupation, Mrs. Remstad?"

"I rent out part of my house, but I live on my income I saved up."

"Your house, Mrs. Remstad—where is it?"

"It's the other part of the Braytons' on Mt. Vernon Place."

"Do you own it?"

"Yes, sir. I own it, and I've lived there for twenty-six going on twenty-seven years. I bought it the same time the Braytons bought theirs."

"Do you know the Braytons, Mrs. Remstad?"

"Not what you'd call know them, I don't. I see them go in and out. I know their son John Brayton to talk to, but to the rest of them I just say How do you do, and that's all they say to me."

"You've lived next door for twenty-six years, Mrs. Remstad. How many times have you been in their house?"

"I never crossed their threshold but one time in my whole life."

"When was that?"

"That was at the Garden Tour when I paid a dollar like everybody else. It's the only way I ever get in houses like that to get ideas for when I have to redecorate for new tenants."

"So you're not here in this courtroom because you are a good friend of your next-door neighbor, are you, Mrs. Remstad?"

"No, sir. I'm not any friend of theirs and they're not any friends of mine. I haven't got anything for 'em or against 'em."

"Then why are you here now, Mrs. Remstad?"

"Because I heard that rich woman this morning trying to make out it was on her account Mrs. Brayton killed her husband, and it made me mad, that's why."

"Did the police talk to you during their investigation, Mrs. Remstad?"

"They asked me questions. I answered some. Some I didn't. I wasn't on oath. I wasn't going to tell 'em anything they didn't ask me. Withholding information's no felony in Maryland."

"But you did withhold information? Why did you?"

"Well, I don't like cops any better than anybody else they try to push around. Anyway, if Mrs. Brayton wasn't talking, I didn't see it was up to me to do it. If she wanted to be a . . . a martyr, that was her right. Anyway, the detectives never asked me anything about her except did I know her and did I like her. They had their minds made up. It wasn't up to me to change them."

"All right, Mrs. Remstad."

Chew paused a moment in the intense quiet of the courtroom.

"Where were you the night of May 1st?"

"Right where I belonged. In my house right next to the Braytons'.

I was in the front of it, and I was in the back. Round eight o'clock I was in my conservatory in back, sprayin' these African violets with one of these bomb can things I got."

"Where were you at half-past ten?"

"I was in my front room looking out in Mt. Vernon Place, watching TV and having me a can of beer."

"And you saw John Brayton leave the house?"

"Yes, and he waved up at me like he always does if he sees me, or I call Hello to him."

"After that did you hear a shot fired?"

"I heard something. I'd just gone out back to get me another can of beer and eat a crab cake. I got a piece of my conservatory made into a kitchen and the rest of it's my dining room."

Enoch Chew paused again. "You say you're here, Mrs. Remstad," he went on, very quietly, "because you got mad listening· to Mrs. Ristwich 'trying to make out' that it was because of her Mrs. Brayton killed her husband."

"That's what I said and what I meant."

"Why did that make you mad?"

"Because Mrs. Brayton didn't do it. That's why."

Judge Sansbury pounded sharply with his gavel, silencing the sudden murmur of excitement.

"She never killed him and I know she didn't."

"Mrs. Remstad . . . on your oath and before your God, how do you know that?"

"Because I saw her with my own eyes. Like you say, on my Bible oath and before my God, Mrs. Brayton wasn't even inside her house when the shot was fired."

Judge Sansbury's gavel came down again.

"How do you know that, Mrs. Remstad?"

"Because, like I said, I was spraying these African violets, round eight o'clock, and I saw a light go on in their back yard, and I saw her in her raincoat go to her garage, and I heard her car start and go out."

"Did you see her again?"

"Yes. I was sitting down to eat my cold crab cake at a table I got by my conservatory windows. I heard the noise, a sort of thud, on account of the wall between the two houses is so thick. The same time, I saw the car lights in the alley turn in the garage, and I heard a second noise, and then in a minute, maybe, she came out of the garage across the garden, walkin' slow to the back door. Then the outside lights went off so I knew she was inside. But she was outside when both those shots were fired. On my oath and before my God she was."

Kerry O'Keefe, leaning forward, engrossed, her lips parted breathlessly, her heart lifting, listening, all her attention concentrated on the large woman there in the stand, was aware slowly of the stunned silence of Lieutenant Caspari of Homicide sitting beside her and the taut dismay at the Prosecutor's table. Then, almost as if her eyes had been metallic wisps caught in a magnetic field, she felt them drawn, with a force intensely powerful, till they met the grey eyes fixed on her. Johnny Brayton's eyes were flat, relentlessly bitter, the contempt in them cold, pitiless, bitterly implacable. *I wish I'd rotted in hell before I'd ever met you.* He was saying it again, his mouth hard and his lips white. Then he coolly shifted his chair, turning away, so that his eyes would never be forced to look into hers again.

19

"NINETY MINUTE BATTLE FAILS TO SHAKE SUR-
PRISE WITNESS"

Kerry saw the headline on her landlady's Seven Star Final on
the hall table. Below it was a picture of Mrs. Inga Remstad being
hustled into a waiting car, Mrs. Enoch Chew on one side of her,
Chew on the other. "Defense Attorney Says Witness Needs Rest
After Vicious Ordeal. Will Spend Night At His Home."

She looked at the heavy type of the late news.

"In a stormy hour and a half session, the State fought tooth and
nail to puncture the last-minute testimony of Mrs. Inga Remstad, next-door neighbor witness, whose surprise appearance veteran court-observers regarded as a major upset. In a second dramatic
move, Enoch Chew, chief defense counsel, electrified the crowded
courtroom in the closing two minutes of the session by suddenly
resting his case for the defense.

"Charges of trickery, hocus-pocus, Houdini tactics and worse
were hurled by the prosecution. Charges of police persecution,
police inefficiency and political chicanery were hurled back by the
defense, in an embittered scene in which Judge Sansbury ordered
the jury from the courtroom and threatened attorneys for both
sides with contempt of court. The witness evidenced her stolid
Scandinavian background by sitting unmoved and unshaken
throughout. Mrs. Margaret Brayton, the defendant, sat quietly, but
seemingly as surprised as her attorneys at her neighbor's appearance on her behalf.

"It had been Chew's intention, he asserted, to place Mrs. Brayton on the stand. In view of the tactics of the prosecution, however,

he stated, he refused to submit her to an ordeal as vicious as that to which Mrs. Remstad had been subjected.

"Arguments will be heard tomorrow. Judge Sansbury ordered the jury to remain in seclusion at a downtown hotel, for the first time during the trial."

Kerry put the paper back on the table and went on to her door. Part of her was still numb, as if the contempt and hatred in Johnny Brayton's eyes pinioning hers across the courtroom had been an actual physical weapon, paralyzing her heart as if it left the rest of her free to move, outwardly normal. She was still sitting in the corner of the sofa, the late twilight softly rose-colored through the open garden windows, when Dave Trumper came at eight o'clock.

He glanced at her bag and gloves still on the sofa. "What's the matter, Kerry? I thought you'd be all set up."

"Is it over?"

"So near we don't have to go to court tomorrow."

He sat down heavily, a puzzled scowl on his face. "So she wasn't in the house when the killing was done and she don't open her mouth. Why? What in God's name does she think she's doing, just trying to be convicted of murder? That's sure where she was headed when Caspari read her letter. Up to then she had a prayer. Then Wham and she was a goner. And a blind man could see Remstad wasn't there because she loved the Braytons. Just sore at the oil woman. I don't get any of it."

He took a sheet of paper out of his pocket and sat staring morosely at it. "This is a photostat of the letter Caspari found, from her to her husband. All it says is, Mrs. Brayton can't stand that car out in front of the house and if Mrs. Ristwich had any sensibilities she can't stand it either. It's a public scandal and if he can't keep the dame in Texas he can damn well keep her car out from in front of his wife's house. So what? Mrs. Brayton sits all through Rist-wich's testimony and doesn't bat an eye, and she damn near passes out when Caspari reads this letter. Everything else she sat through like an angel painted on ivory. This kills her. And boy, did Remstad kill us."

He shook his head, still staring at the photostat.

"Homicide's starting from scratch. We start right here. We find out what's the dynamite that blew her sky-high. It's in this letter, some place. And if this is a perfect murder it still belongs to

Rackets—you, the Boss and the Gun Shop. And I never bought that Ristwich dame anyway—I told you it was a flimflam."

He got up. "I'll leave this with you, I've got another copy. And call my doll. Tell her I'm on my way. Anything the kids didn't eat's okay if there's enough of it."

"MRS. BRAYTON NOT GUILTY"

The evening papers carried the headline when Johnny Brayton put his key in the front door lock.

His mother and Lolly were behind him coming up the steps, photographers' bulbs flashing above the heads of the crowd of curious but silent people who had backed away to let them cross the sidewalk from the taxi. The others were coming with Mrs. Summerfield.

"Good evening, ma'am." Old Horace held the door for them to enter.

"Good evening, Horace."

"Will you have dinner with the family, or would you rather have a tray?" *If you're tired from your journey, ma'am.* It was all that was missing from his greeting whenever she returned from a trip of any kind.

"I think I'll have a tray, thank you, Horace."

He took her bag from Johnny and carried it off.

"But chiefly I want a bath in my own tub."

She smiled faintly. "And I'd like to be alone, loves. If you could send Gran and the rest of them home it would be wonderful. You can try anyway."

They stood at the bottom of the stairs as she started up, turning and bending over the rail to kiss each of them on the forehead. "Forgive me, lambs. I'm so sorry." Her eyes were misted as she turned quickly and went on up.

Johnny followed his sister into the Common Room. They were silent, avoiding each other's eyes. It was the way they'd spent long evenings, trying to close their ears to their grandmother's relentless optimism. Even last night, when she'd gone angrily to her room and they'd sat alone, not daring to be confident until the jury had spoken.

"I expec' you'd all like a drink." They both started as Horace came in with a tray and glasses.

"Thanks." Johnny took it from him and put it on the table.

"I wish we could get Gran to go now," Lolly said. "She's been wonderful. But somehow I thought I'd scream if she kept on saying 'It's absurd, utterly absurd.' Until last night, when you'd have thought she'd be on her knees thanking God for Mrs. Remstad, she was shaking with rage. And today she's been furious."

She broke off, seeing the reflected flashes from the photographers' bulbs. "—Make her go home, Johnny! Don't let her start on Mama tonight!"

He went out to let them in, his grandmother sailing past him, her jaw set, eyes gleaming. Behind her were his brother and sister. Miss Elizabeth seemed to have evaporated into parts unknown.

"Look, friends," he said. "Ma's bushed. Let's give her a break. In other words, beat it, kids."

"Right," Pug said. "Come on, Gran."

"You may go. I'm staying. I'm going to see your mother. This utterly disgraceful performance ... in the name of gracious heaven what was she thinking of? *Needlessly* dragging our names through this revolting mess! Great merciful heaven, if it hadn't been for that excellent woman next door—"

"Take it easy, Gran."

Johnny put his hand on her arm, but she jerked savagely away and went swiftly up the stairs, the flower on her white hat shaking with indignation.

"Look—I'm going," Meg said. "With a show of joyous relief, for the benefit of the press." She started for the door and stopped, came back quickly to Lolly and put her arms around her. "Don't be so unhappy, baby."

"I'm not." Lolly's voice was taut. "You go on. Wave to Mrs. Remstad. Somebody ought to try to act grateful to her."

The three of them stood for an instant at the foot of the stairs.

"You got a drink anywhere?" Pug asked. They went into the Common Room. He poured himself a Scotch. "You can't blame the old girl."

"But she's the one that's been so sure . . ."

"She had to be sure," Pug said quietly. "She had to be sure or else it was her own fault. That's what's been driving me crazy —wondering if Camilla Anne or somebody'd get around to what Gran said in her cups one night. Round Christmas, the day after her dinner for General Preston. She said 'If it hadn't been for me telling him he couldn't hope to marry your mother he wouldn't have run away and joined the Army. And if I hadn't put both feet down after Lolly was born she—'"

"Shut up, Pug," Johnny said harshly.

His brother flushed. "Sorry. I didn't know—"

"Has anybody let him know?" Lolly asked calmly.

It was Johnny's turn to flush. "I've been calling him every day from the office, in case we had a wire tap. He was worried, but not scared. It was the only thing she was afraid of—that he might come."

"The subject is now closed," Lolly said.

They sat there, tension mounting, and jumped to their feet at their grandmother's voice.

"Pug! Johnny!"

It was a half-strangled cry, hardly audible. They sprang into the hall and up the stairs where she was staggering down, one hand at her breast, the other clutching the bannisters, her face ghastly. Johnny caught her. They carried her down and laid her on the long sofa in the Common Room. Pug put his hand quickly on her wrist, held it there, then put her hand down at her side, shaking his head at the two. Not a stroke. He nodded at the bourbon bottle and held his thumb and forefinger an inch apart. Lolly poured it quickly and brought the glass to him.

"Here, Gran. Drink this. It's neat. Watch it."

She drank it with his hand guiding hers, her shoulders shaking as Johnny lifted her. She struggled up then and put her feet on the floor. "Lolly. Get my bag. Get Occam, tell him to take me home. Just let him help me down the steps."

She dropped her head suddenly into her hands. "Oh, my God!" Her body was shaking again. "Oh, no, no, no! I can't believe it!" She rocked back and forth in agony. "Oh, Margaret! Oh, what a fool I've been! Oh, why did I make her tell me! Oh, my poor, wretched child!"

The eyes of the three Braytons met, their faces stunned and white.

"Gran," Pug said. "You'd better go to bed. I'll call Doctor—"

"No." She raised her head sharply. "I must go. You come with me, Pug. We don't want anybody to—"

She was shaking uncontrollably. "Give me another drink. I'll be all right. Bring my bag, Lolly. Come to the door and say goodbye. Everything as we always do. Help me up, Johnny."

She held his arm tight as he lifted her, swaying as she drank the second whiskey. Then she stood erect, stiffening her shoulders. "Help me through the hall, if you will."

They hadn't heard Horace coming to answer the doorbell or seen him until they came out as Lolly was running down the stairs with the bag. Or seen the man standing there inside, his hat and briefcase in his hand. They saw him now.

"Sergeant Trumper to see you, Mr. Johnny."

Mrs. Summerfield's fingers dug into Johnny's arm like iron claws.

"Oh, how do you do, Mr. Trumper?—I'm afraid that last drink went to my knees. Now, if Occam's ready . . ."

Horace opened the door and she went on out. Johnny turned to Trumper. He was frightened, and being frightened he was angry.

"Do we have to begin this stuff all over again—"

"You mean the stuff about finding out who killed your father?" Trumper inquired evenly.

"I didn't mean that. I mean my mother. She's just—"

"What makes you think it's her I came to see, Mr. Brayton?" Johnny flushed.

"I'd like to see her tomorrow, if she's up to it. Right now I'd like to have another look at your father's study, if it won't disturb anybody. And I'd like to see Miss Elizabeth Brayton."

His face was inscrutable.

Lolly put her hand on Johnny's arm. "I'm sorry, Sergeant Trumper. She isn't here. We don't know where she is." She went to the hall table and took a brass key out of the drawer. "We've kept the study locked. We want to get my father's secretary and his lawyers in, to go through his things."

Don't want to touch them yourselves. How you hated that guy.

"If you'll give me a couple of days," Dave Trumper said. He added, as unexpectedly to himself as it was to them, "The jury freed your mother. She can't be put in double jeopardy. Why don't you kids relax a little?"

"That's a good idea," Lolly said quietly. He was on his way upstairs when he heard her say, "Come on, Johnny, let's have a drink."

Inside the Common Room she was trembling violently. "Johnny. Are you sure? Is it true she can't be—" She broke off and poured them each a drink. "Here. Take this and sit down. Act relaxed."

"It's Aunt Elizabeth he's—"

"That's absurd."

Her laugh was high-pitched, bordering on hysteria. "My God, I sound like Gran!"

She was laughing and crying at the same time. Johnny jerked her to her feet, shaking her. "Stop it, Lolly. Stop it!"

"I can't bear it any longer!" She collapsed in his arms, sobbing. "Not one word from him to say he was sorry the wedding was cancelled—not a word!"

She ran then, streaking through the door and upstairs. Trumper, coming out of the study, saw her reach the third floor. When he got to the bottom of the steps he saw Johnny standing in front of the fireplace, his elbows on the mantel, his head in his hands. Sergeant Trumper went quietly to the front door and let himself out, so that neither the Braytons nor Horace saw that he was leaving without the briefcase he'd had when he came.

Johnny heard the door close and looked around. But the hell with Trumper. It was all the nights Lolly had sat there with her empty heart, no word from the boy she loved, just from his family thanking them for the return of her engagement ring. He remembered the promise he'd made to her picture. *They don't need to worry. I wouldn't hurt you, baby.* And he'd done this to his sister, his mother, his grandmother, all of them, because Kerry O'Keefe, the college girl policeman . . .

Then, as if the moment wasn't already bitter beyond its measure, Horace came to the door. "Your phone, Johnny. Miss O'Keefe. She wants to know if you could speak to her."

"No!" Johnny shouted at him. "I don't want ever to hear her name again! Tell her to go to hell and stay there!"

Dave Trumper was shaving when Kerry called him at seven-thirty the next morning.

"Did you figure something, Kerry?"

But he knew before she answered that Mrs. Brayton's letter wasn't the reason she'd called.

"No, Dave." Her voice was dead level. "I've got something else. A confession."

"Keep it," he said shortly. "I'll see you later." He put the phone down hard. *College girl cop. I knew she'd crack.*

He was still angry when he got to Mt. Vernon Place at nine o'clock. The girl in the office on Mrs. Remstad's first floor was just arriving. He stepped in behind her, rang Mrs. Remstad's bell and started up the stairs. He was at the top of them when she opened her door, in a house dress and apron, a white cloth covering her shining hair, a dish towel in her hand.

"Oh. I thought that girl had forgotten her key again."

Her face had hardened into the sullen lines it had had on the witness stand two days before. "What do you want? I'm busy now."

With no makeup on she looked older, almost haggard, her suspicion of the police the only thing that gave life to her face.

"Can I come in a minute?"

She held the door open grudgingly for him.

There was a dishpan of soapy water on a table with a newspaper under it, a carton beside it on the floor. Another table was covered with the animal figures she was washing and drying. And packing, apparently.

"Not leaving us, are you?"

"Wouldn't you?" She handed him the broken half of a brick with a piece of paper, creased where it had been tied around the brick, the red dust sticking to it. "—If you got this through your conservatory window?"

Trumper flushed as he read it. It was foul with obscenity.

"Some psycho. You always get 'em."

"Sure," Mrs. Remstad said. "They been calling me on my phone, all last night after I got home, telling me I lied for her and how much did she and Mr. Chew pay me."

"Why didn't you call the police?" It was automatic with him. The look she gave him was answer enough, but she added to it.

"How did I know it wasn't them behind it? Trying to scare me?"

"Oh, now look—"

"You never been a seventeen-year old kid trying to make a living in Chicago and had the cops shake you down every payday or close your show. Or pull you in on a morals charge. Or—"

"Okay, okay."

The phone rang. They both stood looking at it.

"I'll say hello and you can listen."

She picked it up, said "Mrs. Remstad speaking" and handed it to him, watching his face flush again and harden before he slammed it down. He dialled the Racket Squad's unlisted number.

"Put a check on Vernon 6-0000. See if you can catch some of these filthy bastards."

"So I'm getting out. It's too bad I didn't leave her sink or swim like she wanted to. It wasn't any of my business anyway. I don't like being called dirty names. I'm sick of it. So sick I'd like to die myself. And I said everything I got to say."

"I don't blame you, Mrs. Remstad," Dave Trumper said. "I'm sorry. Just don't answer the phone for a while till we get a screen working. I'll take this with me. Maybe there'll be a fingerprint."

He took the paper and the brick, borrowed a piece of her newspaper and wrapped both up, not putting them in his briefcase. He left then, sick, as he was always sick, at the psychotic backwash after any spectacular murder, whether it got to trial or didn't.

Horace came to the door as he rang the Braytons' bell. "Mrs. Brayton's upstairs. She said to bring you up if you should come."

She was at her desk, ethereally remote in a green linen dress, writing a letter. She slipped it under the blotter and got up as Trumper put his briefcase on the floor by the door.

"How do you do, Sergeant Trumper." She sat waiting.

"Your neighbor's having a pretty rough time of it." He was a little angry, suddenly, at this gentle ivory as impervious as steel, in contrast to the haggard unhappy face he'd seen next door. "Helping you out's put her in a tough spot. She's having to leave town till it dies down."

A flash of feeling that softened him shot through her dark eyes, before the faintly ironic smile he'd noticed in the courtroom closely followed it.

"You must think I'm very callous, Sergeant Trumper. I'm sorry. It was extremely kind of her to come to my defense. I—"

"Would you tell me, Mrs. Brayton, just what in hell—excuse me—just what you thought you were doing? Were you just trying to get yourself stuck in this new gas chamber we're going to have?"

He heard himself, as surprised at asking it as he was at the heat he asked it with.

"You mean, unless I did kill him," she said calmly. "And you're not quite sure I didn't, are you? I could see it in your faces yesterday. But truly, I did not. And I was as stunned as you were when Mrs. Remstad took the stand. I had no idea she'd seen me leave the house, or return to it.—And if I had killed him, I think I'd tell you so, now, to keep you from dogging everyone else all over again. Or I'd gladly say now I did it, if I thought I could make it stick. But you'd ask me to take your lie detector test again, and I'd fail it."

Trumper stared at her. "Are you telling me the reason you didn't take it is you knew it'd clear you? Or were you . . . afraid it would point to someone else?"

She was silent a moment. "It would have shown I didn't do it, if it's as infallible as you say. What else it would have shown, or you could have deduced from it, I'm not sure, Sergeant Trumper. For instance—if you'd asked me about the second shot, your polygraph would have shown that I had knowledge of it . . . even though I didn't hear it. And if you'd asked me what I was doing at Gibson Island on the day of the Garden Tour, I should have had to lie, or admit I'd shot off a whole box of .32 caliber shells, just for fun, or maybe to get the desire to shoot somebody out of my heart by shooting at a target tacked to a tree. I would have put you all, and myself, in a worse dilemma, and you would certainly have thought I was at least an accessory before the fact. Or there may have been other reasons, Sergeant."

She smiled faintly. "But as Mrs. Remstad says, withholding information is not a felony in Maryland."

Dave Trumper looked at her intently for a moment. "You haven't answered my first question, Mrs. Brayton. Or don't you want to answer it?"

She looked away in some far distance.

"It's possibly a case of he who rides the tiger, Sergeant. I didn't hear the shots. They must have been fired while my engine was running out in the garage. After I came in and put the chain in the slot across the back door I smelled gun smoke, just a faint whiff of it. I ran upstairs. Dr. Brayton's study door was open, his lights on. I ran in there. It looked as if he had shot himself. But that was impossible—unless he'd gone stark raving mad, and that was highly improbable. At seven o'clock he was reading a poem to me, planning a trip abroad that he wanted me to take with him, 'after he returned from Texas.'"

"You knew he was going there?"

"Of course. And why he was going. Which was to sell Mrs. Ristwich the idea of a noble renunciation of her personal desires and channel them into public service in terms of medical education. I assure you his interest in Mrs. Ristwich was neither physical nor matrimonial."

Trumper nodded. "You say it was impossible he'd have shot himself."

"Psychologically impossible, Sergeant Trumper. He was almost pathologically fastidious about his person. The sight of blood offended him. He barely passed his practical surgery courses and never touched surgery after he got his degree. He used to fly a great deal, and he always carried a capsule, cyanide I suppose, so that he could avoid the horror of a violent death. He didn't like guns. He only had that .32 in his desk because we had a prowler last winter. Actually I never remember to have seen it loaded the few times I've been—"

A flush rose to her cheeks as she stopped.

"—Never, in fact, now I think about it," she went on casually. "But everything pointed to something wrong. That's why it took me several moments to collect myself and call the police."

"In fact you knew at once that he'd been murdered, didn't you, Mrs. Brayton?"

"Did I?"

She looked at him with her strange ironic smile. But there was more than that in her expression. Trumper watched her intently without seeming to watch.

"Perhaps again it's simply that the woman who rides the tiger cannot dismount."

"Did you think it might be your son, Mrs. Brayton?"

"Never." She smiled again. "I admit I was startled when I learned he hadn't gone back to the office library that night. But if any of you thought I was trying to protect my son, you were entirely wrong."

"No." Trumper said. "I never thought that. And I wasn't ever sold on the Ristwich woman. Not after I saw her."

"But if I'd told you that Dr. Brayton was reading me a love poem that for some inexplicable reason has an almost hypnotic effect on me, and that I was so terrified he'd defeat me again that I'd decided to leave the house in the morning and stay at my mother's until after my daughter's wedding, do you think you would have believed me? Or that because I was leaving, I was clearing my desk, burning old bills and papers, when suddenly I knew I had to stay, I had to keep face till Lolly was married . . . and that, just to try to get back some simple sanity, I left the house, and because it was raining and raw I went to a movie the name of which or what happened in it I couldn't tell you even now, even if my life depended on it—if I'd told you that would you have believed me? You'd only have been the more convinced, Sergeant Trumper."

"You could have told the truth."

She shook her head. "I couldn't, and I can't. I'm sorry. You must know that if there were any human way possible to stop you from going ahead, I would take it with all my heart. I know there is none. If, some day, you have to arrest me as an accessory after the fact, it won't really matter. You will have won, I lost. Until then, Sergeant Trumper, I can only pray. Goodbye. You've all been much kinder to me than I have to you—especially that poor child we treated so horribly. Believe me, I had nothing to do with that. My mother is a generous woman until her own somewhat obsolete standards are attacked. Then she's ruthless in the extreme."

Sergeant Trumper got up. "I saw Mrs. Summerfield leaving here, yesterday," he said quietly.

A white line showed round Mrs. Brayton's lips for an instant. She rose steadily to her feet.

"It's been very difficult for her. She feels bitterly toward me, I'm afraid."

"No," Trumper said. "Not now, Mrs. Brayton. Not since you told her the truth. I saw her leave court. I saw her leave here. What is it—this tiger—that you'd be convicted of murder to keep your family and friends from knowing about? And that your mother collapses at when she hears about it, but isn't angry or bitter any more? What is it, Mrs. Brayton? What is it that's worse than what you went through? What means that much to people like you?"

Her face was pale but still serene except for the sadness in her dark eyes, as her lips moved in a smile that did not touch them.

"That's what is known as a rhetorical question, isn't it? No answer expected.—If I were to admit you're right, which of course I do not. Goodbye. You can find your own way out, can't you?"

Trumper picked up his briefcase. "I'd like to see Miss Elizabeth Brayton, if I may."

"She's gone. I don't mean she's . . . taken it on the lam, as she'd say. I merely mean she's not here and I'm anxious about her. If you run across her, will you send her home?"

"I'll see what I can do. May I use the phone in your husband's study?"

"The key's still down in the hall table, I believe."

He let himself in the study and dialled the Racket Squad. "Have somebody see if Miss Elizabeth Brayton's still hanging out in Mike's Bar over by the court house. Call Kerry. I'm on my way over."

He put the phone down and went over to the book shelves behind the desk. In the bottom row were quarto volumes, only slightly out of line, the way he'd left them the night before. But one leather oblong was not a book. It was a briefcase. Or looked like one. He drew it out and put the one in his hand in its place.

Over on Park Avenue Kerry O'Keefe let him in.

"The office said to tell you Miss Brayton's at Mike's Bar," she said. "Not drinking. Watching TV. They've got color TV."

"You packing too?" he asked, seeing the clothes folded on the sofa.

"Yes." She didn't look at him as she put his cup of coffee down on the table. "I'm resigning. I wanted to tell you before I told the Boss."

"This the confession?" He stirred his coffee. "Let's have it. What did you do?"

"I called John Brayton. After you left here last night. To tell tell him about . . . that."

She nodded toward the briefcase on the floor near the arch.

A slow flush was creeping up the back of Dave Trumper's neck. "I didn't know you knew what it was," he said curtly.

"I saw the one the Commissioner had. I'm not trying to excuse myself, Dave."

"You mean you tried to be an honest cop but love conquered all." She flushed hotly. "Yes. If you want to put it that way."

"What did you tell him?"

"I didn't tell him anything. But that wasn't my fault. I'd have told him if he'd talked to me. But he wouldn't."

Sergeant Trumper sat there blowing on his coffee.

"—Dames," he said at last. He got up. "Okay. Get your hat on." Then he said, "Kerry, cops aren't any different from other people. You take your oath. It don't mean this stuff they call our common humanity slips off you like the skin of a snake. There's bound to be a lot of times when it's tough going. You're just lucky Brayton's a pig-headed ass, sugar. Come on. We're going down to headquarters. You go up to the Sixth Floor. Write me a list of everything you know or ever thought about the Mt. Vernon Place setup. I'll be busy a while."

His first business was at the Crime Lab. He handed in the brick, the string and the note. "Get the Dutchman to check this himself. But fast. I'm coming back. If there's a print anywhere, I want it."

Then he went down to the small room on the Fifth Floor and put the briefcase on the Inspector's desk. "Can we run this off in private? It's last night till ten-fifteen this morning, in Brayton's study." He unzipped the case and took out the reel of tape. "I don't know what I got. If any."

He didn't say that Kerry had almost queered the deal. If there was a deal. It seemed for a long time there was nothing. It was not absolute silence that they got, but it was silence in the normal meaning of the word. The faint ticking of a clock normally not heard in a room, the subdued sounds of traffic, the muted honk of a horn in the street outside.

"It's a bust, I guess," Trumper said. Then suddenly he leaned forward, listening intently.

They heard a metallic click and a long swish, as if a key had turned in a lock and a door brushed over the velvet surface of a rug. There was a moment of silence, and another swish, softer, swish-swish-swish, more distinct as it seemed to come closer to the sensitive microphone in the briefcase between the books in the case behind the desk. Swish-swish-swish. It stopped then, and there was another sound, very faint, followed by still another that was hardly a sound so much as a vague sense of movement signified by the lowering of the background sounds, as if something, a person or a thing, had come in front of the small recorder, obstructing the sound wave reaching it.

Then, so abruptly that they all started, another sound.

Tap, tap, tap. Tap, tap, tap, tap.

There was a long silence. Then it came again.

Tap, tap, tap, tap. Tap, tap.

The Inspector's secretary got up suddenly, her face white.

"It sounds like his ghost. It gives me—"

"Sssh."

Tap, tap, tap, tap, tap. Tap, tap, tap.

It came again, in eerie persistence, from the unwinding reel, until suddenly it seemed to break off. There was another swish, sharper, and the background sounds were clearer. A rapid swish-swish was drowned in the sound of heavy footsteps coming closer, rapidly, with long strides, and a voice cut sharply in.

"Mother! What—"

"Nothing, love." Her reply was tranquil, perfectly calm.

"But that noise I heard. What—"

And a light rippling laughter. "Darling, you must have thought I'd taken up table tapping."

"No. It reminded me of the ghosts Lolly used to hear, before you closed her fireplace—"

"I remember. It was the swallows nesting in the chimney. But I thought you were in bed asleep."

"I thought you were."

"I was, lamb. But I woke up and happened to remember something. One of these pilasters has a hollow space behind it. I was trying to find which one, because there are some . . . papers your father kept there. But I'll get an expert when the police are through. Come along. Let's get back to bed."

Swish-swish. A click of the lock again. Silence. Silence until the reel ran out.

And silence in the Inspector's office, as he and Trumper looked at each other. Trumper shrugged. He got up. "I'll wait. See what I pick up tonight."

He went back downstairs to the Crime Lab. The sergeant with a Dutch accent, author of a history of fingerprinting, came out. "You hit the jackpot."

Trumper looked at the cards with prints on them. "You're not kidding. We got everybody.—This guy's family got him off twenty times, promising psychiatric treatment." He handed back the card with his own prints on it. "I'll be up in Records."

At Records on the Fifth Floor he said, "Rush these, can you?"

He went up to the Rackets Division on the Sixth Floor and glanced in at Kerry O'Keefe typing at his desk. "What about rustling us some coffee?"

"Okay." She pulled the sheet out, put it with two others and handed them to him. "It's the best I can do."

When she came back he was staring vacantly at the corner of the room, his photostat of Mrs. Brayton's note to her husband on the desk in front of him.

—Mrs. Brayton in her sitting room. Her face, and her voice, on the invisible television screen within his own mind. The ironic smile, like the smile he'd seen in court when Mrs. Ristwich was telling all.

He started, coming out of concentrated absorption, when Kerry came in, moved a paper for her to put the coffee down, and swung around as a clerk from Records came in and handed Kerry some papers.

"I'll take those," he said curtly.

Kerry's eyes widened a little. She'd only meant to hand them to him.

"Here." He thrust out one of the sheets. "Take this down to Detectives. Tell 'em to haul him in, quick. He's a psycho."

When she came back he was putting on his hat. "I'll be busy. Stick around."

"—Dave." There were two dull spots burning on her cheeks. "Am I being—disciplined? Or excluded? Or both?"

He stopped at the door. "Say a cop makes a mistake, Kerry. We've all done it. You put him on report, or you give him a chance. Personally, I don't think you'd call Brayton again. But I'd be a lousy cop if I staked a murder case on it. That fair?"

"Very fair. Thanks for telling me straight."

"You can go home at five if I'm not back."

She left at five when he wasn't back. At half-past seven he called her at her apartment. "Put on a dark dress and a pair of sneakers. Meet me in Mt. Vernon Place in half an hour."

He was feeding the pigeons by the fountain when she got there.

"We're going in the Brayton house, Kerry. Relax—he isn't there. He's going out to see his grandmother after he puts his little sister on the train. She's visiting a school friend, so he thinks. So does his mother. But that's a dodge. Horace told me—he's the only one in on it. She's on her way to Las Vegas to marry this lad of hers. He called her this a.m. Been buried in the desert, special training, for ten weeks, and didn't even know the wedding was off. He blew his top. Then all of a sudden Mrs. Brayton tells Horace he and his wife can have the night off to see their daughter who's having a baby. So she and the loony sister are there alone. The mixture as before. Come on, we go around through Peabody Alley."

"Mrs. Brayton doesn't know we're—"

"No. Horace only told me this stuff because he's worried about leaving her alone. So I'm standing guard. He's letting me in at eight-fifteen. Mrs. Remstad's phone is in her living room. She'll get a call so she isn't spraying her African violets."

They were at the end of the alley.

"Wait till you see the servants leave. Stay in the garage. I'll give you a signal.—You're coming along so if it's loused up I'm not charged with being alone with lone women."

"Couldn't you get a warrant?"

"I could if I had the time and they didn't put me in a strait jacket when I told 'em what for. Maybe that's where I belong. It's crazy for sure. I don't believe it myself. And when I told Horace I was standing guard, I wasn't kidding."

CHAPTER

21

One door of Dr. Brayton's bedroom opened off the head of the stairs. The door from the bedroom into his study at the front of the house was at the end of a pine-panelled passage between his bathroom and clothes closet. The door from the passage into the study was plain on the passage side, on the study side, ornately carved like the pilasters between the sections of the bookcases. Opened a bare inch, with no light behind it, the carving concealing the give-away planes of a flush door, it gave the illusion of being closed unless one looked carefully. This was the lousing up Trumper had to fear. But standing there in the pine-panelled passage, when he and Kerry had crept silently up the back stairs through the door off the hall, he was taking less chance than trying to hide himself or her behind the long damask curtains there in the study window.

They stood there, waiting, the silence of the house gradually deeper. Then Kerry, back of Trumper and across the little passage way, could feel him tense sharply. He leaned forward, opening the study door a fraction of an inch further. It was not sound but light that had alerted him, as if a curtain had been drawn aside, letting the street glow into the room. It was gone almost instantly, but Trumper, peering out, had seen Johnny Brayton slip behind the curtain, drawing it quickly into place in front of him. Kerry heard Trumper catch his breath. He drew the door noiselessly to and stood motionless. It was silent again. Silent and dark. Then, so suddenly that Kerry was startled, Trumper moved slightly. She heard the metallic click of a key in the study door and the long swish of the door on the velvet rug. In the soft light that flooded the room she could see the outline of Trumper's face by the barely opened door.

Trumper could see Margaret Brayton move quickly into the narrow field of his vision, reach into the bookcase beside the pine pilaster next to the fireplace, and move her hand again. And see the four-foot segment of the bookcase as she swung it open like a door, back against the segment where his second briefcase was, cutting the sound waves from it. He saw her raise her hand then to the solid wall.

Tap, tap, tap. Tap, tap, tap, tap.

Then silence as she stood there motionless.

She raised her hand again. Tap, tap, tap.

Trumper saw the wall swing slowly away, and saw the light in the living room next door.

Kerry O'Keefe saw nothing. But she heard the stolid voice break the eerie silence, her spine cold suddenly at its undertone of pain.

"I didn't want to come in here ever again. I wouldn't have if it wasn't for that detective. It's got so all I can see is him lying there dead. I wished I hadn't done it. I didn't hate him. I loved him. But I couldn't stand him treating me like I was dirt for that woman. Locking me out when I gave up thirty years of my life for him. Twenty-six of 'em right here."

"—I'm so sorry, Mrs. Remstad. So desperately sorry. But Mr. Trumper told me you were going away. I had to see you, to thank you . . . for saving me. And to tell you—"

"You don't need to thank me. I didn't do it for you. I got to die myself some day. Maybe I can explain what I did to him. But I couldn't explain why I sat and let you take the rap. Not when you were trying to keep them from finding out it was me that did it. First I didn't care. If you wanted to go on not letting your swell friends know about me. If you were that proud—"

"It wasn't pride. It used to be. Very bitter pride. But—"

"I know. I felt kind of sorry for you when Meg was just born and you come in here and found the door open. Before that I just laughed. You were such a cocky, scrawny little thing, so proud of being the great Mrs. Pierce Brayton. I never thought you'd stick it out."

"I didn't stick it out because I wanted to. I took the children and went home. My mother sent me straight back. She wouldn't even let me tell her why I'd left. And he wouldn't give me a quiet divorce. To get it, I'd have had to ruin him and ruin my children."

"He knew you wouldn't do that. All he was worried about was you'd tell your father."

"That would have ruined him. And I was ashamed by then. Ashamed of my own failure. And when he promised you'd go and then after Lolly was born I knew you were back again, it was all so terrible I didn't know anything else to do. My children had to grow up in Baltimore."

"I went away when he married you. I could of married him, when he was so crazy in love with me. But I knew I wouldn't do him anything but harm, with the people he'd know. Sure I was in love with him, but I was young. I was getting along fine when he begged me to come back. He'd found these houses, and figured the door. When you were away, and nights he'd come up here to work, he'd come over to me. He didn't like kids."

"That was the only bitterness I couldn't get over. They never asked to be born. I've been so terrified for them, ever since that Sunday last summer when you spoke to him out on the street, when Johnny was there. It was the first time I'd realized he wasn't seeing you any more. I saw he was angry, and I knew how ruthless he could be. I knew what torture you must be going through over there alone."

"I was going crazy. I wouldn't have cared so much if it was you getting some of your own back. He kept saying how beautiful you'd got to be. So in the winter, when he said I should get another place, it was all right. I had plenty of money. I went away. Then I came back on business a couple of days and saw it wasn't you he was getting rid of me for. It was that woman with the car."

"He wasn't in love with her, Mrs. Remstad."

"You never heard her talking to him. His extension phone's in my bedroom, and I heard 'em. And he coulda told me instead of locking me out like I was dirt. I got so I hated him so much I knew I'd kill him if I stayed here, so I went away. But it was all I could think about and I came back, just before Christmas. And that night her car was down there and I put my gun in my fur coat pocket. I was so crazy jealous I was going to kill him right on the sidewalk. I didn't care. And then Johnny came along walking on those pink clouds, engaged to the girl I thought was an entertainer."

"I thought then he was going right along in his father's footsteps. But at least he wanted to marry her."

"I offered him money to, but he wouldn't take it. I saw how

crazy I was then, so I went back upstairs, but it got like it was a disease, all I could think about. I was going to kill him, but I wasn't going to get hung for it. Then it came back to me all of a sudden how I could do it. I knew he had a .32 in his desk if I could get in to get it. I had some shells. We always used to reload cases. It was easy to make the blank with the dried blood. I knew you opened your house for the Tour, so I just waited. When all those women came I paid my dollar and walked right upstairs. I unlocked the door and got his gun. They all laughed fit to kill when I passed them on the stairs going down."

"If Camilla Anne had only told me you'd been there. I'd have known. I could have saved you both."

"Not with him treating me like he was. I went way out in the country the next morning early and fired all six chambers so the gun'd be dirty and they couldn't tell more than one shot was fired. Then I was ready, and the very next night I heard him talking to her about this glorious week and he was staying home that night. I was figuring how I could get you and Johnny out—I forgot his sister—and then I saw you go out the back way, and Johnny go to meet that girl, and I went right in. If he'd just said one decent word to me! He looked around at me like I was a mangy dog and said 'How did you get in here?' I sat right down on that chair. He went on writing. And I . . . I shot him, just like they said. And then I heard you coming up the back stairs before I got the door closed."

"I . . . when I came in here, it was so terrible. And . . . I knew what had happened. He'd told my father a story about . . . the blank with the dried blood. But I . . . I hadn't known he got it from you."

"It was this fella I had my act with. He got tight one night and told me the way he'd killed his wife and nobody ever asked a question. That's how I met Pierce, because in our act we'd shoot cigarettes out of each other's hands and all of a sudden I knew he was crazy, going to shoot me for keeps because I wouldn't marry him. I got off stage but he winged me and blew his own brains out right there. They called for a doctor and Pierce and another doctor came up. It was just like lightning hitting a haystack with him and me. Only they hauled us all to jail and got our fingerprints. And that's why I came here tonight."

"I . . . don't understand, Mrs. Remstad."

"Because this detective took a note somebody threw through my window to get it fingerprinted. I never thought about mine being on it too. And they got a record. He'll see I'm a crack shot and he'll find out Pierce testified for me. And then he'll start thinking about that letter you wrote to Pierce. They all thought 'Mrs. R.' was Mrs. Ristwich. But you went all to pieces because you thought they'd know it was Mrs. Remstad you meant. That's when I knew you were trying to keep me out of it and you didn't hate me any more. That's why I got up there. But that detective, he'll be back."

"Oh, no . . . no!"

"I wanted to tell you so you didn't think I did it for spite to hurt you and the children when I won't be around here. I'm . . . going away tomorrow. I just can't stand it here any more. You tell Johnny goodbye. I always used to pretend he was my kid. If there was only some way I could bring him back. I wished I hadn't done it. I just couldn't stand him treating me like he did."

There was silence then. A long, long silence. There was no sound that Kerry could hear, until finally she heard the soft swish and saw the narrow line of light turn into darkness. She heard the click of the key in the lock.

It was in an almost trance state that she saw Dave Trumper pull the door open and the ball of light from his small flash bounce over the velvet rug as he drew the briefcase out from the bottom shelf behind the desk. In the same semi-trance she felt his hand touch her arm. The light guided them back through the bedroom. He opened the door softly, listened and beckoned to her again. She followed down the back stairs and out into the garden. Trumper moved quickly across through the garage into the alley.

"—Trump."

"Shut up," he said roughly. "Christ, I don't want to do it. It's my job.—How wrong can you be? I thought they'd hate each other's guts."

She followed him through the alley, up Charles Street into Mt. Vernon Place, past the Braytons' brownstone steps to Mrs. Remstad's. He went up and rang the doorbell, not hers but her third floor tenants'. He waited until a small anxious figure of an old woman in a robe came peering down the stairs. When she opened the door he had his billfold in his hand, his badge pinned to it. He held it out.

"Police officers. We're checking a report. You go on back to bed. We won't disturb you."

He went up the stairs, Kerry behind him. At Mrs. Remstad's door he stopped, waiting for the old woman to disappear up the stairs. Then he raised his hand to knock, dropped it and turned the knob cautiously. The door was not locked. He pushed it open quietly and stepped inside.

"Mrs. Remstad. It's Trumper. Could I—"

The blast shook the room. He leaped forward to the bedroom door. It seemed an eternity to Kerry before he came out of it, in his hand two notes, with the envelopes she had not had time to use. He read them and handed them to Kerry. One was to the police. "I can't face ill health," it said. "It's best this way." The other envelope said "To Detective Trumper." "It was me that did it, just like you people said. If it don't have to come out, please don't let it. But it's not the reason I'm doing this. My life was over when he didn't need me any more. I wished I hadn't done it. Inga Remstad."

Trumper put the notes in his pocket. He crossed the room to the telephone and turned back to Kerry.

"Go next door. Tell Mrs. Brayton. Tell her to wait up, I'll be over. Then go home. Just get the hell out and do as you're told, will you, O'Keefe?"

But as she started for the door he said, "Wait. You can go through here."

He went to the bookcase where the porcelain animals had been glued to the shelves to keep them from toppling over when the door they camouflaged was opened. It swung around easily, the solid back of the bookcases in Dr. Brayton's study there in front of him. That moved slowly as he pushed. The light from Mrs. Remstad's room made a long oblong across the velvet carpet and up the bookcases on the other side. If Trumper saw John Brayton standing in stunned silence in the dark periphery he gave no sign of it. Kerry did not see him until Trumper went through the door and switched on the desk light.

He was standing there, his face white.

"Taking your pound of flesh to the last ounce, aren't you."

"That's right," Trumper said curtly, his own eyes hardening. "Officer O'Keefe. Go through the bedroom and tell Mrs. Brayton

178

Mrs. Remstad shot herself. Tell her to come in here. I want to talk to her when I'm through on the other side."

He went back into Mrs. Remstad's living room and pulled the bookcase door shut.

"Why didn't he leave it?" Johnny Brayton said bitterly. "Or does he want it to be a big surprise for the reporters? Isn't it enough that the poor woman's dead?"

"I don't know." Kerry's voice was taut. She went toward the bedroom door. "You tell your mother. And tell Sergeant Trumper I've gone home."

She saw his whole body sag then, slump together, as he went unsteadily to a chair and let himself down, his head in his hands, the last shred of pride gone, whatever arrogance there'd been the moment before dissolved.

"The poor damn woman."

She heard it, a sobbing whisper, and saw the tears streaking down his face, as she turned blindly, running through the bedroom, down the stairs to the front door. The police cars were just pulling to the curb when she ran across Mt. Vernon Place, unconscious that she was running, with the tears pouring down her own face, until she was home.

In the small sound-proof office the Inspector and Dave Trumper listened to the second tape winding slowly off the reel, the voices of the two women strangely moving. There was silence for a long moment after the technician turned the machine off.

Dave Trumper spoke first.

"I told Mrs. Brayton I didn't have authority to commit us, but even when the law was an eye for an eye it didn't say the whole world had to know everything. John Brayton was there. He knew something was going on from the tapping business the night before. He thought maybe he could help, and he came home instead of going to his grandmother's and got behind the curtains in the window. It was a bad shock. He didn't really come to till he heard the shot next door.—Mrs. Remstad's will leaves all her dough to the Children's Hospital. You see any use blackening her name, now she's paid up?"

"Put the tape in a box," the Inspector said. "If the Commissioner and the Chief want to hear it, okay. If not, that's it. The Commissioner was saying this morning it'd surprise people the secrets we keep when it's families and kids are going to suffer. You take a week off, Trump, and give Kerry one. And tell Mrs. Brayton. How did she take it?"

"The way you'd expect. I told her I thought it'd be closed as far as we were concerned. She said, 'You've won, but maybe I haven't lost. I'd hate it for her, as I would for us.' She's one sweet lady. Well, so long. I'll take Rackets, Boss. No more special assignments in North Baltimore for me."

It was round noon when Trumper was leaving Kerry's.

"If it hadn't been for the fingerprints I don't think we'd have cracked it. I didn't spot that 'Mrs. R.' in the letter till the Dutchman said 'You've hit the jackpot' and there were her fingerprints, mine and the psycho's. Funny, reading about a raid thirty-two years old. Too much of a coincidence this beautiful blonde moves in next door to the doctor that testified for her, less than five years later, and he don't remember her. Not that girl he wouldn't forget. She was a honey. And she wasn't a crack shot, she was a professional crack shot. But I still couldn't figure it till I read in your notes about her coming over the day of the Garden Tour. When she asked if anybody could get in it didn't sound like the tour-goer she said she was on the stand. Then I got to wondering why did she cement her animal figures down to keep people's dirty mitts off 'em when nobody ever came to see her and the ones on the other side of the fireplace weren't cemented?

"But what strikes me funny now is me getting sore telling Mrs. Brayton poor Mrs. Remstad was having to get out of town all because she'd helped her. She said 'You must think I'm very callous. I'm sorry, it was extremely kind of her to come to my defense.' But no wonder she smiled that kind of smile of hers.—You mind if I call my doll and tell her I've got a week?"

He came back from the telephone in a minute and picked up his hat.

"Dave." Kerry was standing there, her eyes not meeting his. "Do I . . . do I go back to regular duty?"

"You go home, sugar. Try to forget you're a cop for a week. Then come back. You're still with us. So long." He went to the door. "You're a good cop, Kerry. I'm proud of you, girl."

She went slowly in and got her suitcases out of the closet. And heard him coming back, knocking on her door again. She went out, not stopping to look through the one-way glass before she opened the door.

"—Oh."

"May I come in, Kerry?"

She hesitated, then stepped aside. Johnny Brayton came on past her into the living room. She closed the door, holding the knob tight for a moment before she let it go and came on in. He was standing by the Dutch door, looking out into the garden with the mimosa tree.

"Trumper told me you were leaving today," he said at last.

"That's right."

"I don't . . . suppose there's anything I can say. Except—"

"There's nothing to say, Johnny. It's been . . . horrible for you. I'm sorry."

"But I didn't have to make it horrible for you. If I'd listened to you, if I'd had half the guts you had, I wouldn't have been the kind of arrogant fool I was.—But . . . I never thought I was doing you a favor asking you to marry me. I was doing myself a favor, Kerry. I wasn't ashamed to take you to the house."

"I knew that, Johnny. Don't—"

"I didn't have much to offer you. I don't even have that much any more. I . . . I hated you because I loved you so much, Kerry. I still do. Now you know the skeleton in my distinguished Baltimore closet, you know that even if you'd really been a sitter and a jail-bird you were a hell of a lot better than the bunch of snobs and hypocrites—"

"Your mother's neither one. She's wonderful."

"She'd have been better off if she hadn't tried to save face all these years."

"You can't say that, Johnny. You can't sit in judgment on people."

"I know. I didn't mean to. It's just so heartbreaking, is all. So useless. I don't know. All I know is I love you. But if you want me to go, just tell me. I haven't any right to ask you to let me stay and let me try some way to make you love me again."

"I've never stopped loving you, Johnny. If you're going out to the West Coast—"

He shook his head. "I'm staying here. I'm not going to duck and run. Unless you couldn't stand it.—Or if you can stand me and my grandmother and Camilla Anne—."

A smile lighted her eyes and vanished. "The last two'd be pretty hard.—I'm still sort of battered and bruised, Johnny. And I know you are. Maybe if we . . . if we could just start over. Start from scratch."

"Oh, Kerry!"

He crossed the room to her. Then he smiled gravely and said, "Miss O'Keefe, may I offer you my coat?"

It wasn't seersucker, but he started to take it off. "And who buys the coffee?"

"Oh, Johnny! Oh, darling—I love you so!"

They started over. But not from scratch.

The Dark Lady
from Belorusse

JEROME CHARYN

The Dark Lady
from Belorusse

A MEMOIR

ST. MARTIN'S PRESS ❦ NEW YORK

B

CHARYN

A THOMAS DUNNE BOOK.
An imprint of St. Martin's Press.

THE DARK LADY FROM BELORUSSE. Copyright © 1997 by Jerome
Charyn. All rights reserved. Printed in the United States of America.
No part of this book may be used or reproduced in any manner what-
soever without written permission except in the case of brief quota-
tions embodied in critical articles or reviews. For information, address
St. Martin's Press, 175 Fifth Avenue, New York, N.Y. 10010.

Design by Nancy Resnick

Library of Congress Cataloging-in-Publication Data

Charyn, Jerome.
    The dark lady from Belorusse / Jerome Charyn.—1st ed.
       p.   cm.
    "A Thomas Dunne book."
    ISBN 0-312-16808-X
    1. Charyn, Jerome—Homes and haunts—New York (N.Y.)
2. Novelists, American—20th century—Family relationships.
3. Bronx (New York, N.Y.)—Social life and customs. 4. Jewish
(State)—New York. 6. Charyn, Jerome—Childhood and youth.
7. Charyn, Jerome—Family. I. Title.
PS3553.H33Z462   1997
813'.54—dc21
[B]   97-15351
                                         CIP

First Edition: October 1997

10   9   8   7   6   5   4   3   2   1

For Faigele and Sergeant Sam

Letter from Mogilev

$\mathcal{W}e$ would walk the streets, a prodigy in short pants and his mother, so defiantly beautiful that all transactions stopped, and we'd enter a slow-motion world where women, men, children, dogs, cats, and firemen in their trucks would look at her with such longing in their eyes, that I felt like some usurper who was carrying her off to another hill. I was only five in '42, a nervous boy who couldn't spell his own name. My mother wore her silver fox coat, designed and cut for her by my father, Sam, who was a foreman in a Manhattan fur shop. The coat was contraband, and should have gone to the Navy. My father's shop had a contract with the War Department to supply the Navy with fur-lined vests so its admirals and ordinary sailors wouldn't freeze to death aboard some battleship.

It was a darkly romantic time. The Bronx sat near the Atlantic Ocean without a proper seawall, and there was talk of attack squads arriving in little rubber boats off some tricky submarine, getting into the sewer system, and gobbling up my native ground. But I never saw a Nazi on our walks. And what power would any of them have had against the shimmering outline of my mother in her silver fox coat? She was born in 1911, like Ginger Rogers and Jean Harlow, but she didn't have their platinum look: she was the dark lady from Belorusse.

We weren't on a pleasure stroll. It was our daily trip to the post office, where my mother was expecting a letter from Mogilev, in White Russia, where her brother lived, a schoolteacher who'd raised her after their own mother had died. I'm not sure why this letter couldn't have been delivered to the mailbox in our building. Had the Germans seized Mogilev, and my uncle could only write via some secret system in the Soviet underground?

The postmaster would always come out from behind his window when my mother appeared. He was a cranky little man who wore slippers and liked to shout at his clerks. But he was kind to the dark lady's little boy. He would take me through his side of the wall and show me the "graveyard," a gigantic sack where all the dead letters lay, sad undeliverable things, with postmarks from all over the planet. I would sift through the pile, look at the pictures on the stamps, smell the glue, while the postmaster squeezed my mother's hand. But not even this wizard of the mail could produce a letter from Mogilev.

She would tremble on the journey home as we climbed hill after hill. She walked like a drunken lady. It was from my mother that I learned how memory could kill. She could survive as long as she had word from Mogilev. But there was no word in the middle of a war, only mountains of dead-letter boxes between Belorusse and the Bronx.

She started smoking cigarettes. And I had to smother a fallen match and slap at the little fires that seemed to collect in her wake. I would dust the walls with a dry mop and attend to my mother's goose, opening the oven door to stab at the bird with a fork, until it was the way my father liked it, dark and crisp and unchewable.

I would put his whisky on the table, pour him a shot, and jabber endlessly, ask him whatever nonsense came into my head, to camouflage my mother's silences. But as soon as he left the house, she would pretend that her brother was calling from Mogilev (we didn't even have a telephone), and she'd laugh and cry in a Russian that was so melodious, I would get confused until I believed that *all* language was born on a phantom phone.

Her English had no music; it was halting and cruel, like a twisted tongue. But I was a clever little bastard. I would clutch at her phrases like building blocks and sing my own backward sentence-songs. "In the sea, mama, drowns many broken ships." I'd never been to the sea. But I could imagine the great Atlantic where those German subs prowled like crocodiles. My mother had promised to take me across the bridge into Manhattan and watch the ocean liners that lay hobbled in the Hudson and couldn't get into the war. But there was always that letter from Mogilev on her mind, and she didn't seem able to plot the simple logic of our trip.

And so we were marooned in the Bronx. My mother got more morose. She would stand in front of the mirror for an hour with a pot of rouge and a canister of lipstick and paint her face. Then she'd start to cry and ruin all the work she did, enormous teardrops eating into the paint with their own salty acid. I'd follow her into the street and head for the post office, people staring at this flaw in the dark lady, the tracks in her face. It couldn't have made her less appealing, because the postmaster was twice as attentive.

"Some coffee, Mrs. Charyn?" he said, and coffee was hard to find. He'd have pieces of candy for me, and cups of cocoa, which marked my own lips. But my mother was deeply discouraged. The pain had eaten into her ritual.

"No letter Mogilev?"

"It will come, Mrs. Charyn. Russian letters are notorious. They ride very slow, but they never fail."

He'd dance around her in his slippers, scowl at his clerks, pirouette with his coffeepot, but my mother hardly noticed. She hadn't risked disappointment day after day to become part of his coffee club. He couldn't have charmed her with all the candy in the world.

And I was lost at sea. I had to pilot my mother from place to place, undress her, cook my father's goose. But I was getting lucky. I didn't have to go to school. Kindergarten had been canceled in the Bronx. There was a terrible shortage of teachers, and someone must have figured that five-year-olds like me could sit at home with wooden blocks and a pound of clay. I didn't have time for clay. I had to groom my mother, coax her into shape, fool my father into believing she was perfectly fine. I fed him Scotch and gin. He was wall-eyed when he left the dinner table. He would ask my mother questions, and I would answer, once, twice, until I got slapped.

"Mind your business, Baby."

Baby, that's what he would call his own kid to make him suffer. I couldn't read or write, but I could listen to the radio. I heard the battle reports, how the British commandos were making amphibious landings in the middle of the desert, and knocking the hell out of Hitler's Africa Corps. I asked my father to call me Soldier or Little Sergeant, but he never did.

Dad was the sergeant, not me. Cutting fur-lined vests for a lot of admirals had kept him out of the war, but he still had his own uniform: a white helmet that looked like a shallow pot and a white armband with a complicated insignia (a blue circle with a triangle of red and white stripes sitting inside). My father was an air-raid warden with the rank of sergeant. He would patrol the streets after dark with a silver whistle around his neck and make sure that every single window in his assigned radius of blocks had a blackout curtain. If a light blazed from a window, he'd warn you with his whistle and shout, "Lights out, smarty." And if that didn't work, he could call the cops or summon you before the Civilian Defense Board. He was an impeccable warden, my dad, heartless within his own small hegemony, willing to risk the wrath of friends, neigh-

bors, anyone who misbehaved. He'd herd you into a cellar if he
ever caught you in the street during an air-raid drill. Some people
wouldn't listen to Sergeant Sam, some rebelled, beat him into the
ground until other wardens arrived, or a cop rescued him. Even in
'42, his first year as a warden, he had a medal from Mayor La-
Guardia, chief of Civilian Defense. I caught LaGuardia on the
radio. "We have our soldiers in Brooklyn and the Bronx, brave
men who go forth without a gun, who guard the home front
against saboteurs and unpatriotic people. What would I do without my wardens?"

And if dad came home with a bruised eye and a broken whistle, his armband torn, a big dent in his white hat, it was the Baby
who had to search for Mercurochrome, while my mother sat forlorn in the living room, dreaming of Russian mail. He was much
more solicitous in moments of sorrow, almost endearing with dirt
on his face. He'd clutch my hand, look at FDR's picture on the
wall, while I swabbed his eye with a cotton stick.

"Baby, shouldn't we write to the President?"

"He's busy, dad, he's drowning in mail. A warden can't complain. How would it look if you snitch? You'll give the Bronx a bad
name."

Of course I couldn't speak in full flowing sentences. My melody
went something like this: "Drownin', dad, the prez. Eatin' vanilla
envelopes. And you better be quiet. The Bronx will kill a tattytale."

Dad got my drift.

"Who's a tattytale?"

But he wouldn't have slapped me with Franklin Delano Roosevelt on the wall. Even in her distraction, my mother blessed FDR
whenever she lit a candle. The blood that flowed in him was our
blood too.

Anyway, dad couldn't have written to Roosevelt. He was as un-
lettered as I was, as feeble with the pen. He could barely scratch a
few words in his Civilian Defense reports. And so he suffered quietly, licked his wounds, and we went to church on the high holi-

days, with his face still black and blue. I had to dress my mother, make sure her mascara didn't run. We didn't belong to that temple on the Grand Concourse, Adath Israel, with its white stone pillars and big brass door. Adath Israel was where all the millionaire doctors and lawyers went. The services were held in English. The assistant rabbi at Adath Israel was also a painter and a poet. He gave classes at night for kids in the neighborhood. We called him Len. He was in love with the dark lady. That's why he encouraged me, let me into his class. He wanted us to join the temple, but my father wouldn't go near any place that didn't have a cantor. That was the disadvantage of English. A cantor would have had nothing to sing.

We went to the old synagogue at the bottom of the hill. It was made of crumbling brick; portions of the steeple would rain down from the roof. There had been three fires at the synagogue since the war began, and the "incendiary bomb," as we called it, was always about to close. But we had Gilbert Rogovin, who'd been a choirboy here and had studied at the cantors' college in Cincinnati, Ohio. Our cantor could have made a fortune singing holy songs on Fifth Avenue, but he always returned to the Bronx. He was a bigwig at the Cincinnati Opera House. He played Spanish barbers and mad Moroccan kings when he wasn't with us.

He was married to the diva Marilyn Kraus, and he would always bring her to our crumbling synagogue. She was a Herculean beauty, six feet tall, with the hands of a football player and a full, floating figure. When she trod up to the balcony, where all the women sat, the stairs shivered under her feet. The balcony was full of opera fans who worshiped Marilyn, called her Desdemona, and I wondered if this Desdemona was another dark lady from Belorusse.

I had the privilege of sitting with my mother and all the other women, because I was only five. Desdemona hunkered down next to us on our narrow bench, her enormous hands cradled in her lap, like a despotic queen of the balcony. She waved to the cantor, who wore a white robe and was about to wave back when he discovered the woman near his wife. The breath seemed to go out of his body. He was just like those firemen who had seen my mother for the first time. Lost in her world of letter boxes, she didn't even smile at him. The cantor was all alone; he couldn't pierce the devotion in her dark eyes. He stood among his choirboys, started to sing. But he wasn't like a postmaster dancing in slippers. He was the custodian of songs. He brought my mother out of her dream with his opening syllables. A woman swooned. I had to run and find her smelling salts . . .

He leaned against the gate with a cigarette in his mouth. A cantor wasn't allowed to smoke on the high holidays. But Rogovin could do no wrong. Desdemona wasn't with him. She must have gone back to their suite at the Concourse Plaza. My mother and I had ventured out of the synagogue with Sergeant Sam, who'd become a local hero because of his little calvaries as an air-raid warden. He was like a special policeman with a wounded face. The cantor saluted him. "Sergeant, I'd like to borrow your boy."

None of us had ever been that close to the cantor, who had little white hairs in his nose. He wore a strange perfume, smelled like a certain red flower at the Bronx Zoo.

"It's an honor," my father said. "But how can I help you? The boy is five. He doesn't have working papers. He can't spell."

"It's a sad story. My old mother has been pestering me to have a child. I had to invent one."

"You lied to her, Cantor?"

"It's scandalous. But mom's half blind, lives at a nursing home in the Bronx. Have to make mom happy before she dies."

Rogovin sobbed into his handkerchief. I'd never seen a cantor cry. His tears were the size of my mother's crystal earrings. Dad took pity on him.

"Cantor, please . . . we'll lend you the boy." He turned to my mother in bewildered fury. "Do something. We can't let the cantor choke on his tears."

I'm not sure if my mother was dreaming of Mogilev at that moment. But she came out of her trance long enough to slap Rogovin in the face. Dad was even more perplexed. The wives of air-raid wardens weren't supposed to perform criminal acts, and assaulting cantors in a public place was worse than criminal; it was a sin against God, because God favored a cantor above all other beings. God loved a good song.

My mother slapped him again. Rogovin wasn't surprised. I saw him smile under the hand he used to cover his mouth.

My father made a fist. "I'll kill you," he said to the dark lady.

"Sergeant," the cantor said, "you shouldn't provoke Madame. She'll just go on hitting me."

"I don't understand," dad said.

"It's simple. My missus was in the balcony with Madame. They got to talking about me . . ."

"Balconies. Missus. I don't understand."

I was just as baffled. I hadn't been able to hear Desdemona whisper a word.

"Foolish," my mother said to dad. "Is no nursing home, is no blind ladies. His mother eats, drinks like a horse."

"I don't understand."

My mother seized Rogovin's thumb and placed it near her breast. "Is clear now? The cantor is lust and lecher."

Rogovin bowed to me, kissed my hand like some kind of Continental, and ran to his hotel.

My father had been so diligent in producing fur-lined vests, his boss was sending him to Florida for a week. Most wartime vacations had to be canceled, because the Army and Navy were running munitions and men on the railroads. But dad had a special pass, signed by Secretary of the Navy Frank Knox. I didn't learn about Florida until a little later—Miami Beach was a furrier's paradise, where manufacturers and their prize workers would have a yearly fling with local prostitutes and dark ladies from Havana and New Orleans. And when I grew aware of the word *prostitute,* around the age of six or seven, I understood the arguments my mother had with Sergeant Sam about his sojourns at the Flagler Hotel. She would hurl a shoe at his head, empty the perfume bottles he'd brought back from Florida, set fire to the photographs he'd hidden in some secret pocket of his valise. He'd always return terrifically tanned, looking like Clark Gable with a guilty grin.

But Gable could have been a ghost in '42. My mother didn't even watch him pack. He left in a hurry, without his air-raid warden's hat, gave me five single-dollar bills to spend in his absence, a small fortune from one of the Navy's favorite sons. I was glad to see him go. I wouldn't have to groom my mother, make her presentable to dad, hide her sorrow from him, cook his goose, load him down with whisky so he wouldn't discover her long silences.

The day he was gone her suitor arrived. I don't know what else to call him. He advertised himself as my uncle, but he didn't have our famous cheekbones and Tatar eyes. He couldn't have belonged to that tribe of Mongolian Jews who terrorized the Caucasus until they were conquered by Tamerlane the Great. Chick Eisenstadt was a big ruddy fellow who'd once worked with my mother in a Manhattan dress shop. She'd been a seamstress before she got married. The whole shop had been in love with her, according to Chick, but he was the one who linked his own history with hers long after the dress shop disappeared. He'd floundered until the war. Chick was the only one of my "relatives" who'd ever been to Sing Sing. It was convenient to have a convict in the family. He could tell you stories of the biggest outlaws. And he knew my father's timetable. He would appear whenever Sergeant Sam wasn't around.

He took us for a ride in his Cadillac. Chick wasn't supposed to have a car. Gasoline had been rationed, and there was a ban on nonessential driving. But Chick was a black marketeer who gave generals and war administrators silk stockings for their wives. He had a card that authorized him to chauffeur "essential people," like doctors and tycoons from war plants. Cops would peek into the Cadillac, glance at my mother, smile, call me "Roosevelt's little pioneer."

We crossed into Manhattan with Chick, who took me to the ocean liners that lay tilted in the harbor, like sleeping beauties with smokestacks, and I was seized with an anxiety I'd never had before. An ocean liner was larger than my imagination. It was like the imprint of a world I couldn't fathom from the Bronx. The one bridge I had was Chick.

He never bribed me, never offered expensive gifts that would have made me despise my own dad. But he took us to the only White Russian restaurant on the Grand Concourse, Bitter Eagles, where his cronies would ogle us; he'd sweat in the middle of a meal, sitting with his secret family. Sing Sing had ruined his health. He had a chronic cough, and his hands still shook from the beatings his fellow prisoners had delivered to him. Chick was thirty-five, three years older than my mother, but his hair had gone white in Sing Sing, and he looked like a wartorn cavalier.

He stared at my mother, helpless before her plate of pirogi, and said, "Faigele, what's wrong?" My mother's name was Fannie, but her admirers and friends called her Faigele, which was supposed to mean little bird in my Tatar dictionary.

"Mogilev," my mother said. One word. And Chick could intuit the entire tale.

"Your brother, the schoolteacher. His letters are no longer coming. And you're worried to death."

"The Nazis are sitting in Mogilev," I said. "Chickie, I heard it on the radio."

Chick watched my mother's grief. "Radios can lie. It's called propaganda."

"The Germans are paying the radio to tell lies?"

"I didn't say Germans. It could be the White House. And the President doesn't have to pay. Don't you get it? The President talks about a defeat that never took place. Hitler relaxes and starts to get sloppy. And we turn the tables on him."

I wouldn't argue with Chick. A black marketeer ought to know. But I didn't believe that Roosevelt would ever lie about Mogilev.

"Faigele, if there's a letter, I'll find it."

We went to the post office after lunch. The postmaster stood in his slippers, eying my mother and her black marketeer, who eyed him back.

"Mister, could one of your own men have been tampering with the mail?"

"Impossible," the postmaster said as Chick stuffed his pockets with silk stockings.

"Come on, I'll help you look for the letter. It has to be here."

They searched the back room, inspected every pouch, but there were no letters from Mogilev. "I'm sorry, Mrs. Charyn," the postmaster said. "Russian mail has been trickling in, but not a scratch from Belorusse."

Faigele took to her bed. "My two bitter eagles," she mumbled, blinking at me and Chick. It was a complete collapse. Chick's own doctor came, examined her, said he couldn't cure heartbreak and withered emotions. He recommended a rest home in the Catskills where he sent all his worst cases.

"Doc," Chick said, "she's not a case. She's a glorious woman, Faigele. She's expecting a letter from Mogilev."

"You're the wizard. You can produce silk stockings. Why not one lousy letter? But what's it all about? Did she leave a boyfriend behind?"

"A brother," Chickie said.

The doctor rolled his eyes. "Isn't it unnatural to miss a brother so much?"

Chick grabbed him by the collar, and I didn't know it then, but it was a very brave act. This doctor was Meyer Lansky's personal physician. He'd poisoned people for the mob. He was the highest-paid internist in the Bronx.

I brought Chick and him a glass of my father's best schnapps. And then Chick explained to him the story of Faigele and Mordecai, who'd come from a family of small landowners in the Tatar town of Grodno, where Meyer Lansky was born. Mordecai was the oldest at ten, with a couple of kid sisters—Anna, five, and Faigele, two—when their mother died (their dad had run to America and made his own life). A ten-year-old boy couldn't hold on to the family fortune. He had to lease himself, become a little slave to protect his sisters. He was sold into the tzar's army at fifteen, escaped, "kidnapped" Anna and Faigele, hid out with them in the marshes, landed in Mogilev in the middle of the Russian Revolution without papers or a crust of bread. The boy was sixteen and he learned to steal. In a time of shadowlands, he became a shadow until he could reinvent himself as a schoolteacher. He had forged documents from a commissar of education who'd been killed. He had pupils in his first classes who were older than himself. He had to bribe an inspector from Minsk: it was like the tzar's government without a tzar, but the Cossacks had been told by some Soviet prince to love all the Tatar Jews. Mordecai saved his money and was able to send Anna out of Belorusse in 1923. But Faigele wouldn't go. He pleaded with her. The inspectors would catch him soon—an illiterate teacher. He couldn't breathe until his little sister was safe.

"But I am safe," she said, "here with you."

He'd start to cry, this gaunt man who was always on the verge of getting TB. She left for America in 1927. He promised to join her in six months but never did.

She became a Manhattan refugee, lived with her father and a stepmother who begrudged every bit of food she swallowed. She went to night school, worked in a dress shop, dreaming of Mordecai. She had to get out of her father's house. Enter Sam, the furrier who never lost a day's work during the Depression.

Faigele married him, but nothing could sustain her—not children, not God, not romance—nothing except those letters that would arrive religiously from Mogilev.

The doctor licked his schnapps. "Chickie, a glorious woman, righto, but where do you fit in? You're not the husband, you're not the brother, you're not the father of this little boy."

"None your stinking business," said Chick, already drunk. "I fill the empty spaces. I'm satisfied."

"If you want to revive her, friend, you'll just have to forge that letter . . . pretend you're with the tzar's police."

"I don't have to pretend. But how will I get Russian stamps?"

The doctor tapped my skull. "Baby, where's your mother's stash of mail?"

I steered them right to the little wooden chest my mother had brought from Belorusse; the letters were inside. Chick was mainly interested in the stamps and the quality of paper and Mordecai's penmanship, but the doctor began to read the letters in whatever Russian he still had at his command (he was born in Kiev).

"The man's a poet, Chick."

He recited from the letters, but Chick cut him off. "Keep it to yourself, doc."

"Are you insane? Poetry belongs to the world."

"But the letters belong to Faigele."

Every stamp had a different face. I saw the brown eagle of Belorusse; Tatar princes and kings; Stalin, the little father of his people, looking like a walrus. The doctor pulled a pair of scissors out of his medical bag. He wanted to cut off a few of the stamps; Chick told him to put the scissors back. He wouldn't mutilate my mother's property.

"I give up," the doctor said, while Chick and I went down to the stationery store, where I helped him pick out a blue envelope and a pad that could have passed for Russian paper. Then we

walked to Bitter Eagles, found a man who was willing to trade
Russian stamps in his family album for the promise of butter, eggs,
and Colombian coffee.

Chick went to work practicing Mordecai's pen strokes. Time
seemed to clot around him and the letter he was going to write.
The doctor abandoned wife, children, mistresses, all his other patients, including Meyer Lansky, to mastermind a letter from
Mogilev made in the Bronx. I brewed cups of black tea and fed
them coffee cake from Bitter Eagles.

It took Chick an hour to do "Dear Faigele" in Mordecai's Russian hand and get the first paragraph going. They had to tiptoe
around the war because Chick wouldn't load the letter with lurid
details. "I am only starving a little bit," he wrote in schoolteacher
Russian and signed Mordecai's name. He addressed the envelope,
I glued on the stamps, and we all fell asleep in the living room on
different chairs.

A knocking sound came right through my dreams. I got up,
stumbled to the door. The postmaster stood in his slippers with a
letter in his hand. He was very excited. "Gentlemen, it arrived,
right out of the blue." Chick offered him some of our fabulous
coffee cake, speckled with dark chocolate. "Delicious," he said.
No one thanked him for the letter, which had come in a crumpled white envelope, all the stamps missing. The postmaster left.
Chick tore up *our* letter and we went in to wake up my mother
and give her the other letter from Mogilev.

She danced out of bed like a mermaid with a nightgown on (I'd
never seen a mermaid, so I had to imagine one). She savored the
letter, but she wouldn't read it until she prepared our tea. The
doctor was startled by her metamorphosis. Faigele's coloring had
come back. She disappeared into the bedroom and closed the
door.

"The angels would be envious of such a creature," the doctor
said.

We waited like orphans until my mother came out. She

wouldn't share Mordecai's language with us. "Is still schoolteacher," she said, summarizing the plot. "But without school. Was bombed."

The doctor returned to his practice. Chickie had to go out of town. My father got back from Miami with his movie-star tan, but Faigele was the one who had all the flush. He put on his air-raid helmet and patrolled the streets. I imagined him in the blackout, looking for renegade cubes of light. Poor Sergeant Sam, who could never really capture the dark lady, or her radiance.

Bambi

It was after she heard from Mordecai that my mother began to notice me again. "Baby, you look so thin." She woke from her bout of amnesia and remembered that she hadn't shopped in a month. Baby had done all the marketing. I had to pay the butcher out of my mother's purse, use my fingers as an abacus, teach myself to bargain like a tycoon. I still couldn't spell or master long and short division. The war was turning me into an ignoramus, and the dark lady took my education into her own hands. If the Bronx couldn't supply a kindergarten, she would create one.

We taught each other how to spell. She'd been the princess of her class at night school, dreamt of becoming a scientist, like Madame Curie. She still had the dog-eared copy of *Bambi* her class had given her as a wedding present. We sought refuge in the book. That forest of talking animals and pesty little birds took us out of the Bronx, and bit by bit Faigele began to recall the prickly landscape of English she'd lost after night school.

We had to sight each word, sound it on our tongues, before it would give up any secret. Words would float along a line like ships caught in a white sea, and you had to lend yourself to them like a sea captain, or you'd never learn to read. We spent a week traveling across the first page, and we had our own compass (a dictionary I'd found in a garbage barrel), but the compass was a tricky one, almost as hard to read as *Bambi* itself until we grasped some of its signs. And then it steered us into the book, and we both began to cry, because it was a powerful elixir to read about a baby deer and his mom who could have been Faigele and me.

When Bambi's mom was killed by hunters who were known as "He," both of us had to stop reading for a month. We couldn't go on with the story, even with our compass. My father caught us moping. "Crazyheads," he called us. "Only crazyheads would believe what's written in a book."

Dad wasn't a reader. He couldn't understand how anyone could mourn people on a page. But Bambi and her mom were dearer to us than our own blood and bones. And when our mourning period was over, we went back to the book, digging cautiously at the words, since we were beginners and could only deal with a bit of heartbreak at a time. We went through the motions of keeping house for Sergeant Sam, but we belonged to Bambi. And it's cruel to say, but I didn't see any resemblance between my dad and Bambi's, the old Prince of the forest who was aloof to everyone, yet adored Bambi at a distance. With his helmet and his armband and his military bearing, Sam could have been one of the hunters who crushed the forest animals or trained them as pets. In my own mind, he was a man with a gun.

Mom and I were delirious when Bambi beat the heck out of a young buck and started going steady with Faline. Faigele would laugh and search my crown for bumps.

"Where are the antlers of Jerome?"

But I couldn't grow horns. I was a little boy who had to crawl with Faigele through his first book. Bambi exhausted us; we were irritable at the end. We didn't have the stamina to start another book, and our souls were still deep inside the forest. I'd watch

Faigele light a cigarette and scan the book, let it fly to whatever page it wanted, and chant to herself. "Bambi braced with his hind legs and hurled himself at Ronni [one of the bucks who was interested in Faline]."

"Mama," I said, "what is *braced?*"

"Metal . . . to help your mouth."

"But a deer couldn't go to the dentist, mama."

"Then is a mystery."

"Couldn't we ask Chick?"

My "uncle" had stopped calling on us. He knew that dad was back in harness as an air-raid warden. And Chick had never liked to sneak around in the bushes. If he couldn't come in his Cadillac, he wouldn't come at all. It was frustrating as hell to have a part-time uncle who was kind to you a couple of weeks a year: Chickie, who was like the old Prince of the forest, nice and proud, but with ration books instead of antlers.

Mom wouldn't have given in and gone to Chick, but she was curious about the word *braced*. She started fixing herself in the mirror, with every little tube that could color your face, and we went downstairs and walked to Bitter Eagles. It was an hour after the big White Russian lunch. Bitter Eagles had emptied out. A hurricane could have gripped the restaurant. There weren't any pirogi or pickled cabbage inside the steam table. The black chocolate coffee cake was gone. A hundred empty tea glasses sat in their silver holders near gutted pots of strawberry jam. Behind the silver holders, at a separate table, was Chick, staring at some void until my mother came in. It wasn't the same Chick who could write a letter from Mogilev. He had stubble on his chin. His white hair wasn't combed. It might not have been noticeable in another man. But Chick had his suits made at Feuerman & Marx (the most aristocratic uptown tailor), and he looked like a vagabond if even one of his shoes wasn't shined.

He danced out from behind the table in a Feuerman suit that had buttons with orange veins. The handkerchief in his coat was also orange. His cuff links had painted orange borders. "Faigele, is your sergeant somewhere at sea?"

"Is not about a sailor," she said, putting *Bambi* on the table. Chick shouted at the waiter until glasses of bloodred tea appeared with the last Russian coffee cake in the Bronx. Then he sat down again, turned to the book with its broken spine and faded image of Bambi on the cover with antlers like a crown of bony knives and forks.

"Helluva book. Read it to my daughters."

What daughters? Chick had never discussed any daughters in front of me. I took it like a slap. He must have had a wife when he first met Faigele, a wife and a daughter or two, and that's why mom had never married him.

She showed him *our* sentence from the book.

"Braced," he muttered. Chick had gone to law school and dropped out after a year. His biggest diploma, he liked to say, had come from Sing Sing.

"Chickie, doesn't the President have a leg brace?"

"Roosevelt has nothing to do with this . . . Bambi can brace himself, tighten the screws in his legs. But the difference between Roosevelt and a deer is night and day."

"Braces are braces," I said, and at least I got him to laugh. Chick was our local Robin Hood who gouged the rich and gave to the poor. He didn't exactly give. He charged the poor cut-rate prices, sold them tubs of butter at cost. But he'd interfered with another Robin Hood, Darcy Staples, a dentist who was attached to Ed Flynn, boss of the Bronx. Darcy was Flynn's lieutenant, an under-chief who ruled the Grand Concourse like his own kingdom, an Irish Protestant in a sea of Jews. He kept an office at the Darcy Arms, a mecca he'd built in his own name. The mecca had already collapsed once. It was made of steel wool and rusty wires and a kind of cheesecake cement. Rats ate the steel wool in the walls and bled out their entrails in Darcy's cellar. He was in the business of ration stamps and wartime contraband, like Chick. They were often partners. But Darcy had decided to punish Chick. Was it greed or jealousy or plain spite? A boy of five couldn't have read such rivalries. Darcy was holding an important shipment of ration books and squeezing Chick to death. He claimed the government was watching his office, and he couldn't move the stamps. Chickie would have to collect them himself.

"He'll murder me, Faigele. He's that kind of man."

"But he wouldn't dare to murder me."

"Why not?"

"He's my dentist."

Darcy was everybody's dentist. Patients would come from Westchester and Long Island to sit in Darcy's chair. That was his advantage. All his deals were made with the smell of ether and chloroform hanging over you. He could dope his enemies and get rid of them, or fill a friend with laughing gas. Darcy's office was the real hub of the Bronx. Boss Flynn would appear with his retinue. He was FDR's point man on the East Coast. He left Darcy to deal with mundane matters. Darcy's gang would break a couple of heads when they had to. Most of the men on his payroll were cops who did a little moonlighting for their dentist. He was my dentist too. And he'd give me special candy that didn't rot your teeth. He was a handsome man with silver hair. I didn't love Darcy the way I loved Chick, but I never had as much fun as the time I spent in Darcy's chair. Darcy caressed my mouth with a long metal toothpick, and its curled head would make a gentle noise against my teeth. He wouldn't fob me off on any of his assistants. I was little Charyn, who had the dark lady as his private kindergarten teacher.

We went to Darcy without an appointment, because otherwise we'd have had to wait for weeks. "Faigele," Chick had told us. "I'd like to blow up Darcy's cheesebox one of these days . . . don't spar with him. Be direct. Ask him for Chickie's merchandise." But it wasn't that simple. Darcy's cheesebox sat near the Bronx County Building. And there was a constant flow of traffic between the county court and Darcy's office. Every single judge who wanted to insure his future had to consult with the dentist. And so we sat with judges and police captains in Darcy's outer room, while his own lieutenants picked their teeth. We were eleventh or twelfth in line, but when Darcy popped his head out of his private office, he ignored the judges and motioned to us. I ran right in and jumped on the chair, which was older than Darcy and Boss Flynn and had to be lowered and raised with a little wheel.

"Ah, Mrs. C, it's a pleasure. Does the little one have a tooth-ache? . . . Baby, open your mouth."

"Is a different toothache," my mother said.

"Then sit down with Baby, and I'll administer to both of you."

"Doctor, is Chick who has the ache."

The dentist lost a bit of his gaiety. "He's a genius, then. Hires you as his camel."

"Yes," my mother said. "I am the camel."

It was a Bronx term, used by black marketeers. A camel carried contraband in one or two of his humps.

"I envy Chick. But it's a pleasure doing business with a camel like you."

"Is treasury agents in other office?"

"Wouldn't pollute my own practice, would I now? What would my patients think?"

"Tell me Chick's sin."

"He's working his own charities in my yard. Undercutting my prices. Selling wares only to unfortunate people who nurse their misfortune at my expense. They can go into business for them-selves, considering what Chickie charges. I'm the warden here, I'm the bishop. I set the ceiling and I set the floor on each article, not Chick. And you had better instruct him, dear Faigele."

"I will instruct," mom said, like a shrewd kindergarten teacher.

And Darcy gave her a shoebox filled with ration books that she didn't have to hide in any hump. This shoebox was the dentist's particular mark. There were hardly any briefcases in the Bronx.

Leather couldn't be found in 1942. It was on the list of rationed goods. And lawyers at the courthouse began to copy from that prince of the Grand Concourse. They carried their files in a shoebox secured with a rubber band. Rubber was also rationed, and the lawyers' rubber bands were as precious as milk and meat and gold.

We returned to Bitter Eagles with the shoebox. Chick went out of his mind. He danced on the tables and drank vodka in the afternoon. His white hair shone in the dark corners under the ceiling. "Ah, my little ones," he said from his perch, kissing the shoebox like a crazyman. "We'll rejoice together, or my name isn't Chick."

"What rejoice? I have to wash potatoes, prepare Sam's stew."

"Faigele, I insist."

"Insist," mom said, "but you don't have husband who eats like a horse."

"Darling, I'll ask the chef to fix him a meal."

"Don't darling so much."

"Ah, it was a slip of the tongue," Chick said, coming down off the tables and leading us to the door. He let me hold the shoebox while he wobbled in the street. Mom could never be ashamed of Chickie. She took him by the arm, steadied Chick, and we sailed across the Grand Concourse with the wind on our backs and stopped at a certain marquee.

We weren't dumb, Faigele and I. You could get an awful lot from the radio. *Bambi* had been turned into a picture, but how could we know it was Hollywood's biggest hit? When we caught that name on the marquee, we didn't even smile. It was as if the territory of our book had been invaded, had been pulled from our hands. We went inside with Chick.

And when we saw Bambi on the screen, both of us were alarmed, because we knew his mom's fate. The forest was thick and dark, a hiding place for hunters and their dogs. Bambi's mom disappeared from the picture, but we couldn't cry. We'd been mourning her from the first image.

Chick seemed to grasp our long silence. "Gorgeous," he said, "but it could never hold a candle to the book." And we walked home without him. The picture must have marked us, because it felt like we were up on the screen, waiting for the hunters to arrive. And they did. They attacked Chick, took his bundle of ration books, robbed him right outside Bitter Eagles, beat him up, four men wearing handkerchief masks tucked under their eyes. No one would talk about them, but they couldn't have fallen from the sky. Their swagger was perilously close to the policemen who moonlighted for the dentist. Darcy had taken Chick out of the black-marketing business. But he was still our prince, and he paid for Chickie's room at Cedars of Lebanon. That's how one Robin Hood behaved with another.

Faigele and I had to sneak into the hospital when Chickie's wife and daughters weren't around. Mom didn't like to play the hidden bombshell, but she was fond of Chick. And she wouldn't desert him when he was riding on some hospital bed, in a somber sea, with black marks under his eyes. His white hair had begun to yellow. He had bandages on his nose and mouth. Mom had cooked a coffee cake in her oven, with almonds and the dark chocolate that Chickie loved. He stuffed a morsel under his bandage. "Piquant," he said.

It was hard for Chickie to talk, but I had to ask him something. "What's *piquant?*"

"Tart and tasty," he said.

And we had to leave before his wife arrived. I was learning more and more about her. She was a holy terror named Marsha who'd gone to Hunter College and become an English teacher at William Howard Taft, the high school that belonged to the Grand Concourse. The whole school was afraid of her. Marsha had a big mouth. She could sing reprimands while she recited some great poet out of the past. I envied Marsha, mistress of the English language, and worried about meeting her. What would she do to mom and me with a tongue that was so powerful and piquant?

But we met a different monster outside Chickie's room. Darcy Staples, wearing a silk scarf and a coat with a fur collar, and carrying a bunch of cornflowers shaped like the devil's ears. He'd come with his usual band, a judge and three cops.

"Morning, Faigele . . . ah, you've already seen Chick. A terrible accident. Four lubbards taking advantage of a businessman. Out-of-town boys, they were. They'll be punished. I've spread the word."

Mom took out her handkerchief, folded it like a mask, and put it on in front of the dentist.

"Darcy, am I out-of-town boy?" she said, and steered me to the door. But we couldn't escape Bambi's forest. The hunters' hounds must have tracked us home. Sergeant Sam was lying in bed with a woeful look and a very fat bandage that covered his hand like a boxing glove; the bandage was tinged with blood. In a rush to meet some admiral's demand for fur-lined vests, dad had nearly cut off his thumb. He'd have to be replaced as foreman at his own shop while the thumb healed. The War Department couldn't wait for Sergeant Sam. Meanwhile he could collect workman's compensation, but it was a pittance compared to all the extras he usually got. Something else ate at Sam. He'd let down all the admirals with a stupid accident. He'd been sculpting fur collars much too fast, had sabotaged his own hand with a wickedly sharp knife.

He got out of bed after a week to put on his warden's hat. Dad made his rounds with that bloody boxing glove, which he had to wear in a sling while he clutched an enormous flashlight in his one free hand. He must have had a romantic air in the dark winter light, because people began to call him the Count of Monte Cristo. But dad wasn't feeling romantic. Phantoms had begun to invade his head. They told him he'd be fired, that he'd never be foreman again. Not even the Christmas bonus his boss had sent him could soothe Sergeant Sam. It was only a kiss-off, he said, a sign that they were getting rid of him. "Baby, I'm dying. Hold my hand."

I held his hand. "Dad, dad, it isn't true."

But he slipped into a morbidity that paralyzed him. I had to comb his hair, help him put on his metal hat, or he wouldn't have made his rounds as an air-raid warden. Where was Faigele? He'd fallen outside her affections. The dark lady couldn't seem to lend him the least bit of her heart. I accompanied Sam to his headquarters, a storefront on Sheridan Avenue that everybody called the Church. There was nothing churchlike about it. It had a long, dirty window shade that blocked out all the light. I felt like I was descending into the mouth of a cave. There were calendars of naked women on the wall, but I couldn't really catch much more than a general blondness and one or two brown nipples. The Church had a sofa without any cushions, a lamp that barely lit up its own outline, a couple of chairs, a gunmetal gray filing cabinet and desk. A woman tended the desk. She must have been some kind of dispatcher. She had short hair and chubby fingers and she smoked cigars like a man. Her name was Miriam, and she was very fat. She kept a map of our district over her desk; all the streets looked like little dark canals.

"Charyn," she said, with the glowing ashes of her cigar like a raw red wound in the cave's particular midnight. "I can fill in with another soldier. You don't have to trouble your bad hand."

"Baby will walk with me," dad said.

Two other wardens came into the Church, carrying big sacks on their shoulders. They saluted Sergeant Sam and emptied their sacks on the desk. I couldn't make out all the objects, but I could swear I saw a radio and some toasters. These men were camels with metal hats. They were taking advantage of the blackout to move merchandise around. And I wondered if they were also burglars. They could have climbed through a ground-floor window in the dark, pillaged a couple of living rooms on their rounds.

"A poor crop," the first one said to Miriam.

"Jackie, you shouldn't advertise yourself in front of the boy."

"Baby's all right," the second one said.

I went outside with Sam, propped the flashlight against my hip and pointed it at the roofs, while dad looked straight ahead. The Count of Monte Cristo.

He was just as melancholy in the morning. He wouldn't move. There was a long river of sadness that seemed to run right through his side of the family. A grandfather who ate the bitter ground at some backwoods asylum. Cousins who died of convulsions. I couldn't coax Sam out of bed. I had to go to Cedars of Lebanon with the dark lady.

Chick was in a panic. "The dentist cleaned out all my goods. I don't have a single tub of butter left . . . or a lousy silk stocking."

"So you'll be naked. But how did dentist know where to look?"

"Faigele," Chick said behind his mask of bandages. "The whole inventory was at Bitter Eagles. In a back room."

"Is black market? I will never eat again."

But we went to Darcy's cheesebox. The dentist took us right away. He didn't even ask me to sit in his chair.

"Shall we do some business, dear Faigele?"

"Is monkey business, Darcy dear. I would like you not to be such a dybbuk. Give back what belongs to the man in the hospital bed."

"I'll hound him into the grave . . . until you come and work for me."

"You need a dental assistant to dance without clothes?"

"I'm not that fond of cabaret," Darcy said. "I run a card game. It's strictly legal. I have judges, barbers, and the borough president at my Monday-afternoon games."

"And should I serve sandwiches?"

"I want you to deal the cards for me."

"I'm not a gambler."

"That's the whole point," Darcy said. "The men will trust you. A beautiful woman with a five-year-old tot."

"Is soon six."

"That's colossal. Bring Baby along. I don't want professionals. I want a woman who can look those men right in the eye, even if she deals them a pair of deuces all night."

"Is an afternoon game."

"I was only taking liberties with the language, dear Faigele, not with you. Your husband's sick. I can't cure him, but I can offer you a hundred dollars for each afternoon, and I will personally cart Chick's stuff back to that stinking restaurant of his."

"Is White Russian, best food in the world."

"Wouldn't demean the menu, would I? But will you work for me?"

"And you will make the whole Bronx not to bother Chick?"

"On my life."

"Then I will deal cards for you . . . but what is a pair of deuces?"

Darcy laughed. "Lord, I am in love with this woman." He dismissed his other patients, herded them out of the office, and we spent the afternoon playing poker in Darcy's private salon.

I wasn't with the dark lady at all her poker lessons. I had to take care of dad. She cooked for him, changed his bandages, fell asleep with him in the same bed, but her spirit seemed worlds away from Sergeant Sam. Mom had fattened her vocabulary at my expense. Darcy was teaching her all the language of a croupier. She could count and distribute chips, fling cards across a velvet tablecloth, and snap out a little song with every card she delivered. "Possible straight flush . . . pair of aces . . . full house."

Mom brought me along to the first poker game. She was wearing a blue dress. The gamblers couldn't keep their eyes off Faigele. "Jesus," said Fred R. Lions, our borough president. "Darcy, you broke my heart. You can't bring your own weapon to the game. It isn't fair. I'll never see my way to a royal flush with her around."

"Should I change the dealer, Mr. Lions?"

"I'll rip out your lungs. She'll deal for us until eternity."

"She's not a circus animal, Mr. Lions. She's Faigele, and you'll please address her as such."

"Faigele, Faigele," mumbled the president of the Bronx. "She's Joan Crawford, or else I'm a blind man."

"Crawford, Joan Crawford," the other gamblers said.

"She's Faigele. I wouldn't have Joan Crawford in this house. And the child is little Charyn, known as Baby to his friends."

But Fred R. Lions wasn't so wrong. Mom could have passed for Joan Crawford's younger twin. Both of them were dark ladies. One was born Lucille Le Sueur in San Antonio, Texas. The other was born Fannie Paley in Belorusse. One was the pony in a chorus line and a card dealer in Detroit before she grew into the dark lady of MGM. The other was an orphan who was practicing her English at the most aristocratic card game in the Bronx.

Darcy liked to say I was his sheriff who rode shotgun for Faigele. But mom didn't need a sheriff. I sat on a tall stool with its very own ladder that allowed me to climb up and down at will. I ate a lot of potato chips. I answered the telephone for Darcy. I opened each fresh deck of cards, tearing off the cellophane with my teeth, while mom smoked cigarette after cigarette, and held that game together with the force of her own dark eyes. She'd slap a hand when she had to.

"Don't peek at neighbor's cards, Judge John."

No one contested her, no one griped. The game was Faigele's. And soon people were fighting for a seat around the poker table. The gamblers always tipped her, always left my mother some largesse. I was elected to carry twists of five- and ten-dollar bills inside my shirt pocket. We were almost growing rich in that second winter of the war. Sergeant Sam could sit home with his damaged thumb. We didn't have to depend on workman's compensation.

My mother had become partners with Chick. He had no one else to move his merchandise. She would go from the card game to Bitter Eagles in the borough president's black limousine, and she'd have to tell all of Chickie's camels (housewives and retired furriers) what to deliver and where. The chef fixed a late-afternoon box lunch, which she brought to Cedars of Lebanon, with Baby at her side. I smuggled splits of champagne into the hospital in one of Darcy's shoeboxes.

He was almost healed, Faigele's black marketeer. The bandages had come off his nose and mouth. The bruises under his eyes were now a pale green. He had only one soft scar on his lip. We closed the door of Chickie's room and climbed onto the bed with him. I poured champagne. We had caviar that looked like the crimson seeds of a Chinese apple. Mom toasted blinis on the radiator. We had Russian coffee cake with the hospital's tepid tea. Faigele was tipsy, not from champagne, but from all the nervous energy, after having to control a roomful of gamblers. Her eyes began to flutter. She hugged Chick and me. She would have danced with us on the bed, done some crazy Bronx cancan, but the door opened, and a woman came in, near my mother's age, with a long nose and the unremarkable features of an old maid. She was clutching her own lunch basket and two girls with long noses and unremarkable eyes. I didn't need much imagination to guess who they were. Marsha Eisenstadt, the holy terror of William Howard Taft, with her daughters, Cordelia and Annabel Lee.

Chick was terrified, but I watched him gather his wits like any good businessman. "Marsha," he said, "come and meet my associate, Mrs. Paley Charyn."

"The Park Avenue Paleys?" Marsha asked.

"No. Sheridan Avenue and Belorusse."

"Ah, that Paley Charyn, the card dealer, with her own illiterate boy."

"It's wartime," my mother said, pulling all her grammar together. "The kindergartens are closed. Please don't insult my son."

Marsha looked at my mother and realized that she wasn't another Bronx bombshell her husband had picked up on one of his black-marketing trails. The dark lady had destabilized her. Marsha's engine had broken down. Faigele was outside the harm of her vocabulary.

She said, "Bastards and bums," which didn't sound much like an educated lady. And she left with her daughters, who hadn't even kissed their dad.

"Faigele," Chick said, "I swear, it's only a marriage of convenience."

Mom began to collect the debris of our meal. She dropped the empty splits into the shoebox, put the remains of the caviar inside Chick's night table. "And what other kind of marriages are there?"

"Marrying you," Chick said.

"And we would have lived in the forest with Bambi and all the black marketeers."

We walked out with the shoebox and never saw Chickie at the hospital again.

Ringworm

$\mathcal{I}$t was considered the Bronx disease. I'm not sure why. But every time you noticed a boy wearing a big hat in the thick of summer or spring, you could always tell what the hat meant. Ringworm. Blisters that would erupt on your scalp like the circular mouths of a volcano. But this volcano had nothing but skin inside and a crust that was shaped like Saturn's rings. And the rings themselves resembled horrible, lifeless pink worms. Polio might cripple you, but ringworm marked you as an outcast. You couldn't walk into school with such a big hat hiding a shaved head. You had to remain on furlough until the blisters healed.

I pitied the boys with ringworm, and kept away from them. I was storing up my future, waiting for September and the beginning of the school year, when I could waltz right into the first grade. Mom still loved books, but she couldn't keep up with our kindergarten classes while she was dealing cards and supervising Chick's camels. The load of my education fell upon dad, who couldn't really read or write. And I taught dad how to read while he was teaching me. That was the planet of the Paley

Charyns, which always moved in reverse from every other planet.

Dad would bathe his thumb in a solution of Epsom salts, and he didn't have to wear that boxing glove, but he seemed terrified to return to his shop. What ghosts could there have been waiting downtown at the fur market? Mom offered to take him there, but dad declined. "Go to your camels," he said. "Baby will bring me."

And that's how I had my first subway ride. A few days before I was six. Dad and I were both dressed in brown. We looked like a couple of soldiers. I loved being under the ground. The lights in the subway car would start to blink, and I made a wish: I wanted to move into the tunnels, live there, among the rats, without mother or father, or a room of my own, neither a Paley nor a Charyn, just a rat boy with no connections. But it didn't happen.

We got out of the subway at Pennsylvania Station, and I couldn't get used to the raw daylight. It ripped at my eyes. I walked like a blind man. But I couldn't desert my dad. We crossed a big street and rode up an elevator, stepped out in front of a metal door with a sign in the middle. I could gobble each letter— R-O-Y-A-L F-U-R C-O-R-P-O-R-A-T-I-O-N—because I already knew the name of dad's shop. I jumped into the air, hit the buzzer, and went through the door with dad. My whole head began to ring. I'd never seen such a racket coming out of one place. The factory floor rocked under my feet. Men and women were sitting around an enormous table, shouting, cursing, sneezing, mimicking each other, while they tore at bolts of cloth with knives and shears, and flung these mutilated articles at other men and women, who caught them in midair and thrust them under the driving needles of several sewing machines. But the fury stopped the moment all these men and women saw Sam. They abandoned their tools and got up from the table to shake my father's hand and stare at me.

"The little man of the house," dad said. "Baby. I have to watch him since they closed the kindergartens."

"Who closed the kindergartens?"

"The bosses of the Bronx," dad said. "They're saving money, putting it into their own pockets."

"But we can teach him a trade. The union will have to let in a boy who lost his kindergarten."

A big fat lady sat me in her lap, and I lived between her heart and her sewing machine. I couldn't operate the treadle. My legs were too small. But I could clutch a piece of cloth in my fists, guide it under the fangs of the machine, and watch it grow into half a vest. I never saw one finished article at dad's factory, or the skin of a single silver fox. Fur must have been as hard to find as shoe leather. But how could the factory make fur-lined vests? I asked the fat lady.

"It's a military secret," she said.

The boss had gone to Washington to meet with Navy bigwigs at the War Department, but dad didn't need instructions from him. He put on a blue apron and profited from his visit to the factory. Winking at the women, encouraging the men, he danced around the table and ruled each sewing machine at the Royal fur shop. Without his melancholia, dad was Clark Gable again.

And I stayed home while dad went to work. I inherited his morbidity. Mom had her new vocation, dad had his shop and his duties as a warden, and I had nothing but a dog-eared book. I couldn't feed forever on deer in the forest. I had to make my own life, but I didn't even have a school to go to.

I began to pester mom. I caught her in the middle of preparing her eyes and mouth for the poker game.

"Mom, don't you have to register me for the first grade?"

"I registered you for kindergarten, and look what happened."

"But how will I get to school?"

"I'll bring you in July and ask to see the principal."

"Faigele, the schools are closed in July."

"Then we'll find another solution," mom said, and we ran down to the dentist to meet our fate with a deck of cards. The dark lady had become much more than a dealer. She would accompany

Fred. R. Lions to the Concourse Plaza after the game. Sometimes Darcy was there, sometimes he wasn't. But the Concourse Plaza was where Mr. Lions held court. He didn't have Darcy's silver look. He was a sloppy little guy with a homburg and a rumpled black suit. He kept mothballs in his pockets. He wasn't a black marketeer like the dentist, and he couldn't have gotten elected without Boss Flynn, but he was the Bronx's very own bagman. He collected whatever money was owed to the borough chiefs, calling on Darcy's muscle when he had to, and dispensing small favors from his crimson chair, like some kind of cut-rate pope. And the dark lady lent a touch of glamour to Mr. Lions.

Darcy had hired mom to sit with our borough president and keep him sober. Mom had to memorize his accounts, because a bagman couldn't afford to practice his penmanship and leave a paper trail. She softened his truculence, prevented him from doing damage to Darcy's machine.

America had two wartime capitals: the Bronx and Washington, D.C. FDR ruled the country from his wheelchair at the White House, but it was Boss Flynn who kept him there, who brought out the voters, and held the other bosses in line. "Manhattan?" Lions loved to growl, like Boss Flynn's private little parrot. "Ain't that where the Republicans live?"

Manhattan had a Republican mayor, LaGuardia, but Flynn had banished him from the Bronx. He boycotted City Hall, treated the Bronx like his own enclave. He didn't require any largesse from Fiorello LaGuardia. He had FDR on his side, and he had his own army. Policemen, firemen, and garbagemen in the Bronx were loyal to Flynn. How many people would dare oppose a man who had his own bed at the White House, who played poker with FDR? Even LaGuardia listened to Flynn, and stayed out of the Bronx . . . leaving it to Mr. Lions.

He was a bachelor with his own suite at the Concourse Plaza. His neighbors were the New York Yankees, who lived at the hotel during the baseball season (Yankee Stadium was right down the

Mordecai, 1937.

The Dark Lady (left) and three companions, Belorusse, circa 1926.

Faigele between two friends, Coney Island, circa 1929.

The Paley sisters, Anna (left) and Faigele (right), 1930.

Faigele and Harvey, 1935.

Harvey in his Sea Scout uniform, 1944.

Baby, just before this story begins.

Faigele and Sam, 1933.

hill). Everybody searched for Joe DiMaggio, but Joe had gone off to the war, and we had to be satisfied with Charlie "King Kong" Keller, the only slugger the Yanks had left. Keller had become the main attraction at the Concourse Plaza. Guests would hover close to him, shout "King Kong," and beg for his autograph. And that's the real reason Darcy had to hire mom—not to baby-sit for a borough president, but to counter "King Kong."

The dark lady began to attend more and more functions in the Bronx with Darcy and Mr. Lions. She couldn't take me along to a banquet or a midnight supper honoring Boss Flynn. Dad would often have dinner at the fur market, and like a forest animal, I learned how to fend for myself. I had to stand on a kitchen ladder if I wanted to cook some chocolate pudding. And because I'd been so busy with mom, and had to suffer without a kindergarten, I didn't make any friends. I felt like a frozen child who could only come to life once school began. I bought myself a pencil case, a fat box of crayons, a jar of white paste. I watched the calendar like a hawk. I couldn't afford to let time jump backward and play a trick on me.

But there were more than calendar tricks. One night, when dad wasn't working overtime, and the dark lady wasn't at some bazaar with Mr. Lions, and we were all at the dinner table, dad drank too much whisky and picked a fight with mom. It could have been about Mr. Lions and Darcy and mom's camels, or dad's girlfriends in Miami and at his shop.

"That dentist," dad said, "and his band of thieves." Dad was a member of the Liberal Party, which broke with the Democrats to help elect LaGuardia.

"Fiorello can't show his face in the Bronx."

"Why should he?" dad said. "You have nothing to see but black marketeers."

In their fury they began to hurl dishes at each other. But their fight wasn't about Fiorello, the Little Flower. Mom and dad had traveled outside each other's orbit, and they couldn't find their way back.

It was dad who tossed the last dish. He must have sensed the futility, because he smiled like Clark Gable, looked at the fallout in my hair, blue and white shrapnel from the broken dishes, and offered to take us to the movies. We left the shrapnel on our shoulders and traveled around the corner to watch a war movie, *The Immortal Sergeant,* at the Luxor. It was about British commandos in desert country. I remember the grease on their faces, the netting that covered their helmets, and fortunes of sand.

And I remember our own immortal sergeant grabbing my arm after the movies and asking, "Baby, who do you love more, mom or me?"

We were like bitter commandos standing in the street, without a desert to hide in. I'd been around Darcy and Mr. Lions long enough. I knew about politics. All I had to say was, *Dad, I love you both.* But I couldn't. I was frightened of losing the dark lady.

Dad asked me again. "Who do you love more?"

"Mom," I said. "Faigele."

I dreamt of the desert, without commandos or camels, just hills that looked like the Bronx. And I was one lone boy in a warden's hat, condemned to climbing those hills, with crayons in my pocket and a little pot of glue that leaked out of my pants, like the sticky elements of my own future.

Dad never talked about that conversation outside the Luxor, but I knew he'd bear a grudge against me for life. I'd landed on the far side of his affections, become a stranger in his house. The son of an air-raid warden, I stopped accompanying dad on his rounds, couldn't even carry his flashlight, search the roofs for saboteurs, like Nazi dwarfs who dropped from the sky after sailing across the Atlantic in tiny balloons.

I held close to *Bambi's* printed lines, lived in the white spaces between every word, sweated like a tailor to build my own vocabulary. I had to be prepared for the first grade. I still sat on a stool while the dark lady dealt aces and kings, I still followed her to the Concourse Plaza, but I kept imagining what it would be like to sit in a classroom with children my own age, who wouldn't keep blabbering about royal flushes and black-market butter.

I got through June and July, and then, around the second week of August, my scalp started to itch. Mom caught me scratching, said I had the hives. "It's a weakness the Paleys have. When we're nervous about something, we break out in a rash."

"I'm not nervous, mom."

"Yes you are. You're frightened of the first grade."

The itching got worse. I tore at my own head. Soon my scalp was bleeding. Mom would slap my hands. "Baby, don't you dare." But it didn't matter what I did. My hair started to fall out. Six years old, and I already had a bald spot. Mom dragged me to the doctor. It was the same jovial man who had helped Chick write that letter from Mogilev. Meyer Lansky's personal physician. His name was Katz. He looked at my scalp with a fluorescent lamp that he carried like a torch. I cried when he put on a pair of white gloves and shaved my head. I could see my own round, red sores in the mirror. It was the Bronx plague.

"Ringworm doesn't run in the family," mom said. "The boy is clean. I scrub him with my hands twice a week."

"Faigele, it's a fungus. Could happen to any kid."

"In orphanages, yes. And playgrounds. In summer camps. But the boy doesn't know how to play. He's a bookworm."

"Mom, I'm the only bookworm who can't read."

The doctor bathed my scalp in a black lotion that stank of tar. Then he wrapped my head in gauze and lent me a baseball cap to wear. But the cap couldn't hide my baldness, nothing could.

The news spread like a crazy fire. Our neighbors tried to be nice, but they wouldn't let their own children near me. Other kids hurled water bombs from windows and roofs, shouting "Ringworm, Ringworm." The bombs were made of cardboard, and when they exploded, the noise nearly broke your eardrums. But my biggest trouble came from the Bronx Seabees, a gang of eight- and nine-year-olds who worshiped the Navy and wanted to build battleships and pontoon harbors and bridges. Meanwhile they took it upon themselves to build a harbor out of my hide. They would steal my hats, oblige me to run through a gauntlet of broomsticks and Seabee "bats," which consisted of rolled-up newspaper, tightened with bands of wire. They would whack my shoulders, legs, and bottom, while I covered my baldness and endured the wire's bite.

Their leaders were the Rathcart twins, Newton and Val, redheads with a mean streak and a fabulous IQ. They lived at the Albatross, a housing development for rich people. The Albatross had a central garden and a gate with gold spears. Newton and Val's mom was a world-famous artist, Rosemund Rathcart, who had her own comic strip in the *Daily Mirror.* It was called "Rat Man," and it was about a dishonorably discharged marine, Private Launcelot Perry, who's down and out in Shark Bay, a town that had all the earmarks of the Bronx—a boulevard like the Grand Concourse, a borough hall, a ballpark, a botanical garden. Launcelot Perry sold hot dogs at the ballpark, and lived among the rats, behind a garbage barrel. His fiancée was a nurse, Emma Martins, who tried to redeem the rat man, bring him back to civilization. Launcelot Perry didn't want to get civilized. But that didn't make him any less of a patriot. After the war started, Launcelot began to collect Germans and Japs who were coming in off the bay and skulking around in the tunnels under the ballpark. The Army and the Navy kept offering him a big reward, but the rat man wouldn't grab their money, or go back into the Marines as a lance corporal. He was happy selling hot dogs.

I couldn't read most of the balloons that went with the comic strip, but I saw enough to realize that no one would ever move me as much as the rat man, Launcelot Perry. I was hooked on him for life. He was outside the trap of politics and wealth. The rat man had no aspirations. He wouldn't have been chasing spies if there had been no war.

The rat man's mama, Rosemund, had agreed to conduct art classes at Adath Israel, that temple on the Grand Concourse. She was helping out the assistant rabbi, Len, who'd let me into his class. I had the corner chair, because nobody else would sit next to me. Half the Seabees had enrolled in the class, including the Rathcart twins, but they couldn't lay a finger on me. Whoever said "Ringworm" was kicked out of class.

Rosemund Rathcart was blonder than Betty Grable, taller and leggier than Rosalind Russell. Even with her eyeglasses, she was almost as beautiful as the dark lady. And when she sketched Launcelot Perry on the blackboard, with pieces of colored chalk—his eyes blue as the Hudson, his cheeks with black hollows, his mouth a little pink—I started to fall in love.

"Class," she said, "chalk is only an instrument, like a rapier or a gun." (I was too ashamed of my ignorance to ask what a rapier was.) "It follows instructions, listens to the mind's eye. The very best artists often draw with their eyes closed."

The class had crayons instead of chalk, and sheets of butcher paper Len had to buy on the black market, and we all attacked the paper with our mind's eye. Mrs. Rathcart asked us to invent a girlfriend for the rat man, a rival to Emma Martins.

I closed my eyes and drew a blond bombshell with glasses and long legs. Mrs. Rathcart studied my drawing and the hat on my head, and whispered to Len. He approached me after class. "I'll have to drop you, Baby. Mrs. Rathcart won't teach with you around. She says you're contagious."

"Not with my hat on, Len, not with the bandages. The doctor pours tar on my head."

"I'm sorry. It's her class."

I let my misery sink in for a week and then I told mom.

"She's not a dictator," mom said. "You have crayons. Go back to your class."

"Can't, mom. The artist lady won't allow it."

"I'll change her mind."

"Mom, her drawings are in the *Mirror*. She's a big star."

"Baby, I can burn the biggest stars."

I couldn't imagine Faigele as a firebug, but I went back to class with all my crayons. The blond lady was furious. She screamed at Len, called him a coward who couldn't expel one little boy. She stationed me near the window. I couldn't use Len's butcher paper. I had to watch the other kids draw.

Then I heard a knock, and Darcy came wandering into the class with Mr. Lions and a pair of bodyguards clutching fedoras against their hearts. Mom was with them, wearing the lipstick and mascara of a croupier.

It wasn't our borough president who broke the ice. It was Darcy Staples.

"Is it constitutional, Mr. Lions? An art teacher who's also a man of the cloth, discriminating against his own pupils."

"It's undemocratic, to say the least."

"And what if we wrote him a summons? A temple with leaky waterpipes . . . conducting private seminars."

"I have a permit," Len muttered. "A signed document from the mayor's office and the Board of Ed."

"The mayor's office? We don't accept Manhattan mandates. What you need, Lenny boy, is a Bronx seal."

"This is preposterous," said Mrs. Rathcart. "I won't be intimidated. You're gangsters, every single one of you . . . with your own gun moll."

"Gun moll, ma'am?" Darcy said. "This is Mrs. Faigele Charyn, mother of the slandered boy."

Mom smiled like a gorgeous jackal. "The gun moll will burn out your eyes in a minute." And mom lit a match. "Baby, count to three."

But I wouldn't count. Even if Rosemund could draw Launcelot Perry in her mind's eye, I couldn't take the chance.

"I'm a personal friend of the mayor," Rosemund said. "I know the attorney general of the United States."

"Tut," said the dentist. "You'll still need a Bronx seal."

"The boy has ringworm. He shouldn't be here."

"He's not dancing with the other children," mom said. "He's not kissing them, he's not rubbing heads. Do his crayons carry a disease? My son admires you and your pictures. We all admire you. Darcy, have you ever missed an installment of 'Rat Man'?"

"I couldn't live without Launcelot."

"Miles ahead of Dick Tracy and Donald Duck," said our borough president.

I'm not sure if it was flattery or mom's fiery eyes that moved Mrs. Rathcart and rescued me. But I rejoined the class, scribbled on butcher paper. And we celebrated our victory, drank champagne at the Concourse Plaza. Darcy, Mr. Lions, mom, and me. The waiter wasn't supposed to serve alcoholic beverages to a six-year-old. But the Concourse Plaza was Darcy's own canteen, and he insisted that I take a drink.

"To Faigele," Darcy said, "and our gentleman artist, who will grow up to be another Rembrandt."

"To say the least," said Mr. Lions, smashing the champagne glass in his fist.

It was meant to be a sign of luck. But I had no luck in '43. Mrs. Rathcart retired from teaching, and Len discontinued his art class rather than search for a Bronx seal. And I returned to the land of zero. With water bombs as my companion.

The Seabees kept stealing my hats; Newt and Val would taunt me all the time. "Ringworm, you killed our art class. Your mom's a gun moll and a tart."

"What's a tart?"

"A greedy piece of cake," said Newt.

"She does poke in the box with all the politicians," said Val.

"What's *poke in the box?*"

They knocked me on the head with their Seabee bats, and nobody stopped them. They were collecting tin cans for Mr. Roosevelt. They'd been to the White House with their mom. They'd had tea with Mrs. Roosevelt, who loved "Rat Man" and kept a picture of Launcelot and Emma Martins in her bureau. And Mrs.

Rathcart's own tailor had cut a miniature Navy cape for the twins, a replica of the one that Roosevelt wore whenever he was on a battleship.

"Good night, Ringworm," Val said, while Newt banged my shoulders. "Sweet dreams."

It was the middle of the afternoon, and I was hatless again. A man sidled up to me, clutching a hatbox. He looked like a very elegant tramp. His suit could have come out of Darcy's closet, but the cuffs were frayed, and the pants hadn't been near an ironing board. His shoes were splattered with white paint; he had bits of stubble around his chin. His face was cut with shadows, like Launcelot Perry. The rat man had such a pull on me, I said, "Launcelot, is that you?"

The rat man laughed. Then I saw the white hair under his fedora, and I recognized my mother's erstwhile partner, Chick Eisenstadt, the black marketeer who'd been boarding at Cedars of Lebanon for months. But the hospital had diminished him. He'd lost his flair.

"Baby," he said.

"My name is Ringworm now."

He opened the hatbox, which was stuffed with baseball caps, black market merchandise. He'd gotten a whole shipment of caps, but they were all from the St. Louis Browns, a team that had never been in the World Series. No Bronx kid would ever wear a Brownie cap. The Brownies lived in hell. The Yanks had to toss away their own tickets when St. Louis was in town.

"Chick," I said, "I couldn't wear a Brownie hat. The cops will arrest me."

"They won't," Chickie said. "I bought this supply for you. The little bastards can steal your caps night and day, and you'll always have another one."

"But who told you I had the ringworm?"

"Dr. Katz. And I knew you'd have trouble keeping a hat on your head. So I looked for a gross of whatever I could get."

Chick took off his own fedora and put on a Brownie cap. And I didn't have the heart to leave him alone like that, the only guy on the Concourse in a Brownie cap. So I dug into the hatbox and sported the colors and the rigid bill of the St. Louis Browns.

We were like two orphans together, Chick and me. People must have thought we'd escaped from a lunatic asylum in our billed caps. Chick no longer had much of a station at Bitter Eagles. Mom met all of Chickie's old camels at the dentist's office. She couldn't seem to forgive him for letting his wife break in on us at Cedars of Lebanon. It wasn't Chick's fault that Marsha Eisenstadt called me a dope. But the dark lady was a bit like dad. She just didn't have a forgiving nature.

Chick had become his own camel. He carried what he had to carry—in a hatbox or under his shirt. And he doubled as a house painter to make ends meet. He had expensive children, an expensive wife. He painted apartments along the Concourse, working in a Brownie cap and suits that had begun to rot on his back.

Sometimes Chick would take me along on one of his jobs. We would eat sandwiches under the stepladder, listen to the radio, gulp Russian tea out of a huge, insulated bottle. Chick liked to paint with a very fat brush. He would reach across the ladder and cover the length of a wall with a creamy white that left big spots on my cap. He'd let me paint in the corner with a tiny brush that could do little harm. Then he'd laugh and touch up my strokes. He worked very fast. And soon both of us were covered with the same white spots.

He was like a mom and a dad to me, and I wondered what would have happened if Chick had married the dark lady rather than the holy terror of William Howard Taft. Would he have taken his own son on stepladder picnics inside a world of benzene and plaster dust? It was a dangerous business to start reinventing one of your own parents and give yourself a whole new set of ancestors. A tribe of Paley Charyns was bad enough.

Chickie was my big secret. I couldn't tell mom that I'd started a new kind of painting class. But no matter how hard Chick rubbed our clothes with turpentine, we were still two spotted people. And mom began to notice my spots.

"Baby," she said, "are you turning into a leopard or a giraffe?"

"Both," I said, because I didn't know what to say. "Mom, the clouds are getting so fat, it's raining milk in the Bronx."

The next time I went painting with Chick, I started to climb the ladder with him, so we could work in tandem, make the whole planet a creamy white. I discovered a guest under our ladder. The dark lady in her card dealer's clothes. She saw the paint in our eyes. "My two bitter eagles," she said, "who like to fly near the ceiling."

We came down off the ladder. Chick with his brush, me with mine. Mom began to scold him. "Mr. Eisenstadt, didn't you ever hear of the child labor laws?"

Mom's ex-partner was mortified. "Faigele, did I lose my name in the street? I'm Chick."

"The Chick I remember wouldn't take advantage of a boy with ringworm."

"Mom, he didn't," I said. "Chick got me ten dozen baseball caps so I wouldn't have to go around bald."

"Better bald," mom said, "than dust in your lungs to catch tuberculosis. A boy needs fresh air."

"Faigele, the fresh air was costing him."

"Fresh air is free."

"Not when other boys hit him and steal his hats."

"I'm no sissy," mom said. "I'll fight those boys."

"Half the Bronx?"

"Then I'll hire the other half to fight the half that steals his hats."

And mom stole me away from Uncle Chick, dragged me out of there with my spotted cap.

Desert Boy

$\mathcal{I}$ had a whole colony of hats, a leaning tower devoted to the St. Louis Browns. And I was the little mad hatter who marched in the streets. But I missed that other dad of mine, Uncle Chick. I'd fallen in love with the smell of turpentine and with the white spots on my shoes. I'd had a job, after all, as Chick's apprentice, and I didn't dream of school while I mounted the ladder or ate sandwiches with Chick. I would have been happy to be a house painter, as long as Chick was beside me, listening to the radio. But I didn't have Chick, and I turned melancholic when the school year started without me. I had my crayons and my bottle of glue, but I couldn't venture into P.S. 88, a converted firehouse at the top of the hill, a hundred years old, with dark red walls. I had to watch while every single kid near the Concourse converged on *my* school with their pencil cases.

My heart was like a bitter ball. I had so much malice inside me, I could have burnt the school down if someone had put a match in my hand. But I should have been glad. No one shouted "Ringworm" or stole my hat during school hours, when the Seabees were tucked inside that ancient firehouse, and I was free to roam wherever I wanted. I would visit the soldier who was stationed in Claremont Park. He had nothing to do but sit in the tiny saddle of an antiaircraft gun that was pointed at the blue skies of the Bronx. I'm not even sure this ack-ack gun had any shells. But the soldier sat. He would lower and raise the saddle with the same little lever that Darcy had on his dentist's chair. And he wore a white helmet, like my dad. We were both outcasts, him with his crazy cannon, me with my poisoned scalp, and I had a touch of affection for such a soldier with his unfriendly, crooked face and a cigarette hanging from his chapped lips. He flirted with the housewives who trundled their baby carriages past his little domain, but none of them cared about a simple soldier with an ack-ack gun. He was always alone.

He would ride up and down on his saddle, rotate the gun, pretend he was knocking a German bomber out of the sky, but there was nothing to shoot at, not even a sparrow, a pigeon, or a kite. He was a prisoner of the people, condemned to take part in a ludicrous vigil.

The Seabees loathed him, because he wasn't with the Navy. They would arrive after school, hurl stones at him, taunt him from some distant rock, and if I waited around too long, they would come after me, grab my hat, rub my face in the grass.

The soldier never climbed down from his saddle to rescue me. He had to protect the skies. But once, in early October, while the Rathcart twins and five other Seabees had trapped me in Claremont Park and were punching me with their usual vigor, a powerful wind seemed to sweep off the rocks and slap them into the ground right in the middle of their war chant. "Ringworm, Ringworm." That wind had brown eyes and my mother's swarthy look.

All seven Seabees began to blubber and shout. "We didn't mean it, Harve. We won't touch Ringworm again."

"What's Ringworm's regular name?"

"Baby, Baby Charyn," sang Val and Newt, and they ran out of the park with their miserable pack of Seabees. I was left with my brother Harvey, nine years old, who suffered from asthma. He didn't get along with mom. She'd sentenced him to a school for asthmatics in the desert, at Tucson, Arizona. But the dark lady wasn't being cruel. Harve couldn't breathe the Bronx's wet air. The desert had saved his life.

His skin was much darker than mine, and he was as lanky as a snake. I hadn't seen Harve in twelve or thirteen months. He'd gotten rid of the Rathcarts, but he wouldn't hug me or say hello. He scooped me out of the grass and began to kick me across Claremont Park. They weren't his hardest kicks, but they still hurt.

"You've been ganging up against dad, you and mom."

"Harve, I swear, I took dad to his shop. He doesn't need me anymore. You can ask him yourself."

"I don't have to ask. Mom is never home. Dad has to suck dry beans at the fur market."

"Mom can't help it. She's a politician now. She's gonna keep Roosevelt in the White House."

"Don't lie. She's a card dealer. And she runs a branch of the black market."

"It's only a little branch," I said, and Harve kicked me right into the water fountain. I figured it was safer to keep quiet. I took off the baseball hat. Harve always hated the Browns.

"Dunce," he said. "Put your hat on. Nobody has to look at your ringworm."

"But ringworm isn't as rotten as the St. Louis Browns."

He kicked me where my tail began. I had to walk bent over, like an old guy.

"I've been to St. Louis, and it ain't so bad."

"Did you see the Brownies play?"

"It was winter. The Brownies were asleep."

"Then what's so hot about St. Louis?"

"It's America," he said, and I was trying hard to believe him.

"What about us? We have the Concourse and Charlie Keller and more lions than any other zoo."

"That's right," Harve said. "The Bronx is one big lion cage."

"But lions are American too."

Harve was so disgusted, he stopped kicking me. And we walked home, my brother like a Bronx god with Arizona on his face. Dad was upstairs. Harve must have called him at his shop. He danced and started to cry when he saw my brother. "I missed you, Harvey, missed you very much." but he'd never talked about Harve, never mentioned him all the time Harvey was away. Was it the dark lady's doing? Did mom have some power over dad? And what about little Ringworm? I was the one who picked up Harvey's postcards from the mailbox, delivered them to mom and dad, but none of us could read his handwriting. And I can't recall mom ever showing the cards to Chick. They were Harvey's personal hieroglyphics. Mom took the cards, kept them in the same wooden chest with all her letters from Mogilev. Once or twice I caught her looking at the cards late at night, trying to decipher Harvey's scrawl. But the moment she saw me, mom threw them back inside the chest. Harvey's language was between him and her.

Dad took Harve and me to have an early dinner at Bitter Eagles. We sat near all the Tatar gangsters, who had Harve's Mongolian eyes. The gangsters gave us vodka to drink. They must have felt a certain kinship with my brother that went beyond the shape and color of his eyes.

"Sonny," they said. "We haven't seen you. Where are you from?"

"I live in Arizona," Harve said.

"Do you happen to know Blackie Shamberg? He moved to Phoenix five years ago."

"I'm from Tucson."

"That's a shame," the gangsters said. "Blackie would have enjoyed you. You're his type."

These Tatars wouldn't let us pay for our meal. They offered

each of us a dessert and drank Mongolian tea at our table. They all wore gold bracelets and pinkie rings and chains around their necks. They dressed like parakeets, in yellow green and powder blue.

Harvey told them his name.

"Ah, Faigele's kid . . . It's curious. You have a head of hair, and Faigele's kid is supposed to be bald."

"That's my brother, Baby Jerome."

"Him with the funny cap? Then Faigele has a whole team of boys. But tell her to be careful. Her dentist is about to take a fall."

"What dentist?" Harvey had to ask.

"There's only one. Darcy Staples. And the governor has singled him out. Tom Dewey is declaring war on the Bronx."

Dewey wanted to run against Roosevelt in 1944. He was the Republicans' own dark horse. Dewey beat up all the downtown gangsters when he was Manhattan's district attorney, sent them to jail. And now he was attacking Roosevelt's people in the Bronx. Boss Flynn liked to call him that lousy kid with the mustache. Dewey wasn't really a kid. He was forty-one, but he'd still be the youngest President we ever had, if he could knock FDR out of the White House.

It was dad's misfortune to have the same kind of mustache as Tom Dewey. The gangsters grew suspicious.

"Is he a friend of yours?" they asked Harve.

"That's my dad, Sergeant Sam."

"Ah, the air-raid warden." They shook dad's hand. "Congratulations. You have a terrific tribe."

The gangsters insisted on driving us home in their personal taxicab. We arrived around midnight, a few minutes before Mom. Her hair was swept back like a movie star. Her lips were a gorgeous red gash. She was coming from a soiree at the Concourse Plaza. She wore her silver fox, a scarlet dress, and purple shoes. She wobbled into the apartment with champagne fever in her eyes. But the fever disappeared when she saw Harve. "The desert boy," she muttered. "Couldn't you warn us when you were coming home?"

And that lanky snake lost his swagger. "I did, mom. In my last postcard."

"Who can read your cards?" she said. "Who can read your cards?"

The dark lady took my brother in her arms, held him against the silver fox for a long time.

"Mom," I said, "Darcy's in a whole lot of trouble."

"Who told you that?"

"A coupla crooks at Bitter Eagles."

"You went to *my* restaurant without me?"

"Mom," I said, "we had to eat."

"And what did the bandits have to say?"

"That Dewey's gonna bring down the Bronx."

That red wound opened wide, and the dark lady let out a laugh. "Dewey can't touch us. The dentist will eat him alive . . . Harvey, do I have to search for your postcards? Why are you here?"

"The Sea Scouts are having a parade. I didn't want to miss it."

"You ran all the way from Arizona for one little parade?"

"I had to, mom. I couldn't desert my crew."

Harve was one of the first Sea Scouts in the Bronx. The Scouts were junior cadets that the Navy began to organize and encourage in case the war didn't end and the country ran out of sailors. Boss Flynn and FDR had blessed the Bronx's own fleet of Scouts.

"And how will you get back to Arizona?"

"I'll hitch," Harve said.

"No one in my family will start thumbing rides. Sam, talk to him. Insist."

"Mom, it never fails. I wear my uniform. I look just like a sailor. Everybody stops for me."

"Sam, I'll kill him," the dark lady screamed, and we fed her hot milk. All of us had the hiccups, even dad. Mom kissed Harve good night. "My gangster," she said, "my Sea Scout."

Mom and dad went off to their bed, and Harve and me to mine. I loved to sleep with Harve in the same bed. He'd brought a magic gun with him from Arizona. The gun had a bulb near the trigger, and it could shoot pictures on a dark wall. We watched naked women for half an hour. Their bodies jiggled. They weren't beautiful, not like Joan Crawford . . . or Faigele. They had wandering pink eyes, like crazed barracudas that couldn't seem to look into the light. And I wondered if these were the same wild women dad had met in Miami, only they weren't so wild, and what was Harvey doing with their images in his lantern gun?

"Hot stuff, huh, Baby?"

I was disappointed, but I didn't tell Harve. I would have preferred pictures of Tucson coming out of that gun. Where was that America Harve had been bragging about? I shut my eyes and fell asleep while a naked dancer rolled her belly on the wall.

The world was different with Harvey around. No one called me Ringworm. No one tried to steal my hat. The Seabees would have murdered anyone who bothered Baby. My brother wasn't a prince, like Darcy Staples. He didn't have his own dentist's chair, or a gang of hoodlum cops, but he couldn't get away from politics. The Rathcart twins groveled around him. They could call themselves Seabees, but they weren't real Scouts, and they were hoping Harve had some pull and could help them march in the parade. But what kind of parade would it have been if Harve had to march with Newt and Val?

Maybe he was a prince. Mom let him lie in bed as long as he liked, and she started squeezing oranges for Harve; asthmatics couldn't live without orange juice. And Harve was the only one in the house who could scribble a note to the telephone company, even if his handwriting wasn't terrific. He'd perfected his English in Arizona, solved all the riddles of grammar that ruined mom and me. He laughed at our little reading lessons, said *Bambi* was for infants. He'd gone through the library at Tucson, talked of Jack London and Huckleberry Finn, a man in an iron mask, and a monster called Mr. Hyde. Dad wasn't interested in monsters and tramps, but I looked at Faigele, and Faigele looked at me. Neither of us could recover from all the characters Harvey had ripped out of those library books and stored inside his head. We loved Harve, but I understood why mom had exiled him. Asthma was only an excuse. We would have eaten our hearts out wanting to be like my brother.

He was dad's champion, went with him to the fur market, had lunch with dad and his boss. But dad could afford to love Harve without limits. Dad wasn't a reader. Jack London and George Sand meant nothing to him. He had no use for wild dogs and men in iron masks. He could only measure things with the mark of his knife.

The dark lady was cautious around my brother. She took him to meet the dentist, had him sit with her at a card game. Darcy was in a charitable mood; he let my brother have a hand in the game. No other nine-year-old had ever held cards at Darcy's table. Harve bluffed the police captains, the Bronx senators, and Mr. Lions, and walked away with fifty dollars, but he wouldn't warm to the dentist or acknowledge the gift Darcy had given him: a seat at the poker table.

"What's that?" my brother asked, pointing to an empty chair. "Is it reserved for Roosevelt?"

"No," Mr. Lions said. "But it's the nearest thing. The chief sits there whenever he's in town. Old Flynn."

"That's funny," Harve said with a cat's smile. "I thought it was Governor Dewey's chair."

"God forbid."

The gamblers stared at Darcy, who stroked his silver mustache.

"Boss, should I beat his ears back?" said one of the hoodlum cops. "Faigele's son can't insult us . . . not after we let him win."

"The boy has pluck," Darcy said, "and shut your mouth. Faigele runs a fair game."

"Harve didn't mean anything," I said. "We heard a rumor at the Russian restaurant. Roosevelt locked Dewey out of the Bronx, and

Dewey is gonna take revenge. But he can't touch this card game, can he, Mr. Lions?"

"Not unless he wants to lose his own head of hair. Tom Dewey'll never walk through this door while I'm president of the Bronx."

"He'll walk where he has to walk," Darcy said. Then he turned to my brother and shut Mr. Lions out of his mind.

"Faigele says you're the reader in the family. Devoted to Mr. Jack London. I loved *Call of the Wild* when I was a lad. And Mr. Stevenson's books. But I don't believe in Dr. Jekyll or Mr. Hyde."

Harve shoved the fifty dollars into his shirt. "What do you believe in?"

"Literature, and not tales of a grim boy like Mr. Hyde. You won't find that silly stuff in Chekhov."

"What did he write?" I had to ask.

"Masterpieces," Darcy said, and he rattled off titles as if they were liquid flavors at a soda fountain. *"The Seagull, The Seven Sisters, The Dark Lady with the Little Dog."*

"Uncle Darcy," I said, jumping up and down, "tell me about that dark lady and her dog."

"He's not your uncle," Harve said, "and I never heard of Chekhov. There are no Chekhovs at the Tucson library, or I would have noticed his name."

"Indeed," Darcy said. "Then Tucson is in a very bad state . . . Faigele, will you enlighten this desert rat, inform him of Chekhov's literary repute."

"Darcy," mom said, "your Mr. Chekhov escapes me."

"But he was born in Belorusse, if I remember, minutes from your door. You must have studied him at school."

"School," Mom said, "what school? I was running from the tzar *and* the Revolution. I didn't have time for dark ladies and their little dogs, or any other masterpieces."

"Her name is Anna. She's a divorcée who's come to Nice. She

can't afford to stay at any of the grand palaces on the beach. She has to live at a tiny boardinghouse near the boulevard du Tzarewitch."

"What's a tzarewitch?"

"Don't interrupt," Darcy said. "A tzarewitch is the son of a tzar, his principal heir, but this Anna had no heirs, only a dog whose name was Dog. That's how desperate she was. She couldn't dream up the dog's own individual name. She fell in love with a gigolo who was living closer to the beach. He sucked out whatever little money she had, abandoned her, and Anna decides to drown herself and her dog in the bay. Poor Anna succeeds, but the dog has a much stronger constitution than his mistress, swims back to shore, and is immediately adopted by the gigolo, who employs this dog named Dog to help him seduce other women."

"A masterpiece," said Mr. Lions, bawling into his handkerchief. "The gigolo should have been shot . . . with the dog."

"But that's the beauty of it," Darcy said. "Chekhov doesn't condemn his own people . . . that's why they continue to haunt us. Wouldn't you agree, Mr. Harvey Charyn?"

Harve returned the fifty dollars to the table and walked out of the dentist's retreat. Mom didn't mention Darcy to him again. And Harve joined other Sea Scouts at the Kingsbridge Armory to prepare for the parade. Meanwhile, Mrs. Daniel Kaplan, whose son George had been killed aboard a battleship, lost the red banner in her window with the gold star that was meant to honor George. Somebody had plucked the banner right out of the window. Darcy offered a thousand dollars to anyone who could recapture the gold star. His own police captains couldn't come up with any clues. But I remembered those air-raid wardens who carried enormous sacks on their shoulders the night I followed dad into the Church—his headquarters on Sheridan Avenue. I couldn't ask dad if his brother wardens were thieves; I told Harve, who broke into the Church, discovered Mrs. Kaplan's banner behind a bin, and gave it to mom. Mom called Darcy, and he arrived at the Church with a police captain, looked at all the stolen merchandise, assembled the two guilty wardens and the dispatcher with chubby fingers who smoked cigars like a man. No one arrested them. That would have been a black mark against the Bronx. The dentist simply held his own court inside the Church, punched and kicked the fat dispatcher and her two accomplices, who were going to sell Mrs. Kaplan's gold star to some miserable collector of wartime memorabilia. He locked the Church, shut it down forever, returned the gold star to Mrs. Kaplan, and wrote a check to Harvey Charyn for a thousand dollars. But my brother threw it right back at the dentist.

"Give it to the Red Cross," he said.

Mr. Lions was there, and he was furious. "What kind of boy doesn't want pocket money?"

"This kind of boy," Harve said, and Darcy tore up the check. But it was dad who suffered the most. He lost his sergeant's station. Darcy wouldn't allow *any* wardens to patrol his terrain. Dad couldn't go into the street with his helmet strapped on and make his usual rounds. Air-raid wardens had become pariahs, peddlers of sacred articles. Darcy wouldn't dare accuse dad of the crime, but dad was still tainted. The dark lady kept clawing at him. "You must have known what this Miriam was doing. You have eyes. Didn't you see Mrs. Kaplan's gold star?"

"The Church was dark," dad said.

"You had a flashlight, Sergeant Sam."

"I had to preserve my batteries for the street."

"Faker," mom said. "How much did that fat whore pay you to keep quiet?"

"I never took her merchandise. I never stole. I had nothing to do with the black market."

"Sweet man," mom said, "you looked for every airplane in the sky . . . and the rottenness was all around you."

They slapped each other, and my brother had to get between them. "Mom, leave him alone. He's the best air-raid warden in the Bronx."

"The best retired warden, my dear. Can I show my face to Mrs. Kaplan and the other mothers with dead sons?"

"Mom, dad didn't do a thing."

"That's the story in a nutshell. Didn't do a thing, when he could have reported those lousy burglars."

"He's no cop. And he doesn't have a dentist behind him."

"Darcy's a great man," mom said. "A patriot. He helps the poor, cleans their teeth."

"And their pockets, mom."

"Go on. Slander him. When your father couldn't work, who put food on our table, who gave me a job?"

"Gamblers always know how to pick a pretty face."

"Don't talk that way to your mother," dad said.

"Dad, dad, she's the dentist's bathing beauty."

Dad slapped his own champion. Harve didn't even resist. He took the slap. And then he started to cough. Mom had to boil a big pot of water, pour it into a basin, and have my brother stand with a towel over his head and suck up the steam coming off the basin. Dad shuffled next to him with tears in his eyes. "Harvey, I didn't mean the slap—"

"Sam," my mother shouted, "stop it. He'll choke if he gets excited."

Harve had to stay in bed. He looked like a prisoner in his pajamas. He lived near steam basins and mustard plasters, bottles of medicine and sprays. Mom said his lungs would turn to paper if he didn't sleep with mustard on his chest. Meyer Lansky's doctor came to the house and examined Harve. He told mom to get rid of all her mustard plasters. "Faigele, it's wet air. That's the killer. Send him back to Arizona."

"Doctor, he's a boy, not a postage stamp. I can't send him through the mail."

My brother started to wheeze; it was the asthmatics' whistle, and that's why Harve's enemies in the Bronx called him the Whistler. His lips turned blue. Dr. Katz went into his medical kit, pulled out a dark cigarette that was a foot long. He lit that long cigarette, and made my brother breathe the fumes.

I nearly died. That's how awful the stink was—like the acid coming off a dozen rotting rats. But the wheezing stopped, and Harve's lips regained their natural color. The doctor let my mother have two "sulphur cigarettes." He borrowed mom's vacuum cleaner and started to dust the ceiling and the walls, the mattress and the pillowcases, with a lyrical sweep of his arms and legs.

"Doctor," mom said, "I would never have guessed you did housecleaning on the side."

"It's nothing. I do it for Lansky all the time. He's allergic to dust."

"Will there be dust on the Grand Concourse when my son marches in the big parade?"

"Darling," the doctor said, "you'll have to stand behind him with a broom and a gas mask."

"They'll think he's a mama's boy."

"Mom," I said, "you could cut your hair and dress up like a Sea Scout."

The doctor blinked at my mother. "Baby, it wouldn't work." Then he plucked off my baseball cap and peeked at my scalp.

"When can I go to school?"

"Soon," he said, and ran out the door. He wouldn't accept payment from us. We were Darcy's people. We belonged to the dentist.

Harve hated being an invalid. Mom wouldn't let him go near the armory without me. I was his nurse. I carried the sulphur cigarettes and a bunch of matches in one of Faigele's own shoeboxes. I sat in the stands with other guests while Harve marched downstairs in the main hall. He wore white spats and a webbed belt, a would-be sailor in a little sea of sailors; maybe his shoes weren't properly shined, and none of his nails was a perfect half-moon, but isn't that how Launcelot Perry would have behaved, if the rat man had ever been a Scout?

Harve was smaller than the other Scouts, who were eleven and twelve, and had slept one night on a Coast Guard cutter called *The Courage*. They marched with a certain swagger, but it was mostly a bluff; they didn't have that inward turn of the eye, like the rat man and my brother, a sense of isolation that could only have come from living in a boxcar or behind a garbage barrel . . .

Boss Flynn was grand marshal of the parade. He rode in a Cadillac with Darcy and Mr. Lions, in front of all the Scouts. He was either the biggest, roundest man I'd ever seen, or else it was an optical illusion, with the sun poisoning my eye. He had six chins, and a rose in his lapel that looked like a fistful of blood. He clutched a microphone and kept evoking the President's name. "Franklin Roosevelt . . . how that man loves a parade. 'Ed,' he told me, 'I'm proud of your marching boys, your boys of the Bronx.' "

Mom and dad were at the parade, and dad cried when he saw Harve march in the middle of a swollen file, vulnerable to all the dust in the trees, his lips potentially blue, his lungs ready to rip. But Baby wouldn't cry. I cursed the parade. Mrs. Roosevelt must have put some pressure on Boss Flynn, because he let Newt and Val into the Scouts at the last minute, and my brother had to march with the Rathcart twins, who stumbled in their spats, and broke the Scouts' gorgeous white line.

Harve returned to bed after the parade. We had to endure the intolerable stink of a sulphur cigarette, but Harve recovered a little after he breathed the fumes. It was Darcy who rescued him, found my brother a berth on a military train that was passing through Arizona. We went to the station with Harve. I watched Faigele's eyes begin to flutter. She was about to swoon. She hated Harve, and couldn't bear to see him go. It was Darcy who caught my mother, not dad. He'd arrived at Pennsylvania Station in a cream-colored coat, with a copy of *Jekyll and Hyde* bound in mo-rocco, Harve's initials burnt right into the leather skin.

I think I understand the dentist; he liked me a lot, but he ad-mired Harve, the Whistler who wouldn't take a thousand-dollar reward.

We waved to Harve. He'd never even talked about his school in Arizona, or his loneliness without the Bronx; America was his new mom and dad.

Faigele fell into a black hole; she was too weak to wash her own hair. I had to cook for her, encourage dad to drink his schnapps. Baby had become the little man of the house. I missed Harve. He was my hero. But I could console myself with the rat man, follow his adventures every week. And mom began to climb out of her funk.

"He's better off, isn't he, Baby?"

"Harve has the sun."

"You'll start school, we'll learn how to write, and we'll get closer to Harvey."

"Mom," I said, "even if I went to college, I couldn't read Harve's handwriting. Nobody can."

"Don't lie," she said. "We'll learn."

Mom stood in the mirror, combed her hair, painted her mouth with the luminous red eye of her lipstick, and went down to deal cards for the dentist.

Madame Curie

$\mathcal{H}$er married name was Madame Curie. But she was born Maria Sklodowska in Warsaw, in 1867. Her dad was a lowly teacher of mathematics who lost his money gambling on the stock exchange, and Maria was an infant prodigy who could memorize maps and countries and languages before she was five. She went to the Russian lycée, where she wore out her professors with her knowledge of Spinoza and the laws of physics. But she couldn't attend the university because of her father's misfortune. Maria, the most brilliant girl in her class, became a governess at seventeen. Her mind fell asleep. She lived like a dray horse to support her family. Finally she fled to Paris, continued her studies at the Sorbonne. She fell in love with a French scientist, Pierre Curie, married him, worked in his lab. They discovered radium together, shared the Nobel prize in 1903. But in 1906 Pierre was run over by a dray on the rue Dauphine and died on the spot. Madame Curie went on with their experiments in radioactivity, and was the first woman to ever teach at the Sorbonne. She won a second Nobel prize in 1911. The most celebrated person on the planet, more popular than movie stars and kings, she sacrificed herself to science. The radioactive material in her lab began to poison Madame Curie; her blood turned to water, and she died of leukemia in 1934.

MGM decided to cash in on her life, and produced *Madame Curie,* the biggest blockbuster of 1943, starring Greer Garson, a redhead who didn't really look like Faigele. But she played a dark lady in the film. The whole Bronx fell in love with MGM's Madame Curie. Greer Garson was in the window of every shop; she never posed as a bathing beauty. She was the Bronx's hysterical idea of the perfect woman, a gorgeous widow who wastes away in a laboratory. And because Poland was considered next door to Belorusse, and Greer Garson was much more radiant than all the men around her, Darcy and his tribe of politicians began to call my mother Madame Curie.

"Faigele," Mr. Lions said, "you should have married a physicist."

"How could I have flirted with him, Mr. Lions? There are no Russian lycées in the Bronx."

But I could tell that MGM had moved mom; she must have wondered what it would have been like to live in a world of scientists, where she might have discovered some radioactive material to combat ringworm. Faigele had long-range plans. She'd wait until I finished junior high, and we'd go to high school together, Madame Curie & Son at William Howard Taft. But I couldn't even manage first grade. The sores healed on my head, and I arrived at P.S. 88 one morning in early December with my crayons and pencil case. I still had a couple of bald spots, and everybody, including my teacher, was suspicious. I wore my Brownie cap and sat at a special desk, far from my classmates. I couldn't hear a thing. I was like a shell-shocked boy, an invalid who could only pick up pieces of language.

The school sent me to a hearing clinic in the winter of '44. I rode down to the clinic with Madame Curie and Mr. Lions. I wore earphones for an hour, listened to very strange bells: the silence between the bells was like a separate civilization, where music was outlawed, and nothing could ever begin or end. I thought of that cantor, Gilbert Rogovin, during the silence between the bells, when I realized that you couldn't live without a melody. Our miserable cantor had nourished a whole synagogue with his songs. I missed the chanting he did in his white hat. But I survived, and the clinic told my mother that I wasn't deaf.

I should have been glad, but I couldn't rejoice with mom and Mr. Lions. "Madame Curie," whispered the president of the Bronx. "Madame Curie." He kept purring in mom's ear. He brought us to the dentist, but Darcy's building was flooded with cops. They stole his files, stored in a hundred shoeboxes, and stuffed them into a police wagon. It wasn't the Bronx police. Tom Dewey sent a special prosecutor down on Darcy, and the prosecutor had his own police from Manhattan.

"Put back the shoeboxes," Mr. Lions screamed. He summoned several Bronx police captains, but they couldn't do a thing. Darcy had already been arrested. He languished in Manhattan's criminal court, like the man in the iron mask. Fifty Democrats arrived at the arraignment, citizens of the Bronx who put up Darcy's bail and carried him from the courthouse on their shoulders, shouting "Tom Dewey can't soil our prince."

Mr. Lions wanted to declare a holiday in the Bronx, but the dentist said no. "Let's not draw attention to ourselves." His silver mustache didn't seem so silver. He must have frozen in Manhattan. He kept warming his hands in his own pockets. Dewey was calling him a swindler and a black marketeer. Mr. Lions arranged a party at the Concourse Plaza to raise some cash for Darcy's defense fund. The Bronx police captains were there and all the politicians, except Boss Flynn. Mr. Lions didn't even have a telegram from Roosevelt to read. The White House was suddenly neutral in the war between Tom Dewey and the Bronx.

Mr. Lions had invited an impresario to sing. Gilbert Rogovin arrived from the Cincinnati Opera House. He was much fatter than I remembered him to be. Rogovin wouldn't do any of his synagogue songs. He did Don Giovanni. He couldn't take his eyes off Faigele. She wore a red dress that was like a victory banner. The cantor shivered when he played the Barber of Seville. He shoved ten dollars into my fist. "Tell Faigele I have a room on the third floor. I'll die if she doesn't visit me."

I took his money but I wouldn't deliver the message. He drank half a bottle of whisky and collapsed in his chair, under a thick mask of paint that made him look like a tired clown.

Darcy kept waiting for a telephone call from his chief, a few words that would redeem him and his struggle. But Boss Flynn never called. And Darcy did something foolish. He broke the terms of his bail. He wasn't supposed to leave the Bronx without a permit from the special prosecutor. It was a plot to embarrass Darcy, keep him hemmed in. But he ran to Jersey City to visit a whore and collect a bill, and Dewey's detectives tracked him down and brought him to the Tombs. It was slightly illegal, but they seemed to have warrants that allowed them to cross the Hudson and kidnap Darcy, remove him from his favorite brothel. He could have had another bail hearing, but he decided to rot in the Tombs. The prince of the Grand Concourse chose to live in exile if Boss Flynn couldn't punish Tom Dewey and stop his commando raids on the Bronx.

We visited Darcy at the Tombs. It was Manhattan's own penitentiary, meant for the hardest cases. The dentist had to live around criminals all day. The Tombs was like a huge, abandoned tugboat that was sinking into the ground. It had no windows that I could see, and even if it did, Darcy was still deprived of the precious winter light that floated off the roofs of the Concourse near sundown. He had his own cell, with an armchair and a radio and a little electric coffeepot that Darcy claimed was standard gear for "political prisoners." Mom had baked him some Russian coffee cake, and the dentist closed his eyes when he tasted the dark chocolate.

"It's a dream," he said, and I almost cried, because Darcy had been the best-dressed man in the Bronx, and now he wore the ragged gray uniform of a jailbird. He wouldn't ask his tailor, Feuerman & Marx, to travel downtown and fit him with custom-made prison clothes. And he wouldn't trim his mustache while he was in the Tombs; silver hair wandered all over his face. But the Russian cake had revived him.

He looked into Faigele's eyes. "Has Lions kept you on the payroll? You get your usual cut, whether there's a card game or not."

But there was no payroll; Darcy's assets, visible and invisible, had disappeared with the hundred shoeboxes and his dentist's chair.

"I love you both," he said, grabbing my hand and smiling at Faigele, with bits of dark chocolate between his teeth.

"Baby," he said, "I'll send you to law school . . . we'll need a lawyer like you. The President has abandoned us. I've been breaking heads fifteen years for that man in the White House. We stole the vote for him when he ran for governor. Mr. Frank couldn't win without Syracuse, and we delivered Syracuse, in a barrel of blood . . . Baby, will you go to law school?"

"I promise."

"Ah, I'm content," Darcy said. "I can sleep, knowing that we have a future."

But the dentist had no future. He died of a heart attack in his cell. He was forty-one years old, like Tom Dewey. Mr. Lions had to create a burial fund for him. Darcy wanted to lie near Herman Melville in Woodlawn, the Bronx's own cemetery. Mr. Lions was in a panic. Nobody had ever heard of Melville.

"Mr. Lions," I said, "he must be related to Chekhov. Darcy loved Chekhov."

"Who's Chekhov?"

"A writer."

"Why didn't you say so?"

And he looked up Herman Melville in the Bronx almanac. Melville was a composer of sea stories, and a sailor who lived with cannibals in Tahiti, the almanac said. "His classic, *Moby Dick; or The*

Whale, was largely unread in his lifetime." He stopped writing novels altogether when he was thirty-six, became a forgotten man, with a very long beard. "Herman was rescued from Manhattan's vapors and laid to rest in Woodlawn, among the flowers."

Mr. Lions buried Darcy as close to Herman Melville as he could. The cemetery was very crowded. It sat on a hill, and Darcy couldn't have seen Melville's grave from his own plot. A platoon of politicians appeared at the burial. Boss Flynn had come with his people. He kept blowing his nose into the largest handkerchief I ever saw. "A tragedy," he said. "One of our better sons."

Mom wore a veil on that hill, like Darcy's other "widows." She didn't cry, but I know how sad she was. She'd discovered the English language around Darcy Staples, had crawled out of her immigrant's shell to deal cards and meet the president of the Bronx and other bigwigs.

There were no priests or rabbis running around. Darcy was a Protestant, and maybe that's why Boss Flynn had sacrificed him so fast. Protestants were like outlaws in the Bronx. FDR was a Protestant, but nobody held it against him, because he was from Hyde Park, where all the Protestants lived. But he couldn't have been elected president of the Bronx, like Mr. Lions . . .

One of the mourners seemed familiar in his brown derby. His mustache had darkened in the past six months, but he didn't have any spots on his shoes. It was Uncle Chick, the house painter, who'd prospered away from Bitter Eagles. He'd gone into business with one of Meyer Lansky's lieutenants, and now he was a contractor who supervised the painting of apartment houses and hospitals and parochial schools.

"Faigele," he said, "am I forgiven?"

Faigele was like a sphinx under her veil. "Mr. Eisenstadt," she said, "I liked you better with paint on your shoes."

"That's funny. You gave the opposite impression."

"Why are you here? To pursue me and my son in a cemetery?"

"No. To pay my respects to a dead man."

"Darcy hated you. His cowboys put you in the hospital . . . you still haven't healed."

"He was a warrior. Under the circumstances, I would have done the same to him."

"What circumstances?"

"He was in love with you."

"That's news," Faigele said. "He lived in a bordello."

"He was in love with you. You're the only woman he would have ever married."

"Who told you that?"

"The dentist. He admitted it to me. That's why he had to break my head."

"Men have such wonderful logic."

Mom lifted her veil with one finger. The dark lady was blushing in that cemetery of flowers, where Darcy slept on the same hill with Herman Melville, author of *The Whale*. "How's your missus?"

"We're estranged," Chickie said.

I clucked in Faigele's ear: if she went to William Howard Taft, mom would have to get along with Marsha Eisenstadt, who might become the assistant principal in seven or eight years.

"House painter," mom said, "don't neglect your children," and she waltzed me away from Chick.

Mr. Lions began courting mom a week after the burial. He came knocking at our door with a whole plantation of roses that hid half his head. He wanted to install mom at the Concourse Plaza with her own card game. "We have Flynn's blessing. The Boss is taken with you. He said, 'Faigele ought to climb into our coach. And she can bring aboard that little boy with ringworm.' "

"Baby doesn't have ringworm anymore. Haven't you noticed, Mr. Lions? And why are you sucking up to the man who sentenced Darcy to death?"

"God forbid," said Mr. Lions. "The dentist died of heart failure."

"*Heartbreak* is a better word. He was a political prisoner."

"Faigele, it's an election year. FDR couldn't afford a brouhaha in the Bronx. He had to give Dewey a little bone. Flynn's hands were tied."

"A little bone? Then you can play cards with Flynn and every other boss whose hands are tied."

"Faigele, it's politics. Darcy was my friend."

Mom returned the plantation of roses and said good-bye to the president of the Bronx. She took FDR's picture off the wall. Sergeant Sam nearly choked on his schnapps.

"Faigele, he's President of the United States."

"Not in my house."

Mom had abandoned all her prospects. She no longer had money to burn. I couldn't go into a toy shop, shut my eyes, and pick out some bagatelle, like a pirate pistol or a statuette of Bambi. I liked it better when mom was in the black market.

I would sneak out of school whenever Chick invited mom to lunch at Bitter Eagles. The restaurant had to take him back. The Russian gangsters who huddled near the bar couldn't afford to slap Meyer Lansky in the face. Chick was attached to Lansky's own lieutenant. None of the gangsters had ever seen Meyer, who lived on Central Park West, but they didn't want to tangle with the Little Man. He was the childhood friend of Bugsy Siegel, psychopath and founder of Las Vegas; a disciple of Arnold Rothstein, first tzar of organized crime; a partner of Lucky Luciano, Rothstein's own little tzarewitch. But Meyer had managed to keep his photograph out of the American papers; there were no features about the Little Man, except in the Jewish press, which talked of his donations to synagogues and summer camps. But the Bronx, *and* Bitter Eagles, seemed to know more about Meyer than the Manhattan district attorney and the *New York Times.* Philanthropic gambler, jukebox king, loyal Democrat, he shunned publicity. The Russian gangsters wanted to know if Chick had met the Little Man.

"What's he like? Chickie, does he have cold eyes?"

"Gentlemen, he's as endearing as Santa Claus. Mind, I only met with him for five minutes. He asked how the Bronx could survive without Joe DiMaggio."

"Did Meyer lose his head in the sand? DiMaggio's fighting for America. He doesn't have time for baseball . . ."

"Then you tell that to the Little Man."

The Russian gangsters dug their noses into their vodka glasses. And Chick invited mom and me on a tour of his domain. I watched two hundred painters descend upon a hospital and whiten every wall in half a day. Chickie called it the shock treatment, because no one could match the discipline and the speed of his house painters. He'd underbid all other contractors in the Bronx, and he had to "deliver" a hospital in an impossibly short period, or waive his fee. He would move his arms like an orchestra leader—Chick had his own baton—and tap any of his shock troops who fell asleep on the job.

But he shouldn't have been out in the field with these men. He would spit blood into a dropcloth and wipe the blood with his hand. Mom was right: he hadn't recovered from the beating, and he never would. He was a doomed general, signaling his own destruction with a baton.

"House painter," mom told him, "you ought to be in bed."

"Never. Nobody's gonna cage me. I couldn't breathe without the smell of paint."

"Darling, tell that to your lungs."

Chick turned to me. "Baby, I have to surround a hospital with two hundred men, plan a siege, and spit blood, before your mother calls me darling."

"Stop it," mom said. "You'll give my son the wrong idea."

Chick didn't even have the luxury of returning to Cedars of Lebanon for a little holiday. Meyer Lansky had an argument with his own lieutenant, and Chick fell outside the protective umbrella of the Little Man. Rival contractors sabotaged Chick's "shock treatment." They hired goons to smash the hands of Uncle Chick's best house painters. And they promised to turn Chick into a snowman, to wash him in white paint, and set the paint on fire. The goons threatened his children, strolled into Marsha's classroom at William Howard Taft, rubbed her face in chalk dust, wrote "CHICK EISENSTADT IS A DEAD DUCK" on the blackboard, distributed bubble gum and candy to the students, and disappeared.

Chick hired Russian gangsters to fight the goons, but he had to disband his army of house painters. The tax man had come after him, claimed that he'd been pocketing cash without declaring it as income, that he owed a hundred thousand dollars to Uncle Sam. Chickie couldn't fight goons and the Internal Revenue Service. He went into hiding, wore a false beard.

"Faigele, it's Roosevelt's fault. I have enemies in high places."

"The President doesn't persecute house painters, only dentists who helped elect him. He feeds them to Tom Dewey. But you had generals and admirals on your side. Didn't you pamper their wives with silk stockings? Couldn't you appeal to them?"

"How? And have them admit that they crawled into bed with the black market? They're trying to clean their slate, wipe me off their calendar. They're my enemies, Faigele."

That's where I chipped in. "Uncle, I'll defend you. I promised Darcy I'd become a lawyer."

"Don't forget. I'll need you, Baby, when I'm back in Sing Sing."

We'd have a meal with Chickie once a month. It was always in the afternoon, when Bitter Eagles closed its doors to strangers, and Chick could pluck off his beard. He'd grown gaunt without the restaurant's Russian cake. He'd have coughing fits and sweeten the tea he drank with his own blood.

"Chickie, sign yourself into a hospital, please, or it will be too late."

"I can't surface. Roosevelt will arrest me."

"Idiot. Roosevelt doesn't know you're alive."

"The admirals put me on the President's black list."

"What black list?"

"People who could be a danger after the war."

"You a danger? My poor Chick. The President has closed his eyes to the Bronx. He's lent us to Dewey."

"Lent us to Dewey," Chick said, and it was the last we heard of him. There were no more rendezvous at Bitter Eagles, no more monthly meals. He was a renegade without luck. And we were the losers. We had to mourn a live man, but mom wasn't always sure that Chick was alive.

"Faigele," I said, "all we have to do is search the cemetery. Chick couldn't stand to be buried outside the Bronx."

"And if he died alone, with that ridiculous beard? The cops will throw him into an unmarked grave."

"The cops aren't that dumb. The beard will fall off, and they'll know it was Chick."

"My little Sherlock Holmes," mom said. "The case is closed."

But it wasn't closed. Because those two black marketeers—Darcy and Chick—haunted Faigele, dead or alive. Mom's mind was like my funny bone. It started playing tricks. She'd stand frozen in her mirror, one eye full of mascara, the other eye dark and bald, and mom was Jekyll *and* Hyde at the same moment. And she'd mutter, "Baby, let's go live with the dentist."

I'd have to reason with her, a boy close to seven, in a Brownie cap, with the remnants of ringworm on his scalp, cold little scars. "Mom, I miss Darcy too, but we can't live with him. He's under the ground. And even if I brought a shovel to Woodlawn and dug up Darcy's coffin, we'd never get in. We'd have to keep the lid open, and the birds would eat our eyes."

"Then we'll live with the house painter."

"We can't find him, Faigele. But I'll leave a message on the wall at Bitter Eagles."

"No messages," mom said. "Roosevelt will arrest him."

"Mom, the President can't bother with Chick. He's running against Dewey."

"Then we'll ask Dewey to find him."

"Dewey's a gangbuster. He'd really arrest Chick."

Boss Flynn summoned Faigele to the Concourse Plaza. She didn't want to go, but I persuaded her. "Mom, he's boss of the Bronx and Manhattan and the whole country. He might have some news about Chick."

I had to prepare Faigele's bald eye. I marched her to the Concourse Plaza. Flynn was in the mezzanine, where he'd set up his own headquarters for Roosevelt's reelection campaign. Mr. Lions was with him, but Flynn did the talking, and Lions served the coffee.

"We'll need a woman of character," he said. "Our own Madame Curie. Otherwise the office will be drab. And Mr. Frank has given us his word that he'll drive through the Bronx on one of his whirlwind tours. I wish I could invite you to sit with us in his limousine, but there won't be enough room . . . Fannie dear, wouldn't you like to shake the President's hand at party headquarters?"

"Only if I can ask him about Mr. Dewey and the dentist."

The big fat giant squinted at our borough president. "Mr. Lions, you assured me that Faigele was a sensible girl . . . Here I offer her a presidential handshake, and I get kicked like a dog."

"God forbid. Boss, she didn't mean it . . . Faigele, tell him you're sorry. Mr. Flynn has a kind heart. He's giving you a plum. He's willing to make you manager of the Bronx County Democrats."

"Mr. Lions," mom said, "I'm a card dealer. I don't count coffee cups."

Flynn clutched his suspenders. "The next thing she'll tell me is that she's voting for Tom Dewey."

"No," said the dark lady. "I'm not voting at all."

"That's sacrilege. A Democrat who doesn't vote is a friend of the devil. I promised Mr. Frank that every single registered Democrat in the Bronx would vote for him."

"Mr. Flynn," mom said, "you should have asked me before you made that promise."

"Fannie dear, we own the Bronx. We can lend you glory . . . or toss you out of our camp."

"I only went to night school, Mr. Flynn, but even I know that glory can't be lent."

"Your husband was once an air-raid warden. I can reinstate him, get him a captaincy."

"I still wouldn't vote."

"Boss," Mr. Lions said. "She's beside herself, grieving for the dentist."

"And she blames me. Darcy was a good soldier. He did what he had to do. He was a pauper when I found him, didn't have a dime. I commanded every Democrat under my wing to use Darcy as their dentist . . . and if you persist in your foolishness, you will be a most unfortunate woman, with a family of outcasts on a Democratic island."

"The Bronx is not an island, Mr. Flynn; you only think it is."

And that was the end of the meeting. We never got close to the Democrats again. I liked Mr. Lions, and I liked the Concourse Plaza. But I didn't like them enough to trample on my memory of the dentist. I even bought a Dewey button from a crippled girl in the street, and I was spiteful enough to wear it, but I had to admit that Dewey was no bargain. The dentist would still have his card game and that wonderful chair if Dewey hadn't picked on him . . .

Roosevelt kept his word. He did come to the Bronx, and he rode with Mr. Flynn. The Sea Scouts marched in front of Flynn, like in the last parade, and the Rathcarts were with them. But Harvey wasn't there. He wouldn't leave Arizona to wiggle around in white spats and march in another parade with the Rathcarts. I hid the Dewey pin inside my shirt.

The President was bundled in a big coat. He wore his election hat, an old gray fedora. It felt like every Democrat in creation had traveled up to the Concourse to catch a glimpse of FDR. He was still our god, a god who'd turned on the Paley Charyns. Dad couldn't keep from crying. "Our commander in chief."

That old gray fox with the twisted legs, who'd contracted a child's disease when he was a grown man, who couldn't walk a step without a pair of metal sticks, but had to carry a whole war on his shoulders, under his Navy cape. Hitler called him the man with no legs. Hitler was a liar. FDR could play water polo and swim like a sea lion, and he could have broken Hitler's back in the water. He was only helpless on land. And maybe I was conceited, a snot-nosed kid, but I likened his polio to ringworm. We'd both caught a crazy disease. I'd recovered, but weren't we cousins under the skin? I loved FDR. We all did. He was elected before I was born, and no one, not even George Washington, who'd fought one of his biggest battles on Harlem Heights, just across from Yankee Stadium, had served as long as FDR. It was party politics that kept us apart. The Democrats were making war on mom, and I couldn't abandon her, even if FDR and I had both been through the fire of a child's disease. Polio was worse than ringworm, but at least the sores on my head had given me the imagination to deal with Mr. Frank's twisted legs.

Faigele couldn't even buy on credit at the grocery store: that's how far the Democrats' fat little fingers could reach. Mom had been wrong. The Bronx was a Democratic island. Dad thought of moving to Far Rockaway. We'd have the beach and the boardwalk; and I would have been much closer to the sharks and submarines in the Atlantic, even Herman Melville's white whale. Whales could live two hundred years, according to the Bronx almanac. But Faigele wasn't interested in white whales, and she wasn't going to let Boss Flynn drive us out of the Bronx.

Dad convinced her to leave the Concourse, a boulevard that could only remind her of Darcy and Bitter Eagles. And we returned to the East Bronx, where we'd lived until I was four and a half. It was like a huge bandanna of crooked streets on a relentless checkered plain. Boss Flynn hardly went there. He had one little storefront that he opened a month before national elections and closed immediately after. It would have given him a bad image to register people who wouldn't vote. The dentist had gone into the East Bronx once to break the heads of these nonvoters, and he'd come back utterly compromised; the more heads he broke, the fewer voters there were in the East Bronx.

Now we didn't have to worry about Flynn's fat fingers. We had a bigger apartment, because the rents were cheaper in the East. I had my own bed, and a little radio, and I could listen to "Lux Presents Hollywood," a condensed version of current Hollywood hits with lesser stars in the main roles . . . Tom Neal in *Casablanca* and Barbara Britton in *Madame Curie*. And slowly, slowly, the Concourse became a forgotten landscape, a lost article on a growing boy's map.

I missed one thing: nobody in the East called mom "Madame Curie." But who could I blame? There were no dentists like Darcy floating around, no house painters like Chick, not even a holy terror like Marsha Eisenstadt. Some kind of raw intelligence and electric wit seemed to have gone out of the world. But I had my radio. And I was studying lists of words, writing rude sentences, while I dreamt of that lawyer I would become for Darcy's sake, defending political prisoners and other victims of Republican and Democratic misjustice. Barrister Baby Charyn.

Wyatt Earp

$\mathcal{T}$he East had its Titans, like the West. But they weren't politicians or dentists who broke a lot of heads. Politics didn't count this far from the Concourse. There wasn't even a proper temple where I could have taken art classes. We lived in a kind of isolated anarchy, and within this anarchy was a black man, Haines, the superintendent of our building. Everybody called him Super. He must have been fifty-five, but he looked younger than my own dad. He'd been a foot soldier in the First World War, part of a black regiment that was funneled into the French Army and fought in the Argonne forest. He had battle scars all over his body. He stayed in France after the war, wearing the uniform of a soldier in a French division, and when his uniform began to rot, he returned to the Bronx. Haines had a wife, a girlfriend, four children, and one grandchild, all of whom lived with him in the basement. The Super was a bit like Bat Masterson and Wyatt Earp. He kept the peace in a neighborhood that wasn't known for lawfulness.

Haines wasn't part of any protection racket. He wouldn't charge a shopkeeper whenever he ran in to flatten a drunk who was on the rampage. And any gang that stole goods from one of Haines' stores soon learned to give back the goods or lose its "license" to walk the streets. Haines was a better gangbuster than Tom Dewey. He'd storm a gang's headquarters and demolish the furniture and the chiefs. And if the Irish or Italian fathers of a gang went into the basement looking for the Super, they'd always come out wiser and humbler men. Haines would battle them six at a time, banging heads, biting ears; if one of these dads dared arrive with a gun, Haines would pluck it out of his hand, smash the barrel against a wall, and oblige this dad to eat his own gun.

The cops had little presence in the East, and the shopkeepers of Southern Boulevard and Boston Road understood where the wind blew in the Bronx; their safety could only lie with the battler, Haines. He wouldn't accept money from them, he wouldn't accept bribes, but he couldn't stop them from offering trinkets to his family. The battler was a poor man, but at least his granddaughter had a crib, and his women and children were warm in the winter. That's the only edge he would tolerate. He reminded me of the rat man, Launcelot Perry, who adored dark places and would never have beaten up people for personal profit.

He was also kind to Faigele and her boy with the Brownie cap on his brains. He liked to think of Faigele and himself as foreigners—Europeans, he said. Exiles. But he wasn't European. He was born in the Bronx. He'd had a whole other family in France, a wife and a child he had to leave behind because the gendarmes had come after him (he stole to keep alive). Haines mixed me up with his lost son. I'd go into the basement with him after school and help him shovel coal into the furnace. His face always had a beautiful light against the burning coals. He'd shovel without a shirt, and I could see his war wounds, scars that ran like irregular fingers under the skin. He wouldn't call me Baby. He said I was too old to have a nickname like that.

"Super, have a heart. I'm only seven."

"But I'm not gonna address you like an infant. You have a name. Jerome."

"That's for school," I said. "I'm Baby to mom and dad and my brother, Harvey, and my friends."

"How many friends you got, Mr. Jerome?"

"One at the moment. You."

"Well, that proves my point. And it's a sad commentary if your only friend is a grandpa and a cripple."

"Wish I was your kind of cripple. You're the battler. Our Wyatt Earp."

Haines started to laugh. "That's considerate. Comparing me to a homicidal thief."

"Super, what does *homicidal* mean?"

"Am I your teacher, Mr. Jerome? . . . *Homicidal* means born to kill."

"But Wyatt Earp was a lawman. In Arizona. Where my brother lives."

"Ain't that a coincidence. Well, I met that man when I was a porter at the big station in Los Angeles. I had to carry him off the train, he was so drunk, pissing all over his pants."

"Wyatt Earp?"

"Earpy is what he called himself. He wouldn't go into the toilet alone. Said he'd give me a dollar if I'd help him. His hands were too unsteady to unbutton his fly. Told him I couldn't take a dollar from Wyatt Earp, and it wouldn't be decent if people caught him in the white man's toilet in his condition. Earpy agreed. I took him into the porter's toilet and cleaned him up. And that's when he volunteered his story about the gunfighting business. He wasn't no sheriff in Arizona. He was an armed guard and a detective for Wells, Fargo."

"Who's Wells, Fargo?"

"What they learning you at school? Wells, Fargo was the biggest company in the world for carrying silver and gold. And it seems that Wyatt carried off some of that silver and killed a couple of people."

"Super, I know you wouldn't lie, but I can't believe it."

"Well, history speaks for itself. Just look up Wyatt Earp in the cyclopedia. You can read, can't you, Mr. Jerome? What you gonna be when you grow up?"

"A lawyer," I said.

The Super laughed again. "You mean a crook with the privilege of cheating people?"

"I wouldn't cheat. I'd protect you if you ever had to go and sit in the Tombs."

"Baby, I've been to the Tombs. And the only thing I didn't need was a lawyer."

"I'm not Baby," I said. "I'm Jerome."

And I ran out of the basement with coal dust in my hair . . .

The economy was booming, but dad sat home more and more, saddled with illnesses he'd invent for himself, and mom found a job in a candy factory. She would spend hours dipping cherries into a barrel of chocolate. The factory was in a rotten neighborhood on Edgewater Road, filled with rats who traveled from warehouse to warehouse, and Haines volunteered to walk mom home whenever she had to work late.

Sometimes he brought me along, and I'd marvel how other men would instinctively inch away from him. Haines wasn't very tall. But he had the dancing step of an acrobat and the dark eyes of Wyatt Earp, as I imagined them in my own head. And once, when three men raced out from behind the wall of a warehouse and tried to grab Faigele's purse (with her pay envelope inside), I watched the Super go into gear. He only had to pivot once. His arms lashed out as he turned to protect Faigele and sock the three men in the throat. They bumped into each other without the purse, which was already back under Faigele's arm.

But mom had to pay a price for Haines' gallantry. His girl-friend, Nita, was very jealous. She was a mulatto who looked like Lena Horne, the most beautiful woman in America. Nita was the wild lady of the building. Haines' wife, Mattie, had a weak heart and never left the basement, but Nita would patrol the stairs, pretending to sweep or mop, and she'd grab at the heels of some boy in the building, pin him against the banister rail if she could, and blow hot breath into his ear. I was her special target.

"You tell your mama to leave my man alone."

Nita was carrying a child in her belly, Haines' child, and she was proud of it. Half the neighborhood was in love with Nita Brown, and the other half called her a rattlesnake who could lick the blood out of a man. I was only a little pisser with scars on his scalp, but if I had a garden somewhere, Nita Brown was the only rattlesnake I'd want.

"Nita," I told her, "mom's not Mata Hari. She didn't flirt with the Super. She didn't even hold his hand. I'm a witness. I was there. He walked her home from the factory, and he was right. Three gangsters tried to steal her paycheck."

"Gangsters?" Nita muttered, tossing back her hair. "Were they niggers or ofays?"

"What's an ofay?"

"Any man with a white dick."

"They were ofays, far as I could tell."

"Then he must have planted them . . . he's always using ofays to help him impress a new piece of tail."

"Mom doesn't have a tail," I told her.

"Come here, Baby," she said, and Nita scooped me into her arms. I sat above her belly, could see the tiny golden hairs of her mustache, sniff the perfumed well between her breasts.

"Can you hear him knocking?"

"Who's knocking?"

"My little boy . . . Dynamite. That's what I'm gonna call him."

I had my drink of paradise, and it was in the East Bronx. But it ended too soon. Nita put me down. Her arms had the same golden hairs.

"Maybe I can be your Mata Hari," she said, and she sashayed toward the basement in a blue housecoat, her belly heaving. And I floated around with Nita's perfumed sweat in my nostrils. I didn't care one little titty about school. The kids in my class were so backward, they'd never been to the Concourse, and they'd never had art lessons either. I was the class whiz, who could talk about Bronx politics like no other boy. "The Bronx reelected Roosevelt," I said (FDR was just beginning his fourth term in the White House). "Boss Flynn and Mr. Lions managed his campaign from the Concourse Plaza. They demolished Mr. Dewey. It was a Bronx massacre."

I was swaggering here and there, dreaming of Nita Brown, when I noticed that the pretzel vendor outside school was damn suspicious. He picked his teeth with a golden toothpick, like the gangsters of Bitter Eagles, wore a herringbone suit that was strictly Feuerman & Marx, and had faint white spots on his shoes.

"How are you, Ringworm?" he said, to throw me off my guard. He'd trimmed his false beard, and he looked like the prince of pretzel vendors.

"Uncle Chick, you didn't have to hurt mom. Couldn't you have written her a postcard telling us you were alive?"

"Postcards can leave a print."

"And don't call me Ringworm. It's unkind."

"I had to attract your attention. Your head was in the clouds."

"What are you doing in the East Bronx?"

"I'm a refugee, the same as you and Faigele."

"A refugee pretzel vendor?"

"It's a good disguise. A million gorillas are after me, including Meyer. Somebody whispered in the Little Man's ear that I stole from him and his people when I was a boss painter."

"Did you steal?"

"From Lansky? Never . . . Ah, it's nice to see you, Baby. Will you give Faigele a kiss?"

I told mom about the new pretzel man on the block, thinking she'd scorn Chick and wouldn't even want to see him for old time's sake. But the dark lady was unpredictable. If Chick had risen in the East, had become a racketeer or a union rep, mom would have avoided him. But a pretzel man appealed to Faigele.

I was the one who set the rendezvous, because it might not have looked correct for a married woman to meet with a strange pretzel vendor under the eyes of Boston Road shopkeepers. I picked the public library, which was in a colored neighborhood where the shopkeepers would never go. Uncle Chick arrived with his pretzel basket and a red rose. It didn't matter what he'd done, he was mom's cavalier. And when he saw the dark lady, he began to cry.

"Fool," mom said, "it's a public library." But she took this ex-house painter in her arms, rocked him for a minute, and let him go.

"I'm guilty," he said. "Faigele, I became a pretzel man because of you."

"Imbecile," mom said, "it sounds like a sentimental story."

"But it's true. I hired some gorilla to search for all the Faigeles in the East Bronx, and then I did a little scouting on my own and got a license to sell pretzels outside Baby's school. I figured Baby would find me."

"Why didn't you knock on my door?"

"I can't take risks. I'm a wanted man."

The librarian started looking at him, and Uncle Chick brought us and his pretzel basket into the street. We sat in a colored ice-cream parlor and had chocolate milk shakes. Mom, Chick, and me must have been born under the same moon, because we were all crazy about anything chocolate.

Chick didn't have an address. He ran from room to room, shaking off Meyer Lansky's people. His only fixture in the world was his pretzel basket. But he couldn't forget about his skills as an entrepreneur. He began to organize the other pretzel vendors so they would have a bit of muscle and could force the suppliers to bring down the price of each pretzel. He had to use an alias, Michael Strogoff, which is the name of some Siberian prince. But the suppliers weren't too happy about this Michael Strogoff. They hired a local gang, the Pistoleeros, to knock the hell out of Uncle Chick. They hadn't counted on Haines . . .

The battler showed up while the Pistoleeros were preparing to demolish Chick and his pretzel basket. They swallowed all the pretzels and stripped off Uncle's clothes. Michael Strogoff was caught naked in the middle of his own Siberia: winter in the East Bronx. Haines didn't know anything about a pretzel man's problems. He was patrolling the neighborhood, that's all, keeping the peace. He waded into the Pistoleeros with his hands and feet, kicking, punching faces, stifling the gang's war cries, until he could extricate Chick and the basket. The Pistoleeros surrendered and offered to pay for the pretzels they'd eaten.

"You're grounded," Haines told the gang. "Get off the street."

The battler hardly said a word to Chick, didn't even ask him his name. He helped Michael Strogoff into his clothes, and when mom's Siberian prince took out his wallet to reward the battler, the battler said no.

"If my fiancée ever passes by, give her one of your pretzels . . . not a soft one that's been lying out in the weather, but one that you keep under your napkin."

"But how will I be able to recognize your fiancée?"

"Oh, you can't miss Nita. And she won't be shy about introducing herself."

That should have been the end of the tale, but it wasn't. The Pistoleeros' dads started to brood. What irked them most was that the battler had obliged their sons to give money to an unknown pretzel man. They talked to the suppliers, who talked to some union rep, who was affiliated with one of Meyer Lanky's death squads, and that death squad talked to the Little Man himself. It had nothing to do with pretzels or Pistoleeros. The death squad had discovered who Michael Strogoff was. And it bothered the Little Man that a colored superintendent who liked to play sheriff had rescued somebody on Meyer's own shit list.

This death squad—two Polish bakers from Tinton Avenue in the East Bronx—crept into the basement at three in the morning with guns, knives, and baseball bats and got the Super out of bed, told him he could die peacefully or put up a fuss and watch his women and children suffer. Haines laughed like a jackal. "You'll kill them all, no matter what I do." They stabbed the Super, shot him twice, socked him on the head, but he didn't even go down on one knee. He leapt on the bakers, bit off their noses . . .

The battler and his kin were the only ones who walked out of the basement alive. The cops showed up, sifted for clues. Their single curiosity about the case was that a colored superintendent had survived his own gangland execution. They covered the bakers with a filthy blanket and called an ambulance for Haines.

The Super was never the same. He returned from the hospital with a metal plate in his skull. He had to count on his fingers and couldn't even spell his own name. But he was still the only friend I had. He forgot how to shovel coal, and no matter what I did, I couldn't teach him to hold a shovel in his hands. He'd bury himself in the coal bin and stare at the wall.

"Come on, Super. You're still our Wyatt Earp."

"Yeah," he said. "I'm good for sucking peppermints and pissing in my pants. Just like Earpy."

Nita had a miscarriage. It was mom who attended to her, put wet towels on her head, covered her with all the blankets she could find. "Mrs. Fannie," Nita said in her delirium, "can't me and the Super go and live with the angels?"

"No angels," mom said. "Not right now."

Mom was terribly sullen; she couldn't puzzle out why two bakers from Tinton Avenue would want to kill Haines. Chickie had to enlighten us. He was no longer Michael Strogoff. He'd given his pretzel basket away. We met in the library, and he told us who was behind the bakers. Lansky, the Little Man.

"And you couldn't have warned the Super?" Mom was crying now.

"Faigele, it was a *fait accompli.*"

I didn't even have to ask what a *fait accompli* was. Something that couldn't be stopped, like the fingers of fate.

Mom reached across the library table to slap Uncle Chick. It was the saddest slap I'd ever seen. "That's my *fait accompli,* darling . . . the Super saved your life. You owed him yours."

"Faigele, I couldn't . . . I was too scared. And I wasn't sure where or how the Little Man would strike."

Mom grabbed my hand and we left Uncle Chick in the library. She had to bear her own responsibility for what had happened to the Super. Chickie's love for her had made him surface in the East Bronx as a pretzel man. And Haines had been reduced to being a little boy again on account of those pretzels.

"You can call me Baby, Mr. Jerome."

But I couldn't. He wasn't Baby to me. He was a wounded warrior.

Roosevelt died while Haines was still in the hospital. He'd had a cerebral hemorrhage at the Little White House in Warm Springs, Georgia. I can't talk about America, but I know how the East Bronx mourned him. The neighborhood seemed to run on slow motion. You couldn't find a trolley car in the street. The shops were empty. Flags suddenly appeared in the windows, and pictures of FDR in his cape. And mom was bedeviled, because she loved Roosevelt and hated Roosevelt for deserting the dentist, giving him to Dewey.

"Baby, I didn't vote for FDR . . . I threw an evil spell on the President."

"Mom, mom, millions of people didn't vote for Roosevelt."

"Not in the Bronx," mom said. "I was the only one. Baby, I

loved him so much, the devil took advantage and turned my hate into a big evil bolt that attacked the President's brain."

I'd never be a lawyer. I couldn't prove that mom hadn't killed FDR. She stayed in bed for two weeks and then she went back to the candy factory. Her boss didn't reprimand her. Mom was the best cherry dipper in town. And besides, lots of women were absent without leave after Roosevelt's death. But Faigele couldn't afford to be sick. She was helping Nita Brown.

Nita had to become the new superintendent of our building, or Haines would have lost the basement apartment, and Mattie and the children would have been out on the street. She wasn't strong enough to attend a whole building by herself; mom and the children would sweep the halls and I would run the dumbwaiter after school. I liked being a superintendent's assistant. But we had to cover up for Nita. She was much wilder after the Super lost some of his brains. She would shovel coal without her clothes on. I didn't mind, but tenants began to complain. She was slovenly, they said. A temptress. She would sit on the stairs and fondle her own breasts.

The landlord fired her, gave her a week to vacate with the battler and his brood. Faigele put on her silver fox coat and her best perfume, painted her mouth, and we went to visit the landlord, Harry Harkins, at his office on West Farms Road. Mom didn't have the heart to leave Haines behind in the coal bin, but we couldn't bring him along. It would only have given the landlord ammunition against us.

Harkins owned and managed a hundred and fifty firetraps in the East. We had to wait an hour to see Harry, but when we entered his office, he couldn't stop gazing at mom. He was a man of seventy, with sad, watery eyes. We introduced ourselves, and Harkins kissed my mother's hand.

"Faigele, I'll give you a diamond . . . send the boy away."

Mom tapped him gently on the cheek. "Shame on you, Harry. I'd like you to rehire Nita Brown."

"Haines' witch? Impossible. She has no legal right to be in the building. She's a squatter."

Nothing could persuade Harry Harkins, not my mother's smile or perfume and war paint. We ran from West Farms Road and got on a bus to the Concourse. It was my only visit in the months we'd been away. The Germans had just surrendered, and the Concourse was in a festive mood. There were banners and electric candles all over Temple Adath Israel. Now no one had to worry that Hitler would ever have lunch in the Bronx.

The buildings basked in a silver light that was peculiar to the Concourse, as if sun and moon had met somewhere in the sky and were shining down on the West Bronx. But mom was in a hurry, and we couldn't pause to remember our past. We galloped into the Concourse Plaza, and found Fred R. Lions holding court in the lobby on his crimson chair. He observed Faigele with a politician's gray eyes.

"Will you go away, woman? You're an outcast, you and that boy with ringworm."

"I told you once. Baby's head has healed."

"But he's still wearing that cursed cap of the St. Louis Browns . . . go away."

"You're my president," mom told him. "I have the right to see you."

"God forbid. You're not a Democrat. You've been drummed out of the corps. I'd lose my seat at the Plaza if the Boss had an inkling you were here . . . Faigele, we're orphans now that Mr. Franklin is gone."

"I need a favor."

"Absolutely not."

"Call Harry Harkins and tell him that Nita Brown is precious to you."

"Who's Nita Brown?"

"A superintendent on Seabury Place."

"She belongs to Wyatt Earp," I said.

Mr. Lions winked at us. "I get it. The sheriff who almost put Meyer Lansky out of business. I'd like to meet him. But why should I meddle? What's in it for me? . . . Man alive, I missed you. What a crowd we could pull in if you agreed to deal cards for the Democratic Party."

"I will, Fred. One time only. But call Harkins first . . . *Nita Brown.*"

The borough president's eyes lit with the silver color of the Concourse. He had the bellhop bring him a telephone. He pulled Harkin's number out of a little book, dialed, whispered into the phone, returned it to the bellhop, and winked at my mother. "It's done. Your Nita Brown will never be touched . . . Now will you deal for us, Faigele dear?"

Mr. Lions assembled as many Democrats as he could; they sat around a long table while Faigele dealt for them with a Philip Morris in her mouth. I heard mom sing out the same old rigamarole. "Pair of kings . . . possible flush."

The Democrats were enthralled. They left enormous tips for the dark lady. Mom made more money in two hours than she would have made in a week of cherry-dipping. But she'd dealt for Nita Brown, not the money.

Even when she was in the black market, mom had never bothered much with money. The dentist might have broken heads for a living, but in mom's eyes he was an educated man, an idealist who preferred to dream of Chekhov and the boulevard du Tzarewitch rather than mundane matters of the Bronx. I'm not so sure. It wasn't Chekhov that killed him. It was the Democratic Party . . .

We walked away from Mr. Lions, who followed us down the carpeted stairs of the lobby with all the panache of a Bronx president.

"Faigele, I know about your factory. We've had you watched. One day you'll fall into the chocolate barrel, and no one will ever find you."

"Fat chance, Mr. Lions. I survived the tzar, I'll survive a candy factory in the Bronx."

We didn't return to the East right away. Mom had to rock herself out of that poker deck, like any good dealer. She puffed on her Philip Morris, caught that Concourse light, the dark lady from Belorusse, who lived near chocolate cherries, while dad was hounded by demons. He'd never recovered from his lost status as an air-raid warden. Sam had been happiest wearing his white helmet, barking orders during a blackout. He'd stopped visiting whores in Miami. He was no longer the foreman of a fur shop. He had no shop, and he couldn't enter the equation that existed between mom and me.

I was the protected one, Faigele's Anton Chekhov, who still couldn't write a sentence. But I had my own boulevard du Tzarewitch, my own dark lady with a little dog. This dark lady never drowned in Nice, and her little dog named Dog could have been called Jerome. Dog discovered the world through his own mistress . . . and big, strapping men, who looked at the dark lady while Dog looked at them and could "read" the rapture on their faces. The dark lady belonged to Dog, and mom belonged to Baby, not to the firemen and postmen and the cantors of Belorusse or the Bronx. Their gaze could only empower Faigele and me.

We still didn't return to the East. Mom bought a wire shopping cart with her bounty from Mr. Lions' game. I wondered if she was going to scavenge in the street, search for bric-a-brac that people of the Concourse had left out for the garbagemen. But it wasn't junk that mom was after. It was her old market route. While we lived close to the Concourse, Faigele loved to shop at the Italian market on Arthur Avenue, where she could find exotic, long-nosed vegetables and purple olives and eggs with two yolks.

It was a long trip to Arthur Avenue, and I had to wheel Faigele's cart down the hill, past Claremont Park, to Webster Avenue, a kid in a Brownie cap accompanying his mother who looked like a movie star. I won't remark on all the men who were struck dumb staring at Faigele. We were on a mission, and mom never answered their gaze. We took Third Avenue to Quarry Road and walked around the Catholic hospital for chronic diseases, *into* Arthur Avenue. I thought I was going crazy, because it didn't feel like spring or summer. The shopkeepers must have ordered a second Christmas for V-E Day. Christmas lights were strung across Arthur Avenue in huge wire crowns with colored bulbs caught within the filigree. Santa Claus stared at us from the windows.

It was after lunchtime, and Dominick's was closed, but when a dark lady peered into the restaurant, the countermen couldn't resist: they reopened Dominick's for us. We had noodles with "angry Arab sauce" *(arrabbiata),* and mom drank dark red wine. The countermen wouldn't let her pay. "Signorina, it would insult our honor," they said.

I had to navigate for mom, guide her out of the restaurant, her head full of red wine. Faigele began to totter in her silver fox coat, and I was holding her and trying to trundle the cart. We were about to enter the indoor market when a tattered little band approached us, men in funny uniforms, with gray mustaches and huge, searching eyes. They were Italian prisoners of war in the company of military policemen with whistles and helmets and guns. There was something silly about policemen who looked like animal trainers. It wasn't their fault. They'd been thrown into a comic situation. Italy had surrendered ages ago, and prisoners of war should have been sent home, but not while the Germans occupied most of Italy. Now the Germans themselves were prisoners of war, and Berlin was a city of rats and rubble, but these same Italian prisoners of war who weren't really prisoners were caught in a curious limbo of nonpersons who didn't have a home. A kind provost marshal who was holding them at a camp somewhere in the "interior" (it was a military secret) must have decided to send them on an excursion to a typical Italian neighborhood. At least that's what the countermen at Dominick's had explained to us.

Arthur Avenue had elected to use its old Christmas decorations for these "unfortunate souls."

Weren't they wayfarers, like me and mom? Trapped in the riddle of our own century, celebrating Christmas in May, inside a tiny Italian bubble. They weren't like the firemen who ogled mom; they didn't want to possess the dark lady with their eyes. They were seeking comfort outside a prison camp. And did mom feel her own confinement in their funny clothes and circus-animal gait? They didn't whisper, they didn't leer. They looked. And mom wouldn't withhold herself from these prison clowns. She broke her drunken stride to embrace them, take each prisoner of war in her arms, let them nuzzle the silky fur of her coat, while the military policemen stood amazed, like prisoners themselves, removed from her warmth.

The dark lady kissed each prisoner of war between the eyes. And then she grabbed our little cart and led me into the market's lighted cavern, where I could get away from prisoners and policemen and search for miraculous eggs with two yolks.

I thought of the battler living in his coal bin, and wanted to bring home a long-nosed vegetable or a purple olive that could lend him a little intelligence. But Arthur Avenue couldn't cure the Super. He was an idealist, like Darcy, and look what it cost him. He was a child to his own children in a basement he had once ruled. But he still had the aura of Wyatt Earp. He would wait for mom outside the candy factory, walk her home. And who would dare test his ability to fight? We danced along our own crooked line. The battler, mom, and me, and everybody got out of our way.